# Scotland's Seas:
# Towards Understanding their State

 FISHERIES RESEARCH SERVICES

 SEPA

 SCOTTISH NATURAL HERITAGE

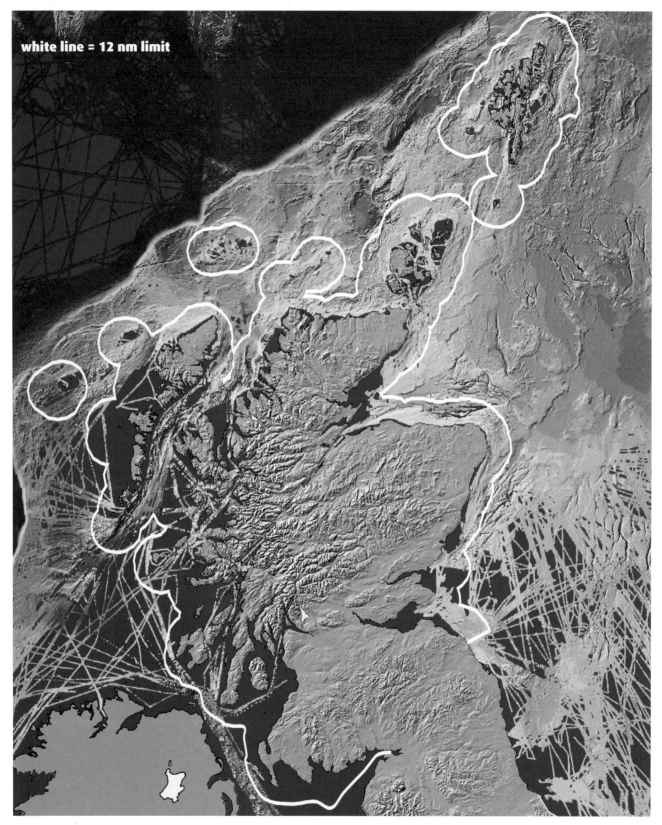

white line = 12 nm limit

The British Geological Survey has compiled a map of the Scottish land and sea areas showing the morphology of the country's terrain. Onshore topography is from NEXTMap Britain (© Intermap Technologies) in which heights of land features are acquired from an aircraft using radar technology. The data have a very high vertical resolution. The marine dataset is part of the Olex bathymetric database compiled, processed and managed by the Norwegian company Olex AS. The seabed image is based upon echo-sounder data acquired mainly by commercial fishing vessels, but also including data from research vessels. The datasets are contributed voluntarily, the data are then individually merged with the central dataset, after which the contributor has access to all of the shared bathymetry. As a result, the data are not complete for the offshore area, but illustrate the advantages of sharing data acquired from different sources.

# Contents

**Documents on accompanying CD**

Annex 1 - Global, regional (North-East Atlantic and European) and domestic (UK and Scottish) legislation and obligations of relevance in Scotland's seas.

Annex 2 - Details of the various marine monitoring programmes and data collection surveys undertaken by FRS, SEPA, SNH and the wider community.

Annex 3 - Reports on various aspects of Scotland's seas published by FRS, SEPA and SNH, as well as examples from other organisations monitoring Scotland's marine environment.

Annex 4 – The Input-Output Approach technical note.

Annex 5 – Data sources used to produce the information presented in Case Study 2.4.

Annex 6 – Computer simulated 'fly through' of the Firth of Forth Bridges derived from multi-beam echo-sounder data.

Annex 7 – SEPA – ADRIS Estuary Classification Scheme.

Annex 8 – SEPA – ADRIS Coastal Water Classification Scheme.

Computer simulated 'fly through' of the Firth of Forth Bridges.

Copy of report

ISBN: 978-0-9546490-9-8

The text pages of this document are printed on recycled paper and are 100% recyclable

Recommended citation format: Baxter, J.M., Boyd, I.L., Cox, M., Cunningham, L., Holmes, P., Moffat, C.F., (Editors), 2008. Scotland's Seas: Towards Understanding their State. Fisheries Research Services, Aberdeen. pp. 174.

# Foreword

Towards the end of summer 2007 the Scottish Government asked Fisheries Research Services (FRS), the Scottish Environment Protection Agency (SEPA) and Scottish Natural Heritage (SNH) to collaborate on assessing the state of Scotland's seas. This report includes contextual information and an initial data inventory and aims to inform the development of the Scottish Marine Bill in 2008. The title *Scotland's Seas: Towards Understanding their State*, reflects this content and purpose. Development of a fuller *State of Scotland's Seas* is underway with the intention of publishing this in 2010.

Such a report has not been published before. The first integrated assessment of the state of UK seas was undertaken in 2002 and the Scottish marine community contributed to that report. The Scottish marine environment and the diverse array of animals and plants that it supports is an invaluable national and international resource. It has provided a wide range of goods and services for centuries and contributed in countless ways to our national identity and 'place' in the world. With marine policy in Scotland, the UK and Europe developing apace, this Scottish report is timely and may hopefully serve as an inspiration to others.

The Scottish Government asked that contributions be invited from the wider marine scientific and academic community. We are delighted to say that the response to our invitation was very positive from organisations based in Scotland and elsewhere in the UK.

This initial review is offered to the Cabinet Secretary as a collaboration from his Government advisers and the wider community, all of whose work is valued and acknowledged. We will continue to work together to produce a comprehensive *State of Scotland's Seas* report in 2010.

**Robin Cook**
Chief Executive, Fisheries Research Services (FRS)

**Campbell Gemmell**
Chief Executive, Scottish Environment Protection Agency (SEPA)

**Ian Jardine**
Chief Executive, Scottish Natural Heritage (SNH)

# Roi-ràdh

Aig deireadh an t-Samhradh 2007, dh' iarr Riaghaltais na h-Alba air Seirbheisean Rannsachaidh an Iasgaich (FRS), Buidheann Dìon Àrainneachd na h-Alba (SEPA) agus Dualchas Nàdair na h-Alba (SNH) tighinn còmhla gus staid na mara ann an Alba a' mheasadh. Anns an aithisg seo, tha am fiosrachadh co-theacsa agus clàr-uidheim de data ag amas fiosrachadh a thoirt seachad gus *Bile Mara na h-Alba* a' leasachadh ann an 2008. Tha an tiotal *Marannan na h-Alba: a dh'ionnsaigh tuigse air an staid* a' dearbhadh an cuspair agus an adhbhar. Tha leasachadh ga dhèanamh an drasda gus aithisg nas domhainn air *Staid Marannan na h-Alba* a' sgrìobhadh airson 2010.

Cha deach aithisg mar seo a' cho-bhualadh riamh ron a seo . Chaidh a' chiad measadh air staid na cuantan anns an Rìoghachd Aonaichte a dhèanamh ann an 2002. Tha na coimhearsnachdan mara na h-Alba, an cuid bheathaichean agus lusan a tha a' toirt taic dha, na goireas luachmhor gu nàiseanta agus eadar-nàiseanta. Tha e air bhathar agus seirbheisean a thoirt seachad airson linntean a agus tha e a' cuir ri ìomhaigh nàiseanta ann an iomadadh dòigh agus a' toirt dhuinn "àite" anns an t-Saoghal. Le poileasaidhean mara ann an Alba, an Rìoghachd Aonaichte agus 'san Roinn Eòrpa ga leasachadh gu luath, tha an aithisg Albannach seo a' tighinn ann an deagh am agus ann an dòchas gun fhritheil seo mar grad-smuain gu feadhainn eile.

Dh'fhaighnich Riaghaltas na h-Alba air coimhearsnachd fharsaing luchd-saidheans is acadaimigeach na Mara a chuir ris a seo. Tha sinn toilichte a ràdh gu robh an fhreagairt a fhuair sinn bhon fhiathachadh seo gu buidhnean ann an Alba agus 'san Rìoghachd Aonaichte uabhasach math.

Thèid am measadh seo a' thairgse do Rùnaire a' Chaibineit bho comhairlichean riaghaltais ann an co-obrachadh leis an coimhearsnachd fharsaing agus an obair a' rinn cuid aithnichte agus luachmhor. Cumaidh sinn oirnn ag obair còmhla gus aithisg *Staid Marannan na h-Alba* a' leasachadh ann an 2010.

Robin Cook
Ceannard Seirbheisean Rannsachaidh an Iasgaich

Campbell Gemmell
Ceannard Buidheann Dìon Àrainneachd na h-Alba

Ian Jardine
Ceannard Dualchas Nàdair na h-Alba

# Executive Summary

Developing *Scotland's Seas: Towards Understanding their State* is a key first step to taking forward the recommendations from the Advisory Group on Marine and Coastal Strategy and the Environment and Rural Development Committee, as well as establishing a baseline against which future marine and coastal policy can be measured. It is a step towards achieving the Scottish Government's vision for seas that are "clean, healthy, safe, productive and biologically diverse" and that are "managed to meet the long term needs of nature and people". This is an interim report that will be followed by a more comprehensive review, the *State of Scotland's Seas*, in 2010.

The Scottish Government's vision is supported by a broad range of legislative and obligatory drivers. At the international level these include OSPAR, which covers the north-east Atlantic, and several European directives, including the Marine Strategy Framework Directive, the Water Framework Directive and the Habitats and Birds Directives. The European policy agenda is aimed at achieving and maintaining "good environmental" or "good ecological" status because there is recognition that the environment and its ecological structure and function need to be maintained if they are to remain economically productive and capable of supporting the health and wellbeing of people. This is being translated into domestic policy through the Government's vision and domestic legislation.

The nature of Scotland's seas owes much to its location at the edge of a continental shelf where water depth plummets from 250 m to oceanic depths of greater than 2,000 m. The warm oceanic waters from the south-west keep Scotland's climate temperate. In addition, they provide a supply of nutrients required for the photosynthetic fixation of carbon thereby maintaining the intricate food chain, and in turn, the seas rich biological diversity.

The Scottish coastline supports much economic and recreational activity. For example, the coastal waters have important potential for renewable energy generation, while the relatively shallow waters of the North Sea are where much of the oil and gas is currently extracted. Scottish ports handle large quantities of crude oil, coal and other 'dry bulk' products as well as providing the embarkation point for over 10 million passengers per year.

Evidence for the state of Scotland's seas comes from a number of indicators and many sources. The organisations with executive responsibility for the collation, stewardship and reporting of data are Fisheries Research Services, the Scottish Environment Protection Agency and Scottish Natural Heritage. Scotland has a long tradition of marine research and various other organisations, including some from outside Scotland, also provide information to underpin interpretation. Data sets that reflect the physical and biological state of Scotland's seas, and other reports derived from these data, have been listed in annexes to this report.

The ocean climate around Scotland is changing in a way that will lead to changes of the distribution and abundance of marine species, and may also lead to changes in the coastline, storminess of the seas and wave heights. Water temperature is increasing at a rate of 0.2-0.4°C per decade and is following similar trends to the wider North Sea and North Atlantic. Thermal expansion of the oceans and melting glacier ice is leading to sea-level rise. Although rates of sea-level rise are variable, 12% of Scotland's coastline is already subject to erosion and this is likely to increase in future. A long-term increase in salinity is being observed while acidification of the seas, because of increased dissolved carbon dioxide, presents a particular challenge to marine organisms.

### Clean and safe seas

There is a strong interaction between the energy within coastal seas, in the form of waves, tides and currents, and the processes of erosion and sedimentation. Sediments are derived from land and coastal erosion and many settle in relatively low energy regions. The result is a patchwork of seabed sediments and some of these areas, such as the Fladen Ground, can be productive for fisheries. These sediments store pollutants that could enter the human food chain, although monitoring has shown a reduction in most pollutant burdens over the past 20 years.

There is a general reduction in contaminant levels in estuarine sediments because regulation has led to declines in the discharges of metals and organic pollutants from rivers. Nevertheless, some historically polluted areas remain and particular attention must be given to an ever increasing number of synthetic substances that are entering the marine food chain, as they may affect biota in subtle but potentially damaging ways. The amount of nitrogen entering the sea, mainly derived from agriculture, has not declined although at present there appear only to

be local effects of this in some of the smaller east coast river estuaries. Toxic algal blooms, which can affect shellfish fisheries and other marine wildlife, do not appear to have a simple cause and there is currently little evidence that they are caused by pollution. Marine litter continues to be a problem on many beaches and this can be a hazard to wildlife. Improved sewage treatment and more appropriate location of discharges has greatly reduced the bacterial contamination of beaches in the past 10 years though again run-off from diffuse agricultural and urban sources still needs more management. Radioactive discharges, marine noise, and discharges of warm water also have effects though generally only local in nature.

### Healthy and biologically diverse seas

Phytoplankton communities are the fundamental basis of marine food chains. New primary production is often focused in regions where rivers deliver nutrients to the sea but in Scottish waters many of the nutrients come from inflow of oceanic water from the Atlantic. This makes Scotland's seas relatively rich in primary production and leads to the richness of marine fish populations. Overall, the primary production of Scotland's seas is in a favourable state but recently there have been major shifts in the distribution of the zooplankton that feed on phytoplankton. Warmer water species have increased and colder water species have declined. The overall effect that this could have on food chains is not known and, as a result, some suggest that the changes in zooplankton populations may be a cause for concern. What effect this will have on the Scottish seas' species of plants and animals (about 6,500, increasing to 40,000 if microbial flora are included) is not known.

Scotland has some of the finest marine habitats in Europe, some of which are very fragile. Although our knowledge of these is improving, many parts of Scotland's seas remain unexplored and it is possible that some of these fragile communities will be damaged or lost before there is any knowledge of their existence. Of the 17 Scottish biodiversity state indicators that have been identified, five are of particular relevance to the marine environment. These help to provide an overview of the health of Scotland's seas. To date, 34 Special Areas of Conservation have been designated in Scotland's seas covering seven different habitat types (56 features) and three species. A recent assessment showed that 97% of features surveyed within these sites were in favourable condition. Further protection has been provided for those sites found not to be in a favourable condition but it may take many decades, even centuries, for full recovery in some cases.

## Productive seas

Government statistics attribute £2.2 billion of marine related industry activity (excluding oil and gas) to the Scottish economy and about 50,000 jobs. Nevertheless, it is difficult to estimate the overall contribution that the sea makes to the Scottish economy or whether this potential is being fully utilised. However, it is clear that the seas provide a basis for a broad range of important industries. More than 99% of UK marine aquaculture is based in Scotland and there are plans to further increase production. Although some wild finfish stocks are not as productive as they might be, shellfish stocks are overall in good

condition. Oil and gas extraction continues to make a major economic contribution (estimated at about £20 billion additional Gross Domestic Product in 2005) with relatively low environmental impacts. Marine renewable energy is likely to become a major new product from Scotland's seas, although there is uncertainty about its environmental impacts.

## Next Steps

The next stage in this ongoing process will be to produce the *State of Scotland's Seas* report in 2010. As part of the process there is a need to improve the coordination of marine science with active industry involvement. There is also a need to develop a greater range of marine indicators which must take account of the multiple impacts to which any sea area is exposed. Finally there is a need to respond to the demands of the European Marine Strategy Framework Directive.

Ensuring that Scottish seas are used in a sustainable manner requires good management underpinned by high quality scientific research and monitoring. This will make certain that, for future generations, Scotland's seas will be clean, safe, healthy, productive and biologically diverse.

The authors welcome feedback on this report and encourage the completion of the short questionnaire at the back of the report. Alternatively comments can be sent to StateofScotlandsSeas2010@scotland.gsi.gov.uk.

# Giorrachadh Gnìomhach

Tha leasachadh *'Marannan na h-Alba: a dh'ionnsaigh tuigse air an staid'* na chiad cheum cudromach ann a bhith a' toirt air adhart na molaidhean a thàinig bhon Bhuidheann Comhairleachaidh air Ro-innleachd na Mara is a' Chost agus Comataidh Leasachaidh Dhùthchail, a bharrachd air a bhith a' steidheachadh slat-tomhais a chleachdar gus poileasaidhean mara is costail eile san àm ri teachd a thomhais. 'S e ceum air adhart gus lèirsinn Riaghaltas na h-Alba a choileanadh airson 's gum bi marannan againn a tha "glan, fallain, sàbhailte, torach agus eugsamhail a thaobh bith-eòlas" agus "air an riaghladh gus feumalachdan fad-ùine nàdair agus daoine a fhreagairt". Bidh rannsachadh nas fharsaing, *Staid Marannan na h-Alba*, a' leantainn na h-aithisg eadar-amail seo ann an 2010.

Tha iomadh inneal-putaidh reachdail is uallaich a' toirt taic dha lèirsinn Riaghaltas na h-Alba. Aig ìre eadar-nàiseanta, tha seo a' toirt a-staigh OSPAR, a tha a' gabhail a-steach ceann an ear-thuath an Atlantaig, agus grunn riaghailtean Eòrpach, nam measg Riaghailt Frèam Ro-innleachd na Mara, Riaghailt Frèam Uisge agus Riaghailt Àrainnean agus Eòin. Tha clàr-gnothaich poileasaidh na Roinn Eòrpa ag amas air inbhe "àrainneachd mhath" no "eag-eòlas math" a choileanadh agus a ghleidheadh oir thathas ag aithneachadh gu feum an àrainneachd agus a structar is gnìomh eag-eòlasach a ghleidheadh ma tha iad a' dol a mhairsinn mar àitean a tha torach gu h-eaconamach agus a tha comasach air slàinte is math an t-sluaigh a thaiceadh. Tha seo ga tionndadh gu poileasaidh dachaigh tro lèirsinn an Riaghaltais agus reachdas dachaigh.

Tha an t-uabhas aig nàdar marannan na h-Alba air a shuidheachadh aig oir sgeilp mhòr-thìreach far a bheil an doimhneachd a' tuiteam bho 250m gu doimhneachd mòr-chuanach de chòrr is 2,000m. Tha uisgeachan blàth nan cuantan bhon iar-dheas a' cumail sìde na h-Alba tlàth. A bharrachd air a seo, tha iad a' toirt seachad beathachadh a tha a dhìth gus carbon a ghlacadh tro photosynthesis, a ghleidheas an dà chuid an sreath-bìdh eadar-fhighte agus beairteas eugsamhlachd bith-eòlasach na mara.

Tha costa na h-Alba a' toirt taic dhan t-uabhas de chur-seachadan eaconamach agus cleasachail. Mar eisimpleir, tha comas aig na h-uisgeachan costail lùth leantainneach a ghineadh, fhad 's a tha a' chuid as motha de dh'ola is gas air a tharraing bho uisgeachan caran eu-domhainn a' Chuain a Tuath. Tha puirt na h-Alba a' làimhseachadh an uiread de dh'ola amh, gual agus bathar 'tioram' eile a bharrachd air a bhith nan ionadan bàrcachd airson còrr is 10 millean neach-siubhail gach bliadhna.

Tha fianais air staid marannan na h-Alba a' tighinn bho ghrunn thaisbeanairean agus iomadh tobar. 'S iad Seirbheisean Rannsachaidh an Iasgaich, Buidheann Dìon Àrainneachd na h-Alba agus Dualchas Nàdair na h-Alba na buidhnean aig a bheil dleastanas gnìomhach airson an dàta a chruinneachadh, a stiùbhardachd agus aithris a thoirt air. Tha dualchas fada air a bhith aig Alba ann an rannsachadh mara agus tha buidhnean eile, a' toirt a-staigh buidhnean bho thaobh a-muigh na h-Alba, cuideachd a' toirt fiosrachadh seachad gus mìneachadh a thaiceadh. Tha an dàta a tha a' meòrachadh staid fhisiceach agus bith-eòlasach marannan na h-Alba agus aithisgean eile a chaidh a tharraing bhon dàta seo, air an cur ann an eàrr-ràdh na h-aithisg seo.

Tha gnàth-shìde na mara mu thimcheall na h-Alba ag atharrachadh ann an dòigh a bhios ag adhbharachadh gun atharraich sgaoileadh is pailteas bheathaichean mara, agus ma dh'fhaoidte gun atharraich an costa, cho stoirmeil is a tha na marannan is àirdean thuinn. Tha teothachd an uisge a' fàs aig ìre 0.2 – 0.4°C gach deichead, a' leantainn air aomaidhean coltach anns a' Chuan a Tuath agus an Atlantaig a Tuath. Tha leudachadh tearmach nan cuantan agus eigh-shruthan a tha leaghadh a' ciallachadh gu bheil àirde na mara ag èirigh. Ged a tha na h-ìrean seo caochlaideach, tha 12% de chosta na h-Alba fo bhleith mar-thà agus tha dùil gum fàs seo anns an àm ri teachd. Thathas a' faicinn àrdachadh fad-ùine ann an ìrean saillteachd, is tha searbhachadh nan cuantan, mar thoradh air barrachd carbon dà-ogsaid air eadar-sgaoileadh, na dhùbhlan sònraichte do bheathaichean mara.

*Marannnan glan is sàbhailte*
Tha tòrr eadar-obrachadh eadar lùths ann an uisgeachan a' chost, mar eisimpleir, tuinn, lìonaidhean mara agus sruthan, agus bleith is grùideachadh. 'S ann mar thoradh air bleith talmhainn no costa a tha grùid, is a' chuid as motha dhiubh sin a' laighe mu dheireadh ann an àiteachan beag-lùtha. Tha seo a' fàgail pàtran de ghrùid air grunnd na mara agus bidh feadhainn dhiubh, mar eisimpleir Fladen Ground, gu math torrach a thaobh iasgach. Tha stòr de truaillidhean anns an grùid seo a dh'fhaodadh a dhol a-steach gu sreath-bìdh an t-sluaigh ach tha sgrùdadh a' sealltainn gu bheil ìsleachadh air tighinn air uallach thruaillidhean thar na 20 bliadhna a dh'fhalbh.

Tha ìsleachadh anns an fharsaingeachd air tighinn air ìrean truailleachd ann am beòil aibhnichean airson 's gun robh riaghladh ag adhbharachadh nach deach an uiread de mheatailtean is truailleachd organaigeach a leigeil ann an aibhnichean. Co-dhiù, tha àiteachan truaillte ann fhathast agus feumar sùil gheur a thoirt air stuthan fuadain a bhios a' dol an sàs ann an sreath-bìdh na mara, oir ma dh'fhaoidte gum bi buaidh aca air biota ann an dòighean seòlta ach cunnartach. Cha deach an ìre de naitroidsean a' dol a-steach dhan mhuir, a' mhòr chuid bho àiteachas, sìos ged nach eil ann an-dràsta ach buaidhean ionadail ann am feadhainn de bheòil-aibhnichean beaga a' chost' an ear. Tha e coltach nach e rud sìmplidh a tha ag adhbharachadh luath-leudachadh algach tocsaineach agus chan eil fianais ann an-dràsta gur e truailleachd a tha aig cnag na cùise. Tha sgudal mara fhathast na dhuilgheadas air iomadh tràigh, agus tha seo cunnartach do dh'ainmhidhean. Thar an 10 bliadhna a dh'fhalbh tha ionadan-otrachais nas fheàrr agus suidheachadh leigeil nas fhreagarraiche air truailleachd bacteriach thràighean ìsleachadh, ach fhathast, tha feum air barrachd riaghladh air uisge a' ruith a-steach bho iomadh rud àiteachail is bailteil. Tha buaidhean cuideachd, gu h-ionadail anns an fharsaingeachd ge-tà, aig leigeil rèidio-beò, fuaimean-mara, agus uisge blàth air a leigeil.

*Marannan fallain agus eugsamhail*
Aig fìor bhonn sreathan-bìdh mara tha coimhearsnachdan phytoplankton. Tha gineamhainn ùr mar as trice a' tachairt ann an sgìrean far a bheil na h-aibhnichean a' toirt beathachadh dhan mhuir, ach ann an uisgeachan na h-Alba, tha mòran den bheathachadh a' tighinn bho uisge a tha a' sruthadh a-steach bhon Atlantaig. Tha seo a' fàgail marannan na h-Alba an ìre mhath beairteach a thaobh gineamhainn, is tha seo ag adhbharachadh beairteas ann

an àireamh iasg mara. Uile gu lèir, tha gineamhainn ann an uisgeachan na h-Alba ann an staid mhath, ach o chionn ghoirid, tha atharrachaidhean mòra air tighinn air sgaoileadh zooplankton a bhios a' biathadh air phytoplankton. Tha àireamh ghnèithean blàth-uisge air a dhol an-àirde agus àireamh ghnèithean fuar-uisge air a dhol sìos. Chan eil fhios fhathast dè buaidh aig a' cheann thall a dh'fhaodhadh a bhith aig an atharrachadh seo air sreathan-bìdh, agus, mar thoradh air seo, tha feadhainn den bheachd gu bheil na h-atharrachaidhean seo ann an àireamhan zooplankton na chùis-iomagain. Cuideachd, chan eil fhios dè buaidh a bhios ann air lusan is ainmhidhean marannan na h-Alba (mu 6,500, a' streap gu 40,000 ma thèid meanbh-lusan a ghabhail a-steach).

Tha feadhainn de na h-àrainnean mara as fheàrr ann an Eòrpa aig Alba, is àireamh dhiubh glè chugallach. Ged a tha ar cuid eòlais a' tighinn air adhart, cha deach pàirtean de mharannan na h-Alba a rannsachadh fhathast, is ma dh'fhaoidte gun tèid feadhainn de na coimhearsnachdan cugallach seo a mhilleadh no a chall mus bi fios againn gu bheil iad ann idir. Dhen 17 taisbeanairean staid bith-eugsmhlachd Albannach a chaidh aithneachadh, tha 5 a' buntainn gu sònraichte ri àrainneachd na mara. Tha iad seo a' cuideachadh gus sealladh farsaing a thoirt air cho fallain is a tha marannan na h-Alba. Gu ruige seo, chaidh 34 Ionadan Sònraichte Glèidhteachais ainmeachadh ann am marannan na h Alba, a' gabhail a steach7 diofar àrainnean (56 feartan) agus 3 gnèithean. Tha measadh ùr a' sealltainn gu bheil 97% de na feartan a chaidh a sgrùdadh anns na làraich seo ann an staid shoirbheasach. Chaidh dìon a bharrachd a thoirt air na làraich nach robh ann an staid cho math, ach ma dh'fhaoidte gun toir e deicheadan,

no fiù 's linntean, gus an tèid feadhainn dhiubh am feabhas.

## Marannan torrach

'S ann air gnìomhan ceangailte ris a' mhuir (gun a bhith a' gabhail a-steach ola is gas) a thèid luach £2.2 billean a chur le staitistearachd an Riaghaltais agus mu 50,000 obraichean. A dh'aindeoin seo, tha e doirbh tomhas a dhèanamh air de chuireas a' mhuir ri eaconamachd na h-Alba uile gu lèir, no a bheilear a' gabhail làn brath air a chomas. Tha e follaiseach, ge-tà, gu bheil a' mhuir a' toirt seachad bun-stèidh do raon farsaing de ghnìomhachasan cudromach. Tha còrr is 99% de thuathanachas-uisge mara an RA stèidhichte ann an Alba is gu bheil planaichean ann toradh a leudachadh fhathast. Ged nach eil feadhainn de sholair iasg cho torrach is a b' urrainn dhaibh a bhith, tha solair mhaoraich ann an staid mhath anns an fharsaingeachd. Tha tarraing ola is gas fhathast a' cur gu mòr ris an eaconamaidh (air a thomas aig mu £20 billean a bharrachd air làn-thoradh dùthchail ann an 2005), is gun bhuaidh mhòr air an àrainneachd. Tha coltas ann gum fàs lùth-mara leantainneach a bhith na bhathar cudromach ùr bho mharannan na h-Alba ged a tha mì-chinnt ann mun bhuaidh aige air an àrainneachd.

## Ath cheumannan

'S e an ath cheum anns a' phroiseas leantainneach seo aithisg *Staid Marannan na h Alba* a thoirt a mach ann an 2010. Mar phàirt den phroiseas tha feum ann air co-òrdanachadh nas fheàrr a leasachadh gus an tig saidheans mara is gnìomhachasan còmhla. Cuideachd feumar raon nas fharsainge de thaisbeanairean mara a leasachadh a bhios a' gabhail ealla ris na grunn rudan a bhuaileas air

pàirt sam bith den mhuir. Mu dheireadh thall, tha feum ann freagairt a thoirt do Riaghailt Frèam Ro-innleachd Mara na h-Eòrpa.

Gus dèanamh cinnteach gu bheil marannan na h-Alba air an cleachdadh ann an dòigh sheasmhach, feumaidh deagh stiùireadh a bhith ann cho math ri rannsachadh is sgrùdadh saidheansail dhen ìre as àirde. Bidh seo a' dearbhadh gum

bi marannan na h-Alba glan, sàbhailte, fallain, torrach agus eugsamhail airson na ginealaichean ri tighinn.

Cuiridh na h-ùghdaran fàilte air fios air ais sam bith mun aithisg seo, agus tha iad a' brosnachadh duine sam bith an ceisteachan aig deireadh na h-aithisg a lìonadh. No faodar beachdan a chur gu
StateofScotlandsSeas2010@scotland.gsi.gov.uk

# Chapter 1
# Introduction and Policy Context
# to Scotland's Seas

## INTRODUCTION

With such high-profile European legislation as the Marine Strategy Framework Directive (MSFD)[1] being agreed in December 2007, it could be thought that assessment, monitoring and management of the marine environment is a new idea. This is far from true. A diverse range of policy has, over the years, developed incrementally the way in which the marine environment is investigated, managed and assessed. However, the tempo of marine policy development has increased rapidly in the last few years and continues to do so.

Some of these policies, both statutory and non-statutory, are the response to global and European obligations, which is appropriate given Scotland's position at the edge of Europe in the North-East Atlantic (Figure 1.1). Obligations include such global policy as the Convention on Biological Diversity (1992)[2] (CBD) and the European Habitats (92/43/EEC) and Birds (79/409/EEC) Directives for the conservation of biodiversity. Also at the European level is the Water Framework Directive (2000/60/EC; WFD). Other obligations are part of a national agenda, such as the new framework for monitoring and assessment of the UK marine environment developed after the publication of *Charting Progress* in 2005[3]. Annex 1 contains a list of legislation and obligations of relevance in Scotland's seas.

As mentioned already, marine monitoring is not new but today there is a renewed emphasis as a greater effort is made to understand the inter-connections between the marine ecosystems and the human activities that rely on them. With sustainability high on the agenda, it is very important that any assessment of the state of the seas, even an initial one, addresses the three pillars of the social, environmental and economic sectors. The Scottish Government's vision for the seas is for a marine environment which is:

"... clean, healthy, safe, productive and biologically diverse ...... managed to meet the long-term needs of nature and people".

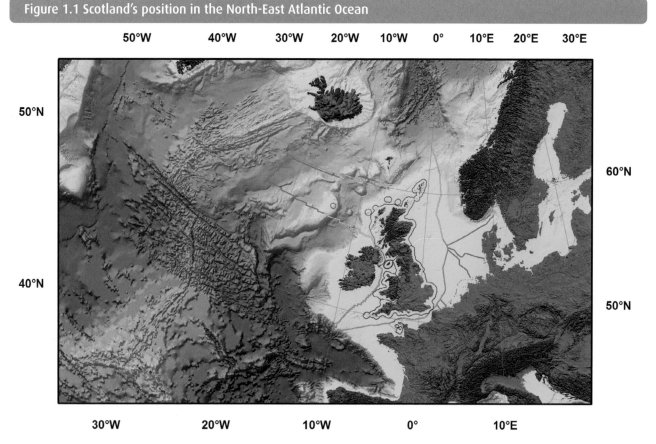

**Figure 1.1 Scotland's position in the North-East Atlantic Ocean**

Red line = 12 nm limit; Yellow line = Scottish fisheries limits; Blue line (West of Scotland) = UK continental shelf limit.

This report has been structured around this vision, to demonstrate how this is being achieved. A full state of the seas is not presented but each element of the vision is addressed and illustrated by a range of case studies.

The report includes:

> **Chapter 1** – the policy context of Scotland's seas explaining how a variety of legislation and obligations, both old and new, are driving policy and creating a context for detailed assessments.

> **Chapter 2** – a description of the physical characteristics of Scotland's seas. This includes details about the features used to understand the nature of the seas and that dictate Scotland's climate and reviews some of the data about our current understanding of the seabed.

> **Chapter 3** – presents an initial review of the 'Clean and Safe' status of the seas with case studies addressing such factors as the amount of hydrocarbons in seabed sediments near oil fields.

> **Chapter 4** – presents an initial review of the 'Healthy and Biologically Diverse' nature of the seas with case studies on phytoplankton and zooplankton, the basis of the food chain on which all else in the seas relies.

> **Chapter 5** – provides an initial review of the 'Productive' status of the seas and marine economic activity, whilst recognising some of the impacts of the various human activities described.

> **Chapter 6** – assesses the effects of climate change on Scotland's marine environment.

> **Chapter 7** – reviews the way ahead as preparations are made for the publication of a full *State of Scotland's Seas* in 2010.

> **Annexes** – These are on the enclosed CD and include:

> > Annex 1 – Global, regional (North-East Atlantic and European) and domestic (UK and Scottish) legislation and obligations of relevance in Scotland's seas.
> > Annex 2 – Details of the various marine monitoring programmes and data collection surveys undertaken by FRS, SEPA, SNH and the wider community.
> > Annex 3 – Reports on various aspects of Scotland's seas published by FRS, SEPA and SNH, as well as examples from other organisations monitoring Scotland's marine environment.
> > Annex 4 – The Input-Output Approach technical note.
> > Annex 5 – Data sources used to produce the information presented in case study 2.4.
> > Annex 6 – Computer simulated 'fly through' of the Firth of Forth Bridges derived from multi-beam echo-sounder data.
> > Annex 7 – SEPA – ADRIS Estuary Classification Scheme.
> > Annex 8 – SEPA – ADRIS Coastal Water Classification Scheme.

**POLICY CONTEXT**
*Global obligations*
World Summit on Sustainable Development
The World Summit on Sustainable Development (WSSD) took place in 2002, setting an ambitious agenda with challenging goals and targets. The UK and Scottish Governments are both committed to delivering the outcomes of the summit which, for the oceans, are to promote integrated sustainable management of oceans at all levels in order to help maintain the productivity and biodiversity of marine and coastal areas and help secure a significant reduction in biodiversity decline by 2010. These will be delivered through the:

> introduction of various policies, measures and tools such as the ecosystem approach[A] marine protected areas (MPAs) and the incorporation of coastal interests in watershed management; and

> introduction and development of effective machinery of oceans governance and partnerships.

*Regional (European and North-East Atlantic) obligation*
OSPAR
In response to widespread concerns about eutrophication and increasing amounts of xenobiotic compounds reaching the seas, international agreements to protect the seas gathered pace in the 1970s. The 1972 Oslo (Convention for the Prevention of Marine Pollution by Dumping from Ships and Aircraft) and 1974 Paris (Convention for the Prevention of Marine Pollution from Land-Based Sources) Conventions formalised agreements following high-profile marine accidents. The Intergovernmental North Sea Conferences of the 1980s required contracting member states to reduce inputs of potentially polluting substances, and led to the first quantitative determination of inputs of these substances to marine waters by 1990. Requirements were rationalised in the 1992 OSPAR Convention for the Protection of the Marine Environment of the North-East Atlantic. This came into force in 1998. It requires the application by Contracting Parties (which includes the UK) of the precautionary principle, the polluter pays principle and best available techniques and best environmental practice. The requirement to determine the pollutant load to the marine environment is now embodied in the Water Framework Directive (WFD), which has been implemented in Scotland through the Water Environment and Water Services Act 2003 (WEWS) and subsequent Controlled Activities Regulations (2005).

A key part of OSPAR's work is its Joint Assessment and Monitoring Programme (JAMP), which coordinates three national environmental monitoring programmes: the Coordinated Environmental Monitoring Programme (CEMP), the Comprehensive Atmospheric Monitoring Programme (CAMP) and the Comprehensive Study on Riverine Inputs and Direct Discharges (RID) to provide a comprehensive monitoring framework. To meet its objective of protecting the North-East Atlantic, the OSPAR Convention has adopted several long-term strategies, with long-term aims:

> **Hazardous substances**
> To reach concentrations equivalent to near background levels for naturally-occurring substances and close to zero for man-made synthetic substances in the marine environment by 2020.

> **Radioactive substances**
> To reach concentrations equivalent to near background values for naturally-occurring substances and close to zero for artificial radioactive substances in the marine environment by 2020.

> **Eutrophication**
> To eliminate eutrophication where it occurs in the North-East Atlantic and to prevent further occurrences.

> **Protection of Ecosystems and Biological Diversity**
> To manage human activity and support the ecosystem approach, make assessments of species and habitats and develop an ecologically coherent network of marine protected areas.

> **Environmental Goals and Management Mechanisms for Offshore Activities**
> To promote the development of goals for the oil and gas industry to prevent pollution from offshore sources, and protection and conservation of the maritime area from adverse effects of offshore activities.

In 2000, OSPAR published the first comprehensive Quality Status Report[4] (QSR) on the quality of the marine environment of the North-East Atlantic. This was supported by five reports on the different parts of the OSPAR maritime area – the Arctic (Region I), the Greater North Sea (Region II), the Celtic Seas (Region III), the Bay of Biscay/Golfe de Gascogne and Iberian waters (Region IV), and the Wider Atlantic (Region V) (Figure 1.2). An interim Overview of OSPAR Assessments 1998 – 2006[5] was published in 2006 with an updated QSR due to be published in 2010; Scottish scientists are involved in the preparation of QSR 2010.

## Figure 1.2 OSPAR regions

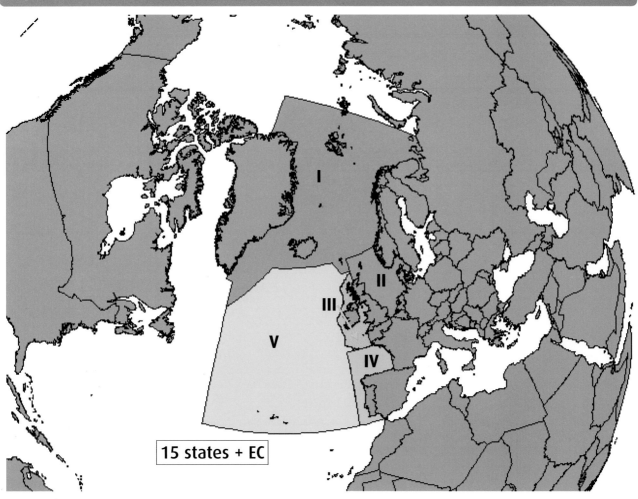

15 states + EC

## European Integrated Maritime Policy

In October 2007 the European Commission announced its vision for an integrated maritime policy for the EU[6]. This emphasised the need for joined-up decision making to deliver economic growth and included a detailed action plan[7] and work programme. It has a number of elements, including:

> maximising the sustainable use of the oceans and seas; due to the importance of shipping and ports, a comprehensive **maritime transport strategy** and new **ports policy** will be prepared;

> building a knowledge and innovation base for maritime policy, including developing a **European Strategy for Marine Research**;

> creating a European network for integrated surveillance, including a **European Marine Observation and Data Network**; and

> delivering the highest quality of life in coastal regions, this will promote tourism to assist outermost regions and islands and develop a **strategy to mitigate the effects of climate change on coastal regions**.

The integrated maritime policy aims to deliver a sustainable development approach for Europe's oceans and seas with the recent MSFD providing the environmental pillar of the sustainable development approach.

## European Marine Strategy Framework Directive

In December 2007 the European Parliament agreed the text for the MSFD, the latest marine legal obligation.

Endorsement by the Council of Ministers is expected in early 2008 with formal completion of the Directive soon after. This Directive will effectively extend many of the provisions of the European Water Framework Directive (WFD) to seas beyond the current WFD limits. The Directive splits European seas into a number of areas. Scotland is mainly within the Greater North Sea (OSPAR region II) and the Celtic Seas (OSPAR region III). These regions are significantly larger that the WFD coastal water bodies. The Directive requires Member States to **"take the necessary measures to achieve or maintain good environmental status in the marine environment by the year 2020 at the latest."** The steps necessary to do this are similar to those required under the WFD:

An **initial assessment** is required to determine the current environmental status of the waters and the environmental impact of human activities; this is to be completed by 2012. Based on the initial assessment, and also by 2012, what constitutes **good environmental status** (GES) has to be determined and **environmental targets** and **indicators** established. Then, by 2014, a **monitoring programme** has to be implemented. This is followed, in 2015, by the development of **programmes of measures**, essentially management actions, to ensure that human activity is managed in such a way that GES is achieved. These must come into force by 2016. The whole process, a **national marine strategy,** is cyclical with regular reporting to the Commission.

| Table 1.1   Comparison of the UK and Scottish Visions with the MSFD definition of GES | |
|---|---|
| **MSFD Definition of GES** | **Vision statement in "Safeguarding our Seas"[8] and "Seas the Opportunity"[10]** |
| "good environmental status" means the environmental status of marine waters where these provide ecologically diverse and dynamic oceans and seas which are clean, healthy and productive within their intrinsic conditions, and the use of the marine environment is at a level that is sustainable, thus safeguarding the potential for uses and activities by current and future generations, i.e.: <br><br> (a) the structure, functions and processes of the constituent marine ecosystems, together with the associated physiographic, geographic, geological and climatic factors, allow those ecosystems to function fully and to maintain their resilience to human-induced environmental change. Marine species and habitats are protected, human-induced decline of biodiversity is prevented and diverse biological components function in balance; <br><br> (b) hydro-morphological, physical and chemical properties of the ecosystems, including those properties which result from human activities in the area concerned, support the ecosystems as described above. Anthropogenic inputs of substances and energy, including noise, into the marine environment do not cause pollution effects | To shape the UK's capability, within National and International waters, to: <br><br> *"Provide, and respond, within a changing climate, to the evidence required for sustainable development within a clean, healthy, safe, productive and biologically diverse marine ecosystem and within one generation to make a real difference."* <br><br> In Scotland, <br> *"to secure a vision of clean, healthy, safe, productive and biologically diverse marine and coastal environments managed to meet the long-term needs of nature and people."* |

The MSFD does not define productive. In the *Safeguarding Our Seas* context productive relates to economic use of the seas and this is the context in which the term is used in this report.

It also provides a legal basis for the ecosystem-based approach to marine management.

Under the terms of the MSFD the OSPAR Regional Seas Convention is promoted as the mechanism by which Member States cooperate to achieve good environmental status by 2020.

The MSFD helpfully includes a definition of GES. This has similarities to the WFD's definition of good ecological status (GEcS) for coastal waters and the UK's vision for our seas (see Table 1.1). Annex I of the MSFD also details a number of qualitative descriptors that will be used for determining GES. Table 1.2 lists the descriptors and sets out parameters that are measured to show the status of the seas together with references to chapters of this report where initial data about that descriptor may be found. The characteristics, pressures and impacts on the marine environment that are to be considered are also stated in Annex III of the MSFD. Table 1.3 lists these, together with initial examples of where such characteristics, pressures and impacts are discussed in this report. Policy makers need to work with scientists, and the wider marine community, to establish how GES of Scottish waters will be measured, based on these characteristics, pressures, impacts, descriptors and the overall definition of GES. It is anticipated that a clearer picture will be available for the *State of Scotland's Seas* report in 2010.

| Table 1.2  MSFD qualitative descriptors for determining GES | |
|---|---|
| **Descriptors** | **Chapter of this report where information provided** |
| (1) **Biological diversity** is maintained. The quality and occurrence of habitats and the distribution and abundance of species are in line with prevailing physiographic, geographic and climatic conditions | 2, 4 and 6 |
| (2) **Non-indigenous species** introduced by human activities are at levels that do not adversely alter the ecosystems | 4 and 6 |
| (3) Populations of all **commercially exploited fish and shellfish** are within safe biological limits, exhibiting a population age and size distribution that is indicative of a healthy stock | 4 and 5 |
| (4) All elements of the **marine food webs,** to the extent that they are known, occur at normal abundance and diversity and levels capable of ensuring the long-term abundance of the species and the retention of their full reproductive capacity | 4 |
| (5) **Human-induced eutrophication** is minimised, especially adverse effects thereof, such as losses in biodiversity, ecosystem degradation, harmful algal blooms and oxygen deficiency in bottom waters | 3 |
| (6) **Sea floor integrity** is at a level that ensures that the structure and functions of the ecosystems are safeguarded and benthic ecosystems, in particular, are not adversely affected | 2 and 5 |
| (7) Permanent **alteration of hydrographical conditions** does not adversely affect marine ecosystems | 5 |
| (8) **Concentrations of contaminants** are at levels not giving rise to pollution effects | 3 |
| (9) **Contaminants in fish and other seafood** for human consumption do not exceed levels established by Community legislation or other relevant standards | 3 and 5 |
| (10) Properties and quantities of **marine litter** do not cause harm to the coastal and marine environment | 3 |
| (11) **Introduction of energy,** including underwater noise, is at levels that do not adversely affect the marine environment | 3 |

**Table 1.3 Indicative list of characteristics, pressures and impacts in Annex III of the MSFD**

| Characteristics | Chapter of this report where information provided |
|---|---|
| Physical and chemical features | 2, 3 and 6 |
| Habitat types | 2, 4 |
| Biological features | 2, 4 and 6 |
| Other features (e.g. chemicals and specific characteristics) | 2, 3 |
| **Pressures and Impacts** | |
| Physical loss | 5 |
| Physical damage | 5 |
| Other physical disturbance | 3 |
| Interference with [...] hydrological processes | 3 |
| Contamination by hazardous substances | 3 |
| Systematic and/or intentional release of substances | 3 |
| Nutrient and organic matter enrichment | 3, 5 |
| Biological disturbance | 3, 4 and 6 |

### Water Framework Directive

The Water Framework Directive (2000/60/EC; WFD) is a wide-ranging piece of European environmental legislation which became law in Scotland at the end of 2003 through the Water Environment and Water Services (Scotland) Act 2003 (WEWS Act). The Directive establishes a new legal framework for the protection, improvement and sustainable use of surface waters, transitional waters, coastal waters and groundwater across Europe in order to prevent deterioration, enhance status of aquatic ecosystems, including groundwater and reduce pollution. The Directive repeals and replaces a number of older directives and incorporates the remaining existing water Directives (the Bathing Water, Nitrates and Urban Waste Water Treatment Directives) into its framework through its protected areas provisions. Classification systems that the directive requires are outlined in a case study in Chapter 3. The language, the sequential steps and the drive to good ecological status of the WDF are very similar to those in the MSFD although there are some key differences, namely:

1) WFD is already in place so the timetable is much tighter. Monitoring has started and the first River Basin Management Plan has to be ready for 2009 which will define the Environmental Objectives and programme of measures. A further plan has to be produced by 2013 with the aim of achieving good surface water status by 2015. The cycle then starts again over 6 year periods.

2) The spatial scale of the WFD only covers inshore coastal waters and transitional (brackish waters and estuaries) out to three nautical miles from the Scottish Baseline. This does, however, include large sea areas such as the Sea of the Hebrides, the Minch, the Clyde and other major Firths.

3) Crucially, the WFD brings in holistic regulations and monitoring programmes that cover the land/sea interface and as most of the contamination that enters the sea emanates from land, control at this point is at its most effective.

An important part of the WFD implementation is international inter-calibration work to ensure that the good ecological status quality boundary is equivalently defined and implemented by all member states. Similar work is anticipated under the MSFD.

### European Habitats and Birds Directives

The EC Habitats and Birds Directives require the UK to identify and designate two types of area: Special Areas of Conservation (SAC), where they support rare, endangered or vulnerable natural habitats and species of plants and animals (other than birds) as listed in Annexes 1 and 2 of the Habitats Directive, and Special Protection Areas (SPA) that support significant numbers of wild birds and their habitats as listed in the Birds Directive. The requirements of these Directives extend out to the 200 nm limit. The collection of sites, known as the Natura 2000 network, is designed to ensure the continued survival of important habitats and species but also encourages the sustainable management of the marine environment as a whole. The continuing challenge in meeting the objectives of the Directives is to work with all those who use and manage the marine environment to allow wildlife to thrive and people to work and enjoy recreation in harmony with the natural heritage.

### Domestic (UK and Scottish) obligations

In 2002, the UK developed a strategy for the conservation and sustainable development of our marine environment, *Safeguarding our Seas*[8]. This introduced a vision for a marine environment which is **clean, healthy, safe, productive and biologically diverse.** The principles of sustainable development, integrated management, conservation of biological diversity, robust science, precautionary principle and stakeholder involvement were identified to underpin policy for the marine environment. This strategy also committed the UK to an integrated assessment of the seas.

### Charting Progress

*Charting Progress - An Integrated Assessment of the State of UK Seas*[3] (Figure 1.3) was published in March 2005. This was the first integrated assessment undertaken across the whole of the UK continental shelf and was based on four peer-reviewed sector reports and an integrated regional assessment based on eight regional areas.

In overview, it concluded:

> "The general picture that emerges from the evidence is mixed. The UK seas are productive and support a wide range of fish, mammals, seabirds and other marine life. The open seas are generally not affected by pollution and the levels of monitored contaminants have decreased significantly. The main contamination problems which are identified are in part due to the legacy of the past and are generally observed at higher levels in industrialised estuaries or areas local to the activity.

> However, human activity has already resulted in adverse changes to marine life and continues to do so. For example, widespread commercial fishing

**Figure 1.3 Charting Progress**

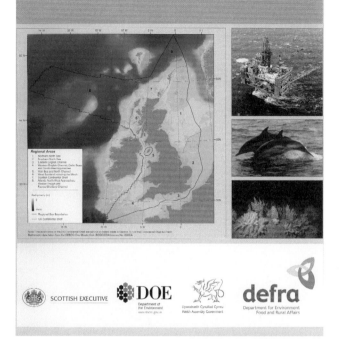

> practices threaten many fish stocks by over-exploitation and damage sea floor areas. There is also evidence that the marine ecosystem is being altered by climate change: for example sea temperatures are rising and the distribution of plankton species is changing. These changes pose a real threat to the balance and integrity of the marine ecosystem."

In addition, a number of lessons learned from the process of compiling *Charting Progress* were identified and a number of recommendations made. The key ones of relevance here were the need to:

> develop marine ecosystem indicators;

> evaluate and revise current marine monitoring programmes; and

> capture knowledge, not just data, and also improve our data and information stewardship.

It is remarkable to note that at the time of *Charting Progress* being prepared there was not a central record of who monitored what, where, when and why for the marine environment and there was no overall coordination of the many programmes.

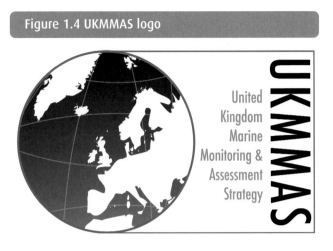

The main mechanism through which the recommendations from *Charting Progress* are being taken forward is the UK Marine Monitoring and Assessment Strategy (UKMMAS) (Figure 1.4). This is co-chaired by the Scottish Government and Defra and is implementing an improved way of managing the marine monitoring programmes, assessment activity and is working towards better stewardship of the collected data.

The UKMMAS strategy became part of core business for monitoring organisations in January 2008. The structure of the mechanism is shown in Figure 1.5. A high-level policy committee (MAPC) steers the strategy, whilst a technical committee (MARG) oversees the work of various sub-groups which themselves address the activities of data gathering to demonstrate the vision is being met. These include three evidence collection groups (the Clean and Safe Seas Evidence Group (CSSEG); Healthy and Biologically Diverse Seas Evidence Group (HBDSEG) and Productive Seas Evidence Group (PSEG)) and sub-groups with responsibility for the production of integrated assessments, data stewardship and monitoring protocols.

One of the collaborative monitoring programmes set up through MARG, the UK Clean and Safe seas Environmental Monitoring Programme (CSEMP), overseen by CSSEG, is long-term and was built on, and continues building on, the datasets from earlier programmes such as the UK National Marine Monitoring Programme[9]. It is also now a significant part of the monitoring network required by the WFD.

### Devolution

In 1999, the UK Parliament devolved certain powers to Scotland. Since then, the responsibility for marine activities has been split between Holyrood and Westminster. Table 1.4 sets out the broad responsibilities.

To further develop Scottish marine and coastal policy in a devolved context, *Seas the Opportunity – a strategy for the long term sustainability of Scotland's coasts and seas*[10] (Figure 1.6) was published in 2005. This endorsed the vision for "clean, healthy, safe, productive and biologically diverse marine and coastal environments, managed to meet the long term needs of nature and people". The strategy set out an objective to "develop better integrated, relevant scientific data on the marine environment and the effects of pressures on it". This current report is a part of that process. A key action of *Seas*

Figure 1.5 UKMMAS Structure

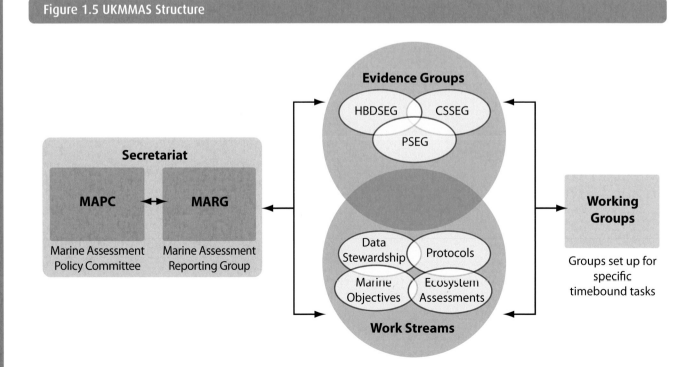

| Table 1.4 Devolved and reserved responsibilities for key marine activities | | |
|---|---|---|
| **Activity** | **Within 12 nautical miles** | **12 to 200 nautical miles** |
| Fishing | Devolved | Devolved |
| Aquaculture | Devolved | Not applicable |
| Nature and conservation | Devolved | Reserved |
| Harbours & harbour orders | Devolved | Not applicable |
| Control of land-based discharges (WEWS Act) | Devolved | Not applicable |
| Planning | Devolved | Reserved |
| Coast Protection Act | Devolved | Not applicable |
| FEPA | Devolved | Executively devolved |
| Renewable energy | Executively devolved | Executively devolved |
| Telecommunications | Reserved | Reserved |
| Oil and gas | Reserved | Reserved |
| Shipping | Reserved | Reserved |
| Historic heritage | Devolved | Reserved |

Executively devolved – Scottish Government administers the activity but has no powers to change the legislation.

*the Opportunity* was to establish the Advisory Group on Marine and Coastal Strategy (AGMACS), a Ministerially chaired group to further the development of marine and coastal policy work by involving stakeholders.

In 2007, reports by both AGMACS[11] and the Scottish Parliament Environment and Rural Development Committee (E&RDC), the latter having started an *Inquiry into the Marine Environment*[12], were published. In terms of marine science and data, the common themes to their recommendations were the need to:

> develop performance indicators;

> prioritise measures to bring available marine data together;

> support Scottish input to marine data archive centres;

> document current marine research and identify process for prioritising new research; and

> undertake research on the science of indicators and the impact of different activities on the marine environment.

Developing *Scotland's Seas: Towards Understanding their State* is a key first step to taking forward the recommendations from AGMACS and the E&RDC as well as establishing a baseline against which future marine and coastal policy can be measured.

| Figure 1.6 Seas the Opportunity |
|---|

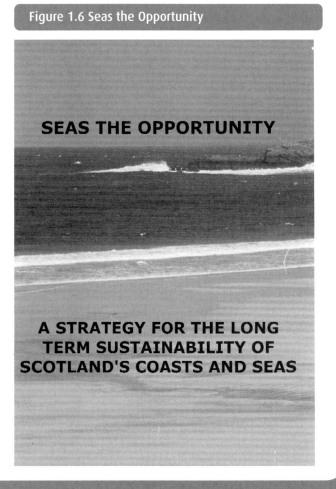

SEAS THE OPPORTUNITY

A STRATEGY FOR THE LONG TERM SUSTAINABILITY OF SCOTLAND'S COASTS AND SEAS

## New marine legislation in UK and Scotland

Following a commitment by the Prime Minister in 2001, the UK Government has been developing new marine legislation. The UK Marine Bill White Paper was published in March 2007 and includes proposals for a new marine management organisation, marine planning, licensing of marine activities, marine nature conservation and managing of inshore fisheries around England and Wales. A draft Bill is expected in spring 2008.

In June 2007 the Scottish Government announced its intention to bring forward legislation for Scotland's marine environment and in its Programme for Government committed to consult on proposed marine legislation. Since January 2008, a Sustainable Seas Task Force, with a membership from the wide marine stakeholder community, has been contributing to the development of a consultation paper for the intended marine legislation. The consultation is expected later in 2008 and is likely to include proposals to cover marine planning, marine nature conservation, streamlined licensing and, possibly, proposals for a marine management organisation. The intended legislation seems to fit with the wider recommendations of both AGMACS and the E&RDC.

### Why this report "towards understanding the state of Scotland's seas"?

The quantity of marine policy is, in itself, insufficient to demonstrate the effectiveness of marine legislation to achieve the overall vision of **"clean, healthy, safe, productive and biologically diverse seas"**. To demonstrate that the vision is being achieved needs: (a) a definition of the state according to some assessment criteria (i.e. what is a healthy sea?), and (b) determination of indicators to measure Scotland's seas against targets, using these to highlight gaps in knowledge. Some would argue that the process should be reversed, using a suite of indicators to define the vision. In practice the vision for clean, healthy, safe, productive and biologically diverse seas needs to be merged with pragmatic metrics of all these requirements. To understand the seas, assessments are needed but these take time. To assist with the current Scottish marine policy development, this report provides a baseline of information and data sources that paves the way for a full *State of Scotland's Seas* report in 2010.

Two initiatives being undertaken through the UKMMAS process will provide valuable tools for Scottish marine policy makers and managers.

> The UK Database of Marine Observing Systems (UKDMOS) will, for the first time, provide a web based portal of who in the UK does what, where, when and why in the marine environment. The database can be found at www.ukdmos.org; and

> Contributory Marine Objectives (CMOs), currently being developed by the three UKMMAS Evidence Collection Groups, will provide statements which will facilitate in the description of clean and safe, healthy and biologically diverse and productive seas. These CMOs will be described by an underlying set of indicators.

This report will contribute to the debate on clean and safe, healthy and biologically diverse and productive seas whilst adopting, where appropriate, thresholds enshrined in legal and other obligations. In addition, Annex 2 summarises the Scottish monitoring programmes listed in UKDMOS.

### Who does marine monitoring and research in Scotland's seas?

Understanding the state of the complex environment of Scotland's seas requires information to be integrated from a range of disciplines, from atomic through the microbial to the ecosystem level. Many specialists have provided the evidence to support policy decisions and assess the state of the seas. Annex 2 outlines the data that are being collected by FRS, SEPA and SNH from Scotland's seas and some of the data collecting programmes conducted by the wider community. These are briefly summarised, where appropriate, in Chapters 2–6.

Annex 3 is a list of reports from FRS, SEPA and SNH that report on the state of Scotland's seas according to the Scottish vision of **"clean, healthy, safe productive and biologically diverse seas"**. To provide a comprehensive list of reports published by the wider community on the aspects of the Scottish vision would run into hundreds of pages, and so Annex 3 also gives examples of existing reports with evidence on the state of Scotland's seas to illustrate the types of publication available from the wider community.

### Indicators

Indicators are representative, concise and easy-to-interpret variables which are used to illustrate the main features of the marine environment. Thus indicators reflect trends in the state of the marine environment and monitor the progress made in realising policy targets. The International Council for the Exploration of the Seas (ICES) has defined the criteria for a 'good indicator' specifically in relation to Ecological Quality Objectives, and these are presented in Table 1.5.

Indicators have become indispensable to policy-makers. They summarise large amounts of data and may relate to trends in pressures, state or impacts. In relation to our vision for **"clean, healthy, safe, productive and biologically diverse seas"**, indicators can be used for three major purposes:

| Table 1.5 | Criteria for a 'good indicator' specifically in relation to Ecological Quality Objectives as defined by ICES |
|---|---|
| **Criterion** | **Property** |
| a | Relatively easy to understand by non-scientists and those who will decide on their use |
| b | Sensitive to a manageable human activity |
| c | Relatively tightly linked in time to that activity |
| d | Easily and accurately measured, with a low error rate |
| e | Responsive primarily to a human activity, with low responsiveness to other causes of change |
| f | Measurable over a large proportion of the area to which the [EcoQ] metric is to apply |
| g | Based on an existing body or time series of data to allow a realistic setting of objectives |

> to supply information on the state of Scotland's seas, in order to enable policy-makers to develop policy and assess any emerging environmental problems;

> to support priority setting, by identifying key factors and gaps in knowledge that cause pressure on the marine environment; and

> to monitor the effects of policy responses.

As shown in Table 1.5, data for indicators must be collected at appropriate spatial, temporal and ecological (i.e. individuals versus communities) scales, with replication for robustness and a measure of quality assurance. Collecting data for indicators can be very resource intensive and consequently baseline data, against which the current state should be assessed, for some species and habitats have not (yet) been collected. A relatively good knowledge of plankton, some fish, bird and marine mammal species and some habitats exists, however, indicators have still to be developed for the less charismatic components of the marine realm including, for example, microbes, the deep sea, benthos, food-web interactions and ecosystem function.

In order for sustainable management to be effective it is important to understand the relationship between the ecological response (e.g. chlorophyll concentration) and the pressure (e.g. climate change). As an example, a decline in seal numbers could result from anthropogenic (e.g. shooting) or natural (e.g. disease outbreak) pressures. Both natural and anthropogenic change may have management consequences, yet indicators will rarely differentiate between these different impacts. The Pressure-State-Response (PSR) framework can be used, alongside policy questions, to develop a set of indicators. This approach can be considered as a tool for organising and presenting information to decision-makers; it shows the links between the causes of environmental problems and society's responses to them. For example:

> **P**ressures on the environment e.g. exploitation of renewable and non-renewable resources, pollution inputs including waste, conflict of interest in use of marine space, invasive/non-native species. The pressures on the environment are often considered from a policy perspective as the starting point for tackling environmental issues, and, from an indicator viewpoint when they are perhaps more readily available for analysis since they can be derived from socio-economic, environmental and other monitoring databases.

> **S**tate of the environment resulting from above pressures, including physical, chemical, biological and socio-economic. The state of the environment may, in turn, affect human health and well-being as well as the socio-economic fabric of society. Indicators of state should be designed to be responsive to the pressures and at the same time facilitate decisions on corrective action.

> **R**esponse of society to prevent negative environmental impacts, to correct existing damage, or to conserve natural resources e.g. designation of protected areas. Responses should be designed to act on the pressures but may at the same time also have an impact modifying the indicators of state.

Reporting areas

As part of the UKMMAS process, and in preparation for *Charting Progress 2*, new reporting areas have been developed. These are shown in Figure 1.7. Where possible, the Summary Assessments used in this report, and where differing geographical analyses are possible, have adopted these areas.

## Figure 1.7 Sea areas adopted in this report

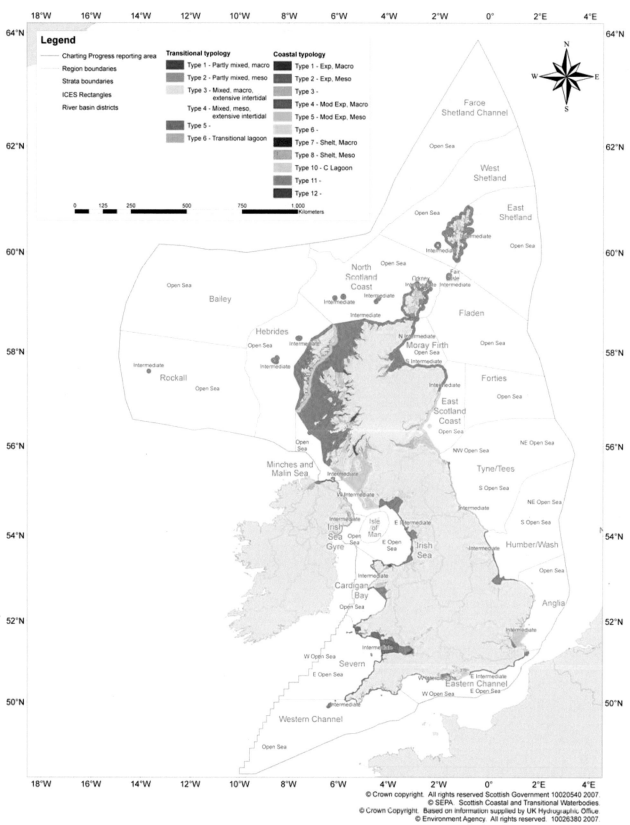

## Summary Assessment

As part of the process of establishing the status of the marine environment, summary assessments are included throughout this report and, more specifically, as part of the various Case Studies presented to highlight, in more detail, aspects of the science being conducted within Scottish waters. To maintain consistency, the summary assessment used in the UK Charting Progress process has been adopted here. One new column, for geographical region, has been

added (Table 1.6). The key to the 'trend assessment', 'status' and 'confidence' are presented in Tables 1.7, 1.8 and 1.9 respectively. These summary assessments present the current status for the specific regions detailed for that assessment and will be further developed in the *State of Scotland's Seas* to be published in 2010. In Chapter 5, summary assessments are also presented, where possible, on the basis of the available production statistics.

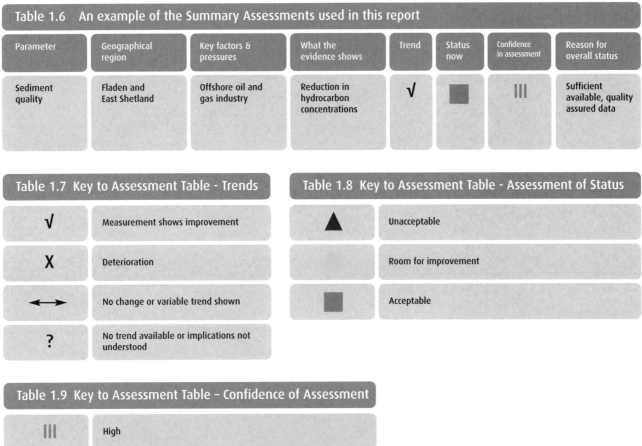

**Table 1.6   An example of the Summary Assessments used in this report**

| Parameter | Geographical region | Key factors & pressures | What the evidence shows | Trend | Status now | Confidence in assessment | Reason for overall status |
|---|---|---|---|---|---|---|---|
| Sediment quality | Fladen and East Shetland | Offshore oil and gas industry | Reduction in hydrocarbon concentrations | √ | ■ | III | Sufficient available, quality assured data |

**Table 1.7  Key to Assessment Table - Trends**

| | |
|---|---|
| √ | Measurement shows improvement |
| X | Deterioration |
| ↔ | No change or variable trend shown |
| ? | No trend available or implications not understood |

**Table 1.8  Key to Assessment Table - Assessment of Status**

| | |
|---|---|
| ▲ | Unacceptable |
| | Room for improvement |
| ■ | Acceptable |

**Table 1.9  Key to Assessment Table – Confidence of Assessment**

| | |
|---|---|
| III | High |
| II | Good/Satisfactory |
| I | Low |
| 0 | No assessment possible |

## CONCLUSION

Scotland's marine environment is of fundamental importance to the country. It influences weather patterns and provides many resources. However, this biologically diverse environment is under pressure from many human activities which, either individually or combined, have the potential to permanently alter the fundamental ecosystem processes. In some cases this may already have happened. It is necessary to ensure that the appropriate scientific

information is collected and analysed so as to provide the required advice which will ensure that Scotland's marine environment is used in a sustainable manner or that impact of the damage that has already occurred is reduced or reversed. The following chapters provide information on both our current knowledge of the marine environment and the on-going scientific monitoring which will form the basis of our integrated assessment of the *State of Scotland's Seas* to be published in 2010.

# Chapter 2
# Physical Characteristics and Modelling of the Marine Environment

## INTRODUCTION

The waters around Scotland are diverse in their physical characteristics. In the coastal zone the coastline varies between deep and narrow sheltered sea lochs on the west coast, shallow bays and estuaries, and long straight stretches of coastline that have little shelter from waves and storms. The major Scottish estuaries are the Solway Firth, the Clyde Sea, the Moray Firth, the Firth of Tay and the Firth of Forth (Figure 2.1).

---

**Figure 2.1   Bathymetry, specific boundaries and selected geographical features of the seas around Scotland**

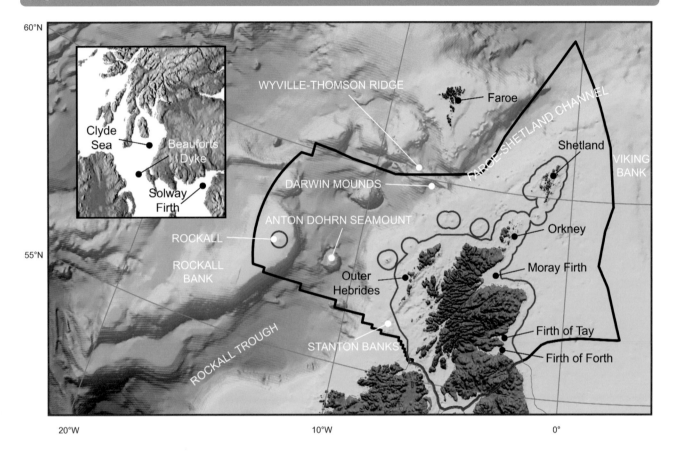

Table 2.1 details the latitude and longitude of the approximate centre of the features included. Red line = 12 nm limit; Black line = Scottish fisheries limits.

---

The offshore environment in Scottish waters ranges from shelf sea areas which are generally shallower than 250 m (average ~100 m) and deep ocean regions with depths greater than 2,000 m. The continental shelf includes the Malin and Hebrides Shelf Seas, Orkney and Shetland Shelf Seas, and the North Sea. The shelf seas are marked by notable features such as banks (e.g. Stanton Banks, Viking Bank) and deep channels (e.g. Beauforts Dyke). It is interesting to note that, in terms of Admiralty surveys, there remain some coastal areas of Scotland for which the survey data has been gathered by lead line only (Figure 2.2).

| Table 2.1 Latitude and longitude of the approximate centre of features included in Figure 2.1 | | |
|---|---|---|
| Feature | Latitude | Longitude |
| Solway Firth | 54.80 N | 3.53 W |
| Clyde Sea | 55.87 N | 4.94 W |
| Firth of Tay | 56.43 N | 2.74 W |
| Firth of Forth | 56.08 N | 3.02 W |
| Moray Firth | 57.66 N | 3.92 W |
| Orkney | 59.05 N | 2.95 W |
| Shetland | 60.31 N | 1.29 W |
| Faroe | 62.13 N | 6.94 W |
| Outer Hebrides | 57.84 N | 7.10 W |
| Beauforts Dyke | 54.72 N | 5.25 W |
| Stanton Banks | 56.21 N | 7.79 W |
| Viking Bank | 60.28 N | 2.41E |
| Wyville-Thomson Ridge | 60.11 N | 7.67 W |
| Rockall Trough | 56.08 N | 11.69 W |
| Anton Dohrn Seamount | 57.47 N | 11.08 W |
| Rockall | 57.57 N | 13.55 W |
| Darwin Mounds | 59.62 N | 7.22 W |

## Figure 2.2 The extent and nature of Admiralty Surveys conducted under the Civil Hydrography Programme (to 31 July 2007)

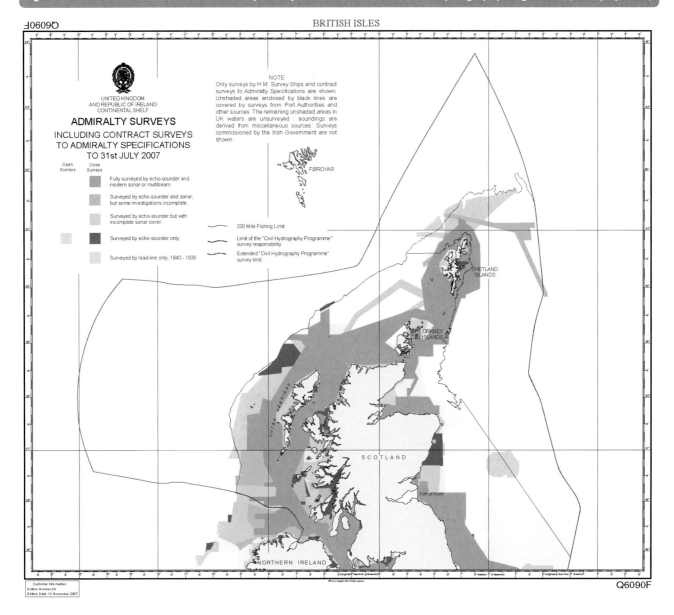

The western margin of the continental shelf is marked by a sharp change in the depth of the seabed. From less than 250 m, the continental slope drops rapidly into water deeper than 2,000 m. The continental slope is a transition area between two systems; the deeper oceanic waters and the shelf sea waters. The deep ocean areas have a complex bathymetry that is broken up by steep ridges (e.g. Wyville-Thomson Ridge), seamounts (e.g. Anton Dohrn) and banks[A] (e.g. Rockall Bank).

These deep waters west of Scotland were the location of some of the pioneering studies of deep-sea research when, between 1868 and 1890, HMS *Lightning* and HMS *Porcupine* first sampled this area ultimately leading to the discovery that the deep sea is not a quiescent, unchanging desert, but is an extremely dynamic region which can

contain an astonishingly high diversity of species. There is, however, still a huge amount not known about this area, but with time, understanding of the deeper waters to the west of Scotland is improving.

### PHYSICAL CHARACTERISTICS
*Weather and climatic conditions*
Scotland has a maritime climate strongly influenced by the oceanic waters of the North Atlantic and prevailing south-westerly winds. As these winds blow over the regions of the North Atlantic warmed by the North Atlantic current, they pick up heat which is delivered to Scotland, giving Scotland a relatively mild, wet climate considering its latitude. As such, changes in the strength of the Atlantic Ocean circulation have a significant effect on the climate of Scotland.

Normally, in the atmosphere over the North Atlantic, a low-pressure area is situated in the north, near Iceland, and a high-pressure area is situated in the south of the region near the Azores. This pattern of sea-level pressure results in a stream of smaller, secondary depressions, travelling in a north-eastward direction between these two regions. The passage of these depressions account for the variable weather experienced in Scotland and although the predominant wind direction is from the south-west, wind direction varies as depressions pass. The depressions are often more intense during winter months bringing with them gales, which in the windiest places (Western Isles, Orkney and Shetland) can occur up to 30 days per year.

The low-lying areas on the west coast of Scotland that are exposed to the Atlantic Ocean tend to have more cloud, less sunshine and be slightly warmer and wetter than the east of Scotland (Figure 2.3). Mean annual air temperatures in low-lying areas are between 7-9°C. However, sea fog (haar) from the North Sea is common in the spring and summer, particularly in the Northern Isles and on the east coast.

Rainfall over Scotland is high compared to the UK as a whole. Total rainfall is 113,150 million cubic metres *per* year of which 73% is estimated to runoff into the sea. This equates to approximately 1 million cubic metres runoff per square km of land[1].

The latitude of Scotland means that there are large variations in day length throughout the year with some northern areas receiving almost 24 hours daylight in midsummer and just a few hours of daylight at midwinter. The duration of light availability is known to produce a varied response in different phytoplankton species. The short, dark winter days that are typical of the north of Scotland mean that phytoplankton growth is considerably reduced between the months of November and February and very low cell abundances are observed in the water column. In contrast, some phytoplankton growth is observed in more southerly latitudes of the UK during the winter period. Extended photoperiod, which is the time that uninterrupted light is present, has also been shown to affect the toxin production of some phytoplankton routinely detected in Scottish waters such as *Pseudo-nitzschia seriata*[2], see Case Study 5.1.

*Currents and circulation*
Scotland's position on the UK continental shelf (Figure 2.1) means that the seas around Scotland are directly affected by oceanic circulation. The ocean circulation in the North Atlantic is dominated by two gyres, the southernmost of this is called the sub-tropical gyre. Although it is often

stated that the Gulf Stream, as part of the sub-tropical gyre circulation, brings warmth and milder conditions to Scotland's shores it is more correct to refer to the North Atlantic Current. This current is partly wind driven and partly driven by the density differences between the warmer, southern water and the cooler, northern water.

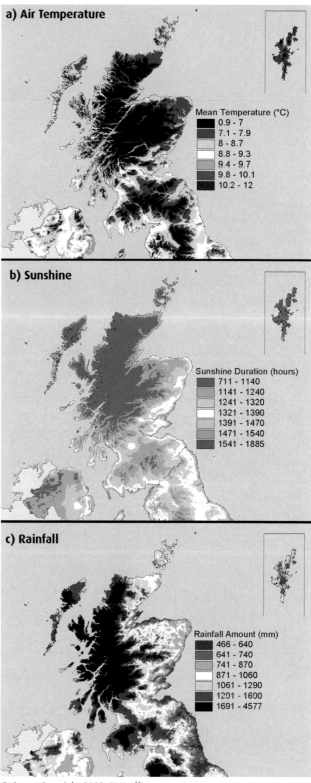

**Figure 2.3 Annual average (1971-2000) meteorological conditions for Scotland**

a) Air Temperature

Mean Temperature (°C)
0.9 - 7
7.1 - 7.9
8 - 8.7
8.8 - 9.3
9.4 - 9.7
9.8 - 10.1
10.2 - 12

b) Sunshine

Sunshine Duration (hours)
711 - 1140
1141 - 1240
1241 - 1320
1321 - 1390
1391 - 1470
1471 - 1540
1541 - 1885

c) Rainfall

Rainfall Amount (mm)
466 - 640
641 - 740
741 - 870
871 - 1060
1061 - 1290
1291 - 1600
1691 - 4577

© Crown Copyright 2008, Met office

Despite the significance of this circulation, current speeds and depth-averaged tidal velocities are relatively low. Currents speeds can be enhanced around topographic features, so areas such as the Rockall Bank and the edge of the continental shelf can have strong currents associated with them.

The map (Figure 2.4) only gives a schematic of the general pattern of currents and does not show the detail associated with the complex circulation of water. Background current speeds can also be enhanced over shorter timescales by complex effects such as mesoscale meanders and eddies, internal tides, internal waves and storm surges.

**Figure 2.4 Circulation in the offshore and coastal waters around Scotland**

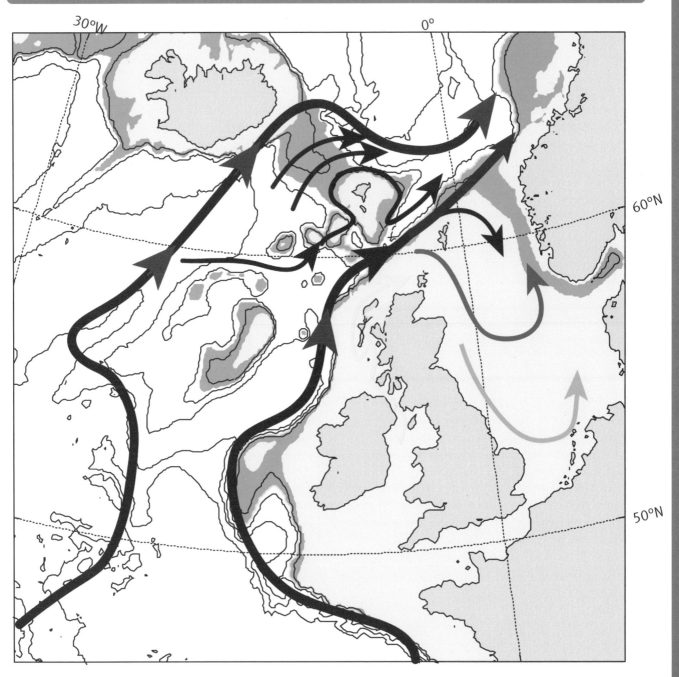

Map shows the circulation of surface waters. Red arrows are the flow of warm, salty Atlantic waters along the continental slope and further west. Yellow, blue and green arrows show the flow of coastal waters. Yellow arrow shows the path of the Scottish Coastal Current. Blue arrow shows the inflow of mixed coastal/oceanic water past Fair Isle (the Fair Isle Current).

As well as the surface circulation shown in Figure 2.4, there is a flow of deep water returning at depth from the Arctic. This is evident from the presence of cold water at depth in the Faroe-Shetland Channel (below 400-600 m) that has its origin in the Iceland, Greenland and Norwegian Seas. Two technical terms often associated with this circulation are the Thermohaline Circulation and, more recently, the Meridional Overturning Circulation (MOC). The MOC has been the subject of intense study in recent years, because of its significant contribution to climate variability and the possibility that the effects of global climate change will weaken the MOC (see Chapter 6). The deep waters from the Arctic, which travel in a south-eastward direction through the Faroe-Shetland Channel, are diverted westward by the Wyville-Thomson Ridge (Figure 2.1) and eventually spill over into the deep basin of the Rockall Trough. There are also intermittent overflows through deep channels in the Wyville-Thomson Ridge that are as yet unquantified. Changes in the properties of the deep water are thought to be indicative of changes in the surface circulation and the wider scale climatic changes. Two hydrographic sections across the Faroe-Shetland Channel have been surveyed by FRS for over a century and are situated at a key point to allow FRS to monitor these changes (see Chapter 6). Since 1994 the addition of current meters has allowed scientists to study changes in the volume of water passing through the Faroe-Shetland Channel.

In addition to the North Atlantic Current, a jet-like current, known as the Slope Current, flows in a poleward direction along the edge of the continental slope (Figure 2.4) as a persistent slope current with speeds in the range of 15 to 30 cm/s, and centred approximately over the 400-500 m isobath. The waters in the Slope Current originate from the Iberian region and some of the North Atlantic Water that reaches the Bay of Biscay joins the Slope Current. The Slope Current is an important source of heat, nutrients and plankton to the waters around Scotland. It appears to vary with the seasons, and can be stronger in winter than in summer. Its strength and direction can also be affected by local winds.

The steep bathymetry of the continental slope acts as a barrier between oceanic regions and the shelf sea systems, reducing the amount of water that can travel from the deeper waters of the North Atlantic into the shallower waters on the continental shelf. Processes that cause mixing of oceanic waters and shelf sea waters are complex but have a significant impact on conditions in Scottish waters. Waters from the North Atlantic enter the North Sea between Orkney and Shetland and around the north-east of Shetland as well as through the deep Norwegian Trench (Figure 2.4).

Tidal currents are predictable and stronger than the residual current in many areas. Tidal currents cause mixing in the water column and therefore often determine the location and extent to which the water column is stratified into different distinct layers. Tidal currents are intensified in localised areas (Figure 2.5), usually where the flow is constrained by topography. This includes areas such as between Orkney and Shetland, the Pentland Firth, off the Mull of Kintyre and Hebrides where tidal streams can be as high as 3.5-4.5 m/s. However, when the transport of water around Scotland is considered, the overall effect of the tides is quite small as tidal currents mainly move water back and forth.

The residual circulation in the North Sea is predominantly anti-clockwise and circulation on the shelf west of Scotland (the Scottish Coastal Current) is mainly northwards. However, this circulation is strongly affected by winds and density-driven coastal currents and jets, which can lead to significant changes and even a reversal of this general pattern for short periods (Figure 2.4).

Flow variability on the Scottish west coast is being studied using a current meter mooring in the Tiree Passage (Case Study 2.1). Such measurements of currents, together with determination of salinity and temperature, provide an essential background understanding of the physical characteristics of Scottish waters which have a direct effect on the ecology of Scottish seas.

### Temperature and salinity

Sea temperatures around Scotland are affected by local climatic conditions (heat flux with atmosphere) and the heat transferred to the shores of Scotland by ocean currents (advective effects). Sea surface temperatures vary with an annual cycle, lagging behind the cycle of atmospheric temperature by around one month.

Average sea temperatures around Scotland reflect the influence of heat transported from oceanic waters (a specific example of the Tiree Passage is presented in Case Study 2.1). On average, the winter temperatures on the west coast of Scotland are higher than those on the east coast. In the summer this situation is reversed as waters in the shallower North Sea warm up more quickly and so summer temperatures on the east coast are higher than on the west coast. The influence of the North Atlantic Current and climate system can also be observed in the long-term variability of sea surface temperatures.

In deeper waters, the circulation patterns strongly influence temperatures, with returning cold water of Arctic origin filling the deep basins below about 800 m and intermediate waters lying between this and the warmer Atlantic waters above.

**Figure 2.5** Mean spring tidal range (m) and peak current flow (m/s) for a mean spring tide for the seas around Scotland

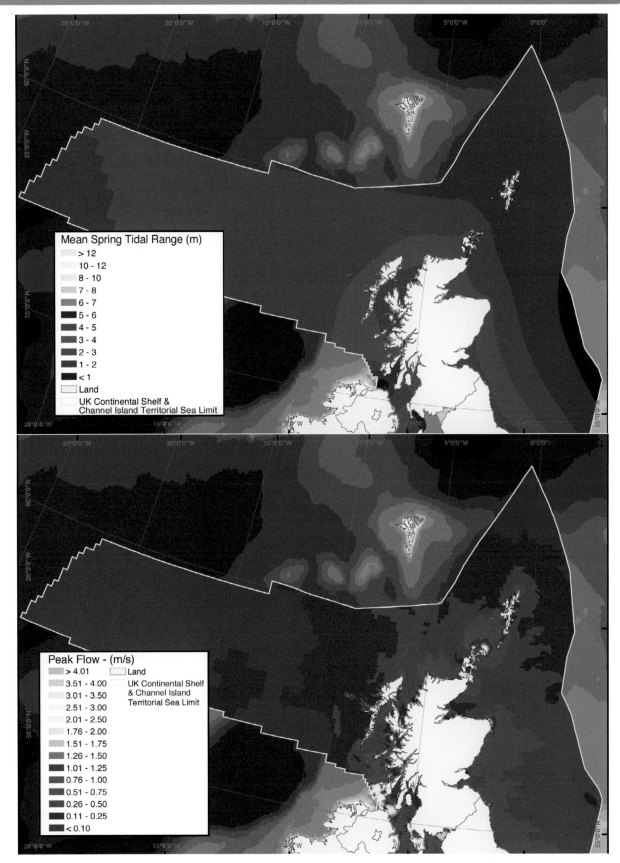

Source: Atlas of Marine Renewable Energy (Bathymetry, Waves, Wind, Tides)
http://www.berr.gov.uk/energy/sources/renewables/explained/wind/page27741.html

Salinity in the open ocean is controlled by the balance between evaporation (freshwater out) and precipitation (freshwater in). In coastal waters the direct input of freshwater from land run-off and rivers dominates the changes in salinity. Many shelf areas are affected by freshwater inputs. Areas of high freshwater influence are the large estuaries and adjacent coastal waters of the Clyde, Solway Firth, Moray Firth, Firth of Tay and Firth of Forth as well as coastal areas on the west coast that receive a lot of freshwater from land runoff and numerous small rivers (Figure 2.6).

The physical characteristics of the waters in the shelf seas off Scotland are important because of their effect on the marine ecosystem. These characteristics are largely determined by a balance between the surface heating from the sun and freshwater run-off from the land, and the mixing influences of the strong tidally and wind driven flows, themselves shaped by the intricate and irregular bathymetry and coastline. The combination of these factors results in regions that are stratified and regions that are well mixed, with complex frontal systems between them (Figure 2.6).

It is also important to note the particular characteristics of sea lochs. Many west coast Scottish sea lochs have restricted water exchange with the surrounding seas, particularly those with a sill at the mouth of the loch.

**Figure 2.6 Water column features on the Scottish continental shelf in winter**

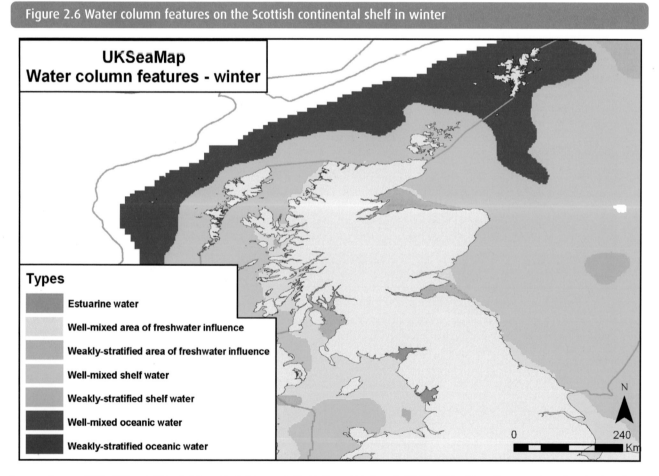

Source: Connor, D.W., Gilliland, P.M., Golding, N., Robinson, P., Todd, D. and Verling, E. 2006. *UKSeaMap: the mapping of seabed and water column features of UK seas.* Joint Nature Conservation Committee, Peterborough.

## Sea-level

Sea-levels are affected over short timescales by the rise and fall of the tide as well as the effects of storm surges. Over longer timescales, the sea-level is affected by global climate change and movements of land masses relative to the earth's crust.

The principal tidal components are the semi-diurnal (twice daily) tides although in some limited regions the diurnal (daily) tides are significant. The UK National Tide Gauge Network, run by the Tide Gauge Inspectorate, records tidal elevations at a number of locations around the UK coast of which 11 are located in Scotland. These measurements, together with those provided by the SEPA Tide Gauge Network (Figure 2.7), provide a long time series of reliable and accurate sea-level data. Tidal range is generally between 4 and 5 m; highest tidal ranges are found in the inner Solway Firth (Figure 2.5) where the mean spring tidal range can be between 7 and 8 m. Tidal range is at a minimum in areas known as amphidromic points. One of these points occurs in Scottish waters between Islay and the Mull of Kintyre; another amphidromic point can be found in the north-east of the North Sea. Tidal range decreases with distance offshore from the north-east coast.

### Figure 2.7 SEPA Tidal Gauge locations and Scottish locations of the UK National Tide Gauge Network (POL gauge)

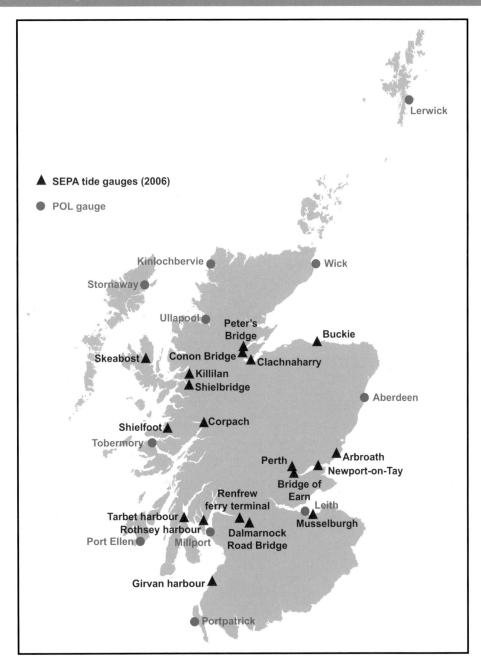

## Background

Temperature, salinity and flow variability on the north-west European continental shelf to the west of Scotland are examined in this case study. Analyses are derived from a range of marine and atmospheric data sources which together comprise a "proto marine observatory".

## Surveys and data sources

The main time series are from a current meter mooring which has been maintained by SAMS in the Tiree Passage between the islands of Coll and Mull (Figure 2.8) since June 1981, and from a hydrographic section repeated at least annually since 1975 across the shelf at the mooring latitude and out to Rockall. Additional time series used are from the UK Tide Gauge Network (main text Figure 2.7) and Met Office weather records.

### Figure 2.8 Location of the current meter mooring in the Tiree Passage between the islands of Coll and Mull

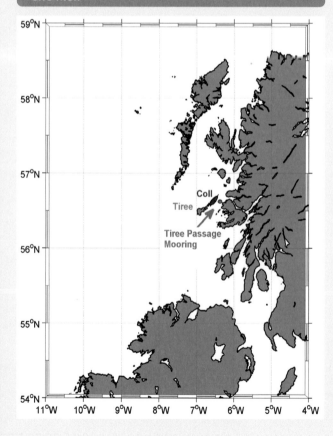

## Results and Interpretation

The mean water temperature in the Tiree Passage is 10.1 °C and the dominant mode of variability in the temperature record is the seasonal cycle, with an amplitude of 3.2 °C. Temperature anomaly time series (deviations from the average monthly values over the last 25 years) from the Tiree Passage and of the full NE Atlantic upper layer show highs in the late 1980s and late 1990s and lows in the early 1980s and mid 1990s. The overall trend on the continental shelf is of warming at a rate of +0.57 °C per decade (Figure 2.9). In addition, it was found that the date of maximum annual temperature has been delayed by 12 days per decade, throughout the time series. However, it should be noted these historical trends do not mean that the rates of change will be the same into the future.

Shelf salinities showed only weak seasonality, in contradiction to previous published analyses. No single determining factor has been found for the longitudinal movement of more saline oceanic waters across the shelf. Prolonged periods of high North Atlantic Oscillation index (NAO) were found to coincide with periods of raised salinity of shelf waters (NAO: high values of this index correspond to warm, wet and windy conditions over Scotland).

The water currents in the Tiree Passage are constrained by the coastline and are dominated by the semi-diurnal tides (12.42 and 12 hours). There is also significant seasonal variation in the flow rate. After removal of the effects of tidal currents, the residual flow has a mean value of 10.8 cm/s directed towards the north which is likely to be caused by the Scottish Coastal Current (Figure 2.4). There were very few, short duration periods of flow reversal. Application of a simple model to the flow in the passage (using tide gauge, atmospheric pressure and wind observations) demonstrates that wind changes are the dominant factor accounting for variability of the northward flow, and both the north/south gradient in sea-level slope and atmospheric pressure are significant in driving the coastal current northwards. Applying this balance model to these year-round data has revealed a bias in previous summer-only estimates of the flow rate of the coastal current. A revised figure for the strength of the Scottish Coastal Current of approximately twice previous estimates is therefore proposed. Residual winter flows correlate significantly with the North Atlantic Oscillation index (r – 0.59) (Figure 2.10).

## Figure 2.9 Monthly temperature anomalies from the Tiree Passage temperature time series

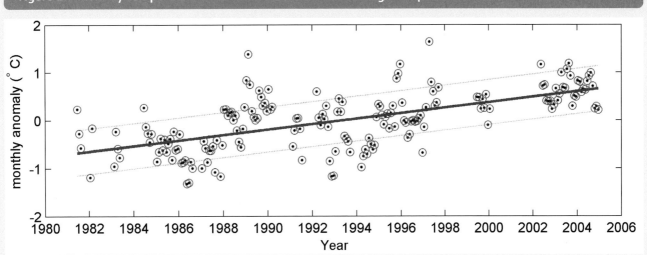

Trend shows an increase in temperature of 0.57 °C *per* decade. Error estimates of 1 standard deviation are shown.

## Figure 2.10 Winter (December, January, February, March (DJFM)) NAO and the winter average northward flow (divided by a factor of two) through the Tiree Passage

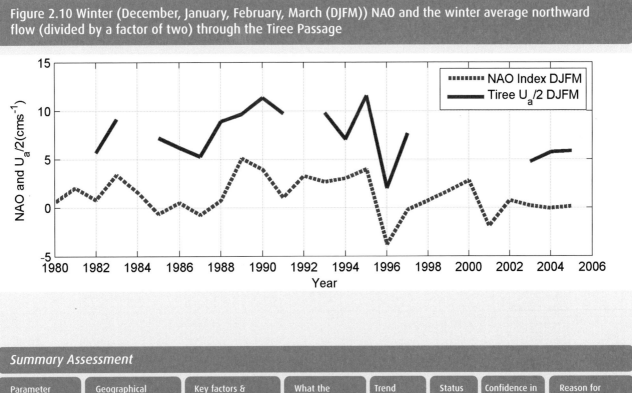

## Summary Assessment

| Parameter | Geographical region | Key factors & pressures | What the evidence shows | Trend | Status now | Confidence in assessment | Reason for overall status |
|---|---|---|---|---|---|---|---|
| Water Temperature | Sea of the Hebrides | NE Atlantic Circulation Patterns | Warning trend overlain by large inter-annual variability | ? | | III | Sufficient available, quality assured data |

Tidal surges caused by storms do occur in Scotland, and mainly affect the east coast. However, storm surges are less significant around Scotland than in regions further south because of the way that the surges grow as they propagate southward. For example, the most significant storm surge ever recorded over the last 100 years occurred in 1953. During that event surge levels of 0.6 m and 0.83 m were recorded at Aberdeen and Leith respectively, but reached 2.97 m in southern England (King's Lynn) and 3.36 m in the Netherlands[4]. The 1 in 50 year storm surge predictions for Scotland are around 1.25 m.

*Waves*

Sea-surface waves are mainly a wind-driven phenomenon, and their height is predominantly determined by the fetch (i.e. distance wind has blown over) and length of time of the wind forcing. The seabed also influences waves in shallow water as waves will become steeper and higher as they approach the shore.

Within Scottish waters, the wave climate is mainly influenced by conditions in the North Atlantic ocean, where the fetch is long enough to establish large swell waves.

## Figure 2.11 Annual mean wind speed (m/s) and annual mean wave height (m)

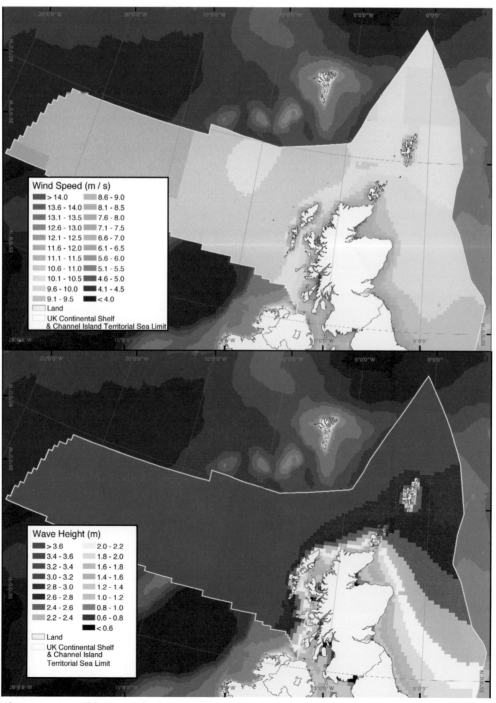

Source: Atlas of Marine Renewable Energy (Bathymetry, Waves, Wind, Tides)
http://www.berr.gov.uk/energy/sources/renewables/explained/wind/page27741.html

The north and west of Scotland (Hebrides, Orkney and Shetland) are most exposed to these conditions. Waves on the east coast of these islands are smaller due to their comparatively sheltered nature. On the east coast of Scotland, conditions in autumn and winter may also be rough in the North Sea due to the wind direction being such that there is a large fetch. Moreover, the Moray Firth is also relatively exposed because of its shoaling bathymetry and exposure to the North Sea. Figure 2.11 shows the significant wave height (the average height of the highest 1/3 waves) and the wind speed for Scotland.

*Turbidity*

Turbidity, a measure of how clear the water is, is generally determined by which particles are suspended in the water column, and their concentration. Suspended solids are generally highest in areas close to land (due to run-off) and in shallow regions where currents and waves are

sufficiently strong to resuspend bottom sediments. Other than biological (e.g. phytoplankton cells) and mineral (sediment) particles, the water colour may also be influenced by Coloured Dissolved Organic Matter (CDOM), that is released by decaying terrestrial and marine plants. Due to the relatively larger release from terrestrial plants, the input of significant concentrations of CDOM is mainly confined to coastal areas with a large freshwater input[5].

Turbidity is highest in coastal areas with a large fresh water input, such as the Clyde Sea, Firth of Lorn and the Forth/Tay river plume. Compared to the southern North Sea, the Scottish North Sea has much lower concentrations of suspended sediment (Figure 2.12). The turbidity of the water influences the productivity, as murky waters limit the penetration of light and can inhibit photosynthesis[5].

**Figure 2.12 Map showing modelled turbidity (mg/l) in coastal waters of Scotland[6]**

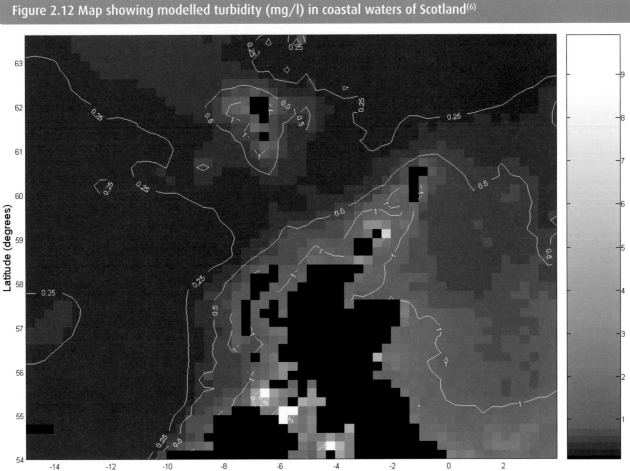

The model data are a monthly average of the Suspended Particulate Matter (SPM) concentration at 45 and 5 m depth from the European Regional Seas Ecosystem Model (ERSEM) for the month of February. Higher concentrations are evident near the coasts, with low concentrations in the deep ocean. High concentrations are also identified near larger estuaries, such as Clyde and Firth of Forth/Tay, and in locations with strong currents such as the region between Northern Ireland and Mull of Kintyre.

## pH

There are no existing observations of pH in Scottish waters. In future, pH is likely to be one of the water property measurements requiring increased attention due to its importance for ocean acidification. The effects of increased acidity of waters will be most pertinent for primary producers (phytoplankton), although through higher trophic links, the grazing community and their predators may also be affected[7,8].

## Sediment concentration and transport

When looking out over the sea, the presence of water is very evident. What is less evident is that within the water is suspended particulate material (SPM) which comprises mineral particles, living plankton and phyto-detritus. The focus in this section is on the mineral particles and the sedimentary processes which lead to the distribution of seabed sediments observed around Scotland. As mentioned above, there is an association between SPM and the turbidity of marine waters. Many monitoring programmes include measurements of suspended sediment and turbidity, often using a device to measure optical back-scatter. However, the more traditional method, of measuring the depth at which the black and white segments of a Secchi Disk (Figure 2.13) are no longer discernable, although of limited use, still provides a quick assessment of water clarity.

## Sedimentary processes and transport

Sedimentary processes affect the coastal and marine environment in a number of ways.  These include:

> the evolution of the coast, the foreshore and the sea bed;

> the transport of contaminants, especially those which have a high octanol/water partition coefficient and thus bind strongly to the fine sediment particles; and

> the species composition and population of benthic communities.

In terms of species composition, the fine muddy sediments with a high organic matter content can support a wide variety of molluscs, worms and crustaceans while sandy sediments tend to support fauna that are adapted to life in relatively mobile substrate.

Sediment resuspension, transport and deposition are mainly influenced by the sediment type and availability, and by the nature of the currents and waves. The movement of most types and sizes of sediment grains will occur only when the waves and/or currents are strong enough to exceed the threshold of motion for particular

**Figure 2.13 Measuring water clarity at the FRS Ecosystem Monitoring site off Stonehaven using a Secchi Disk**

grain sizes. Very fine grains will tend to be transported at the same rate as the transporting fluid but, for sands and gravels, the pathways of sediment transport may be very different to the distribution of the residual current.

The character of the shelf sea bed is highly variable and reflects both modern tidal and current patterns, and past currents that affected sediment accumulation. The sea bed varies from mud to rock and a more detailed description of the seabed sediments around Scotland is presented in Case Study 2.2. However, a better knowledge of seabed sediments is required for habitat mapping, offshore renewable energy, oil and gas development, aggregate extraction, fisheries, environmental monitoring, marine and coastal planning and legislation. Ultimately, modern instrumentation, such as multi-beam echo-sounders, can now provide such high-resolution information. This technique is being used by marine management organisations and the commercial sector to gather depth information that reveals the shape of the sea-floor, and provide acoustic images of the physical properties of the sea bed that can be used to compile detailed and accurate geological maps of the sea-floor. An example of this is

**Figure 2.14 Rock outcrops used to support the Firth of Forth bridges obtained using multi-beam echo-sounders**

A full 'fly-through' of this area of the seabed and further information is available in Annex 6 on the CD.

provided in Figure 2.14 and on the attached CD. The data were collected by BGS from a small area of the Firth of Forth surrounding the road and rail bridges. Using 'fly-through' software, the sea bed can be observed in detail to identify geological features such as the igneous rocks that crop out at the sea-floor. The images (Figure 2.14 and the 'fly-through' on the CD) clearly show how designers of the Forth bridges used these rock outcrops to provide a solid foundation for the construction of both bridges.

On a very different geographical scale, the Frontispiece to this report is a map of the Scottish land and sea areas showing the morphology of the country's terrain. Onshore topography is from NEXTMap Britain (©Intermap Technologies) in which heights of land features are acquired from an aircraft using radar technology. The data have a very high vertical resolution. The marine dataset is part of the Olex bathymetric database compiled, processed and managed by the Norwegian company Olex AS. The seabed image is based upon echo-sounder data acquired

mainly by commercial fishing vessels, but also including data from research vessels. The datasets are contributed voluntarily, the data are then individually merged with the central dataset, after which the contributor has access to all of the shared bathymetry. The database represents the earth's surface as a series of 5 x 5 m cells. Vertical resolution is 1 m in deep areas and 0.1 m at depths less than 100 m. This means that relative depths are highly accurate with an error range of only 1-2%. Quality assurance is achieved by comparing an individual contributor with the large number of other soundings covering the same area. Although the data are not complete for the offshore area, this example illustrates the advantages of sharing data acquired from different sources. What these two examples show is that detailed information is becoming increasingly available. This will be of value to all those interested in the Scottish marine environment.

**EVIDENCE FOR THE STATE OF PHYSICAL CHARACTERISTICS OF THE SEA**

There is a difference in the precision, accuracy and quantity of evidence available on the physical characteristics of the state of Scotland's seas. Some data are periodically collected and cover large regions (e.g. thermosalinograph is an automated sea-surface temperature and salinity measurement system making measurements from a ship throughout its cruise), whereas other data are collected frequently, but only at a few locations (e.g. circulation data, wave heights). A vast amount of data are currently being collected on temperature (both sea surface, and profiles) and the salinity of Scotland's seas.

Table 2.2 summarises some of the physical data collected in Scotland's seas. A considerable amount of these data are collected in the coastal waters, particularly in the Minches and Malin Sea, East Scotland Coast, and Shetland areas. There are often only sparse data available for the offshore areas, although this situation is improving all the time with an increased amount of data being collected in offshore areas. In addition, models are being used to predict physical characteristics for these areas (e.g. waves and circulation).

## Table 2.2 Summary of data collected on the physical characteristics of Scotland's seas

| Physical characteristics | Data collector[1] |
|---|---|
| Air temperature | British Atmospheric Data Centre (BADC), FRS, Met Office |
| Bathymetry | BGS, Fishing Industry, Hydrographic Office |
| Bottom pressure | Institute of Oceanographic Sciences, NASA |
| Changes in seal-level, coast and seabed | POL, SEPA |
| Currents and circulation | FRS, POL, SAMS, SEPA |
| Freshwater inputs from major rivers | SEPA |
| North Atlantic Oscillation index | Climatic Research Unit at the University of East Anglia |
| pH | International Council for the Exploration of the Seas (ICES) |
| Rainfall | BADC, Met Office, SEPA |
| Salinity | FRS, ICES, POL, SEPA, SNH |
| Sea temperature (surface and profiles) | FRS, ICES, Met Office, SAMS, SEPA |
| Sediment concentration and transport | BGS, Satellite Observing Systems Ltd |
| Thermohaline profile | SAMS |
| Waves | Met Office, Surf Observer Program, POL, Satellite Observing Systems Ltd, University of Aberdeen |
| Wind direction and speed | BADC, FRS, Met Office |

[1] The term 'data collector' includes organisations who may act as a repository for data collected by another organisation (e.g. ICES)

## MODELLING THE MARINE ENVIRONMENT

There is a significant challenge associated with characterising the marine environment because of its complexity and limited data. However, perhaps an even greater challenge is to have the capacity to link different data in a manner that can allow us to develop an understanding of marine processes. Models can be used to describe the physical, chemical and ecological processes in the marine environment. This allows the effects of changes in the sea (natural or man made) to be simulated and predictions to be made. These prediction scenarios are often used to aid decisions relating to public and maritime safety, environmental protection and economic development. Increasingly, they will also aid in the assessment of the state of the seas. The continual improvement in computing power permits models to be used to study, for example, the early life history of fish, shelf sea circulation and the environmental impacts of aquaculture. A further example, the use of data from multi-beam echo-sounders to improve computer model performance, is presented in Case Study 2.3. However, there remain many modelling challenges. For example, accurate forecasting of salinity is a major modelling difficulty, particularly around the west coast of Scotland where land run-off is not well described. Also, as models are expensive to produce and their calibration requires hard data they generally have a particular geographic or functional focus which limits their use elsewhere without further development.

### The modelling of Scotland's seas

A considerable number of organisations have an interest in simulating the seas around Scotland at different scales. These range from the inclusion of our seas in global climate models, through to the simulation of coastal flooding/erosion and the disposal of waste. In this context, many Scottish organisations contribute to the international efforts to improve understanding and modelling of our seas. For example, Scotland's west coast has many fjordic sea lochs and there is a need to improve our knowledge of fjordic processes. These environments are challenging to model and are fertile ground for testing improvements to modelling capability. Examples of Government and Academic organisations carrying out modelling in Scottish seas are detailed in Table 2.3.

A specific area of interest is operational oceanographic forecasting of the UK coastal and shelf seas. Recently a strategic partnership between the Met Office and the Proudman Oceanographic Laboratory (Liverpool), Plymouth Marine Laboratory, National Oceanography Centre Southampton and the Environmental Systems Science Centre (Reading) was established to facilitate this process. The National Centre for Ocean Forecasting (NCOF; http://www.ncof.gov.uk/) presently has no Scottish representation.

Commercial organisations also carry out a wide range of modelling around Scotland's waters, for example to predict the impact of waste disposal from fish farming, industrial activity and public sewerage systems, or modelling relating to coastal flooding, coastal erosion and defence, renewable energy and seabed and coastal engineering works.

Specific examples of modelling studies in Scotland's seas include:

> **Aquaculture:** The Scottish Aquaculture Research Forum (SARF) commissioned two modelling studies relating to 'The Assimilative Capacity of Sea-Lochs and The Fate of Aquaculture Waste'. FRS is undertaking research into the modelling of sea lice dispersal;

> **Bathing Water Quality:** Scottish Water commissioned two major modelling studies (Ayrshire Coast and Forth Estuary) to identify how drainage investment could help contribute to bathing water improvement;

## Table 2.3  Organisations involved in modelling Scottish seas

| Task | Examples of Organisations Involved |
|---|---|
| Climate Change Modelling | Met Office |
| Storm Surge Modelling & Coastal Flooding | Met Office, POL, SEPA |
| Oil/Chemical Spill Modelling | Marine and Coastguard Agency (MCA), Cefas |
| Fisheries and Aquaculture | FRS, SEPA |
| Coastal Water Quality | SEPA, FRS |
| Physical, Chemical and Ecological Modelling Research | SAMS, FRS, CEFAS, POL, Universities of St Andrews, Strathclyde, Dundee, Bangor and Southampton. |
| Fisheries and Aquaculture Modelling Research | FRS, SEPA |

## CASE STUDY 2.2   Seabed sediment

Knowledge of the seabed sediments around Scotland is primarily based on surveys undertaken by the British Geological Survey (BGS) in the 1970s and '80s, when the DTI sponsored a major reconnaissance mapping programme based on seabed samples and seismic reflection data. Approximately 15,000 samples were taken a few kilometres apart and a grid of seismic data were collected on a line spacing of 2 to 5 km. Over 50 maps at 1:250,000, 1:500,000 and 1:1,000,000 scales depicting the bedrock geology, the overlying unconsolidated sediments and the seabed sediments were published. Much of this information is also available within various digital products and has been described in six regional reports[9-14].

The existing seabed sediment maps (summarised in Figure 2.15) depict the grain size of the sediments. Samples were classified by grain size (the relative proportions of gravel, sand and mud) and the amount of terrigenous (land-derived) or calcareous materials (derived from the shells of marine organisms).

In general, the sediments around Scotland are sandy or gravelly and originate from deposits during the Quaternary glaciation. Strong currents and wave action may also have prevented deposition of recent muddy sediment or have winnowed it to leave a coarse-grained lag deposit. Muddy sediments occur principally nearshore, for example in estuaries where the sediment is supplied from the main rivers such as the Forth and Clyde. Further offshore, muddy sediments occur in depressions on the sea floor, where currents may be relatively weak, such as the Witch Ground and Fladen basins and in The Minch. They also occur beyond the shelf break (200 m water depth) to the west of Scotland, in the Faroe-Shetland Channel and the Rockall Trough. The concentration of calcareous material varies greatly in seabed sediments reflecting the amount of shell material in different areas; locally, they can be very high (over 75%) in areas such as the sea bed around Orkney and Shetland.

### Figure 2.15 Distribution of seabed sediments around Scotland

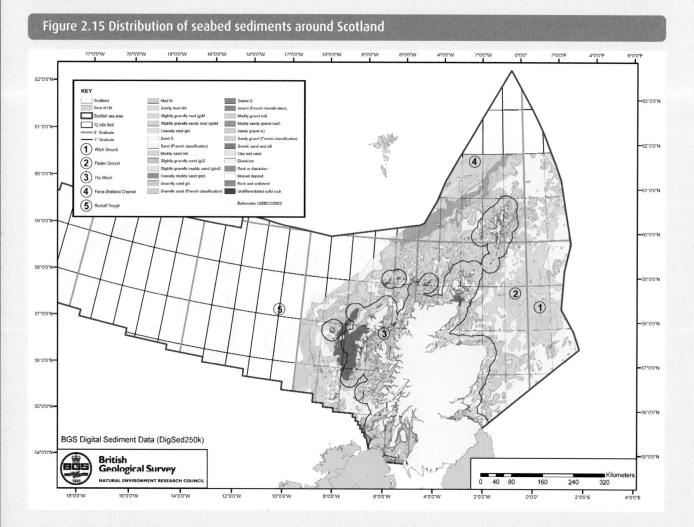

## CASE STUDY 2.3   Modelling bathymetric data

### The Application of Multi-beam Echo-Sounders

In recent years, some areas of Scotland's sea bed have been surveyed using Multi-beam Echo-Sounders. These deliver high resolution depth data which can greatly improve physical process simulation (e.g. water flow/level) in computer models and also help to generate maps of seabed type. Multi-beam data from the Sound of Harris, in the Western Isles, are shown in Figure 2.16. Shaded bathymetry data (purple shallow, red deeper) are presented alongside an aerial photograph. Inset charts in Figure 2.16 show the effect of multi-beam bathymetry on

computer model performance. In this case the greater the agreement between the yellow dots (real data) and the blue dots (model data) the better the computer model is simulating the flow of water. The Sound of Harris data shown in Figure 2.16 were collected under the Civil Hydrography Programme, operated by the MCA. Other areas around Scotland have been surveyed by a range of organisations for commercial, government and academic projects. Greater access to new and existing multi-beam data will help to improve the performance of all models of Scotland's seas.

### Figure 2.16 Multi-beam bathymetry detail and the effect on computer model performance

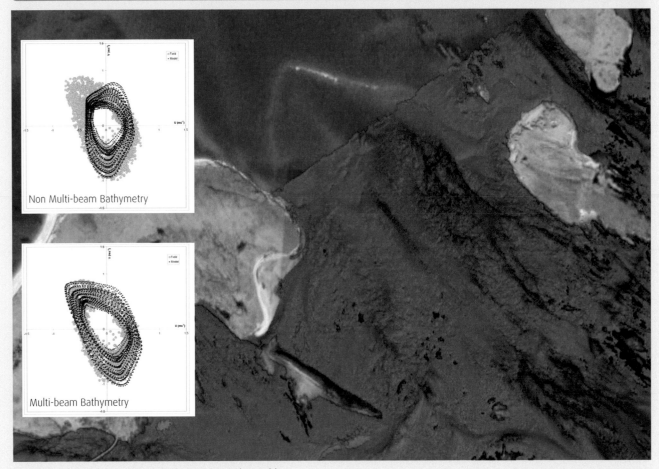

(Courtesy of MCA, Associated British Ports, Google Earth)

> **Coastal Flood Warning:** SEPA currently operates a Firth of Clyde and Clyde Estuary flood warning modelling system;

> **Clyde Estuary:** The existing SEPA model of the Clyde Estuary was upgraded and utilised, by commercial consultants, during the Glasgow Strategic Drainage Plan (GSDP) study;

> **Forth Estuary:** Scottish Power commissioned a modelling study of the Forth Estuary to predict the impacts of changes to their discharge from Longannet power station; and

> **Aberdeen Beach:** Aberdeen City Council commissioned a modelling study to examine options for coastal erosion defence.

### Data

All computer models require real environmental data to work effectively. The disciplines of measurement and modelling are intrinsically linked. A lack of data in any modelling exercise can introduce uncertainty and lead to unreliable results. Much of the data collected in Scottish seas are used to set up models or check their performance. Modelling often benefits from targeted, simultaneous, data collection, where many different parameters are collected throughout the area to be modelled. One key marine environmental data-set that benefits virtually all those involved in modelling is the water depth (bathymetry). The existing quality, and coverage, of bathymetry data around Scotland is, as mentioned earlier, variable (see Figure 2.2). Case Study 2.3 explores the effect of bathymetry on the performance of a marine model.

### Communication

The construction and operation of computer models of the sea include many common steps which are sometimes independent of the final application. At present many of these common steps are duplicated for different modelling studies. All those involved in the simulation of the waters around Scotland would benefit from a greater sharing of model information and data.

Output from large-scale models can often be used to drive smaller, more detailed, models of specific areas of interest. NCOF runs a global ocean model, a higher resolution North Atlantic Ocean model, and an even higher resolution UK shelf seas model. The resolution of the shelf model is 6 km. However, this only poorly describes the Scottish coastline, particularly the west coast. A high resolution sub-model for the Irish Sea (1.8 km) is run by the Proudman Oceanographic Laboratory which also has a research grade 1.8 km model for the full UK shelf. It would be highly desirable to see an operational high resolution model of the seas surrounding Scotland (1.8 km or finer). Access to information from a common model of Scotland's seas would provide more accurate inputs to smaller scale local models, benefiting many types of studies.

### Combining physics, chemistry and biology

Oceanographic processes bring nutrients (phosphate, nitrate, silicate and ammonia) to the surface waters where there is sufficient light to permit the fixation of carbon through photosynthesis. This chemical process requires, in addition to nutrients, trace elements and facilitates the growth of phytoplankton. The capturing of energy is crucial to the overall productivity of the marine ecosystem and will, to an extent, dictate the subsequent fisheries productivity and overall biodiversity in a region. Understanding the physical characteristics, chemical reactions and ecological processes which result in, for example, a substantial fishery is complex and requires the use of computer modelling as well as the adoption of an integrated, multi-faceted approach. This is illustrated in Case Study 2.4 which shows how estimates of new primary production in Scottish waters are produced and discusses their implications. This extended case study provides an insight into what can be achieved when the various marine disciplines are combined. It also makes individual regional assessments right round the Scottish coast, something which, in time, it is hoped can be achieved for many other assessments.

## CASE STUDY 2.4   New primary production in Scottish waters, 1960-2003

### Introduction

Primary production is the fundamental property which sets the productivity of the marine ecosystem as a whole. Impoverished regions which are starved of nutrients and the necessary trace elements required for phytoplankton growth can support only small fishery yields. In contrast, regions where oceanographic processes or major river inputs deliver large quantities of nutrient to the surface waters typically support substantial fisheries. Assessments of annual primary production can provide valuable information about overall yields from the sea.

Photosynthetic fixation of carbon in the oceans requires corresponding uptakes of inorganic nutrient elements (nitrogen, phosphorus, silicon) and trace elements such as iron and copper from the seawater. The annual supply of these elements to the shallow sunlit layers of the water column (the photic zone) therefore sets a limit to the amount of primary production that can occur. In practice, total annual primary production typically exceeds that which can be explained in terms of water column nutrient content at the start of the year. This is because a significant proportion of annual production utilises nutrients excreted back into the water column by herbivores and through the bacterial breakdown of detritus; referred to as 'recycled production'. In contrast, production derived from nutrients supplied to the photic zone by transport, mixing or atmospheric deposition is referred to as 'new production'. In temperate shelf seas where nitrogen is the main limiting nutrient element, new production is usually considered to be represented by the annual uptake of nitrate by phytoplankton, whilst regenerated production is represented by the uptake of ammonia.

The 'recycled' component of primary production reflects the metabolic requirements of the ecosystem since it is based on the within-season re-mineralisation of organic matter. 'New' production reflects the potential for growth and reproduction of higher trophic levels. Areas with a high proportion of recycled production would therefore be expected to exhibit low energy transfer efficiencies between total primary production and higher trophic levels. By considering new, rather than total, primary production as the basis for carbon and energy fluxes up the food web, explaining the production of higher trophic levels can, in theory, come closer.

### Estimating new primary production

Direct measurements of nutrient uptake in the water column require complicated incubations of sub-sampled water supplemented with isotope labeled nutrient at a range of light intensities. These are inherently costly, and can only be undertaken at a very limited number of sites.

Extrapolating from a few such measurements to obtain realistic estimates of new production over an area such as the North Sea is then practically impossible. An alternative is to apply a proxy measure of annual uptake which can be generated from nutrient data sets. Researchers at FRS have used nitrate concentrations in the sea water and inputs of nitrate by rivers and from the atmosphere as a proxy from which to calculate potential new primary production (PNP). Assuming that there are no other advective, or diffusive inputs of nitrate during the annual phytoplankton bloom period, and no significant reliance on nitrate to support production outside this period, then the loss of nitrate from the water column in spring, plus the river and atmospheric input of nitrate during the spring and summer, equate to the depth integrated annual new production. Conversion from production in terms of nitrogen units to production in terms of carbon units is then achieved by assuming that the two elements are related according to the Redfield ratio (C:N molar ratio 106:16).

### Data sources

Shelf seas nitrate data, the amount if oxidised inorganic nitrogen discharged to the sea from rivers and the oxidised nitrogen deposited on the seas surface with rainfall and dust particles were used in the determination. More details for each data source are presented in Annex 5.

### Results

The modelled distribution of annual potential new primary production (PNP) due to removal of nitrate from the water column is shown in Figure 2.17 using the year 2000 as an example. The analysis was restricted to continental shelf waters (shallower than 200 m), so it was not possible to provide summaries for the Rockall, Bailey and Faroe Shetland Channel regions (see Figure 1.7 for details of regions). In addition, the spatial resolution (graininess) of the model output was too coarse to meaningfully resolve small regions such as the Clyde. The Clyde and Irish Sea regions were therefore merged for the purposes of this case study. The year-to-year changes in new production due to water column uptake in each region covered by the data are shown in Figure 2.18.

Annual river inputs of oxidised nitrogen to each of the Scottish regions are shown in Figure 2.19. Inputs have shown an increasing trend only for the Irish Sea and Clyde. In other regions the inputs have been stable or declining. The input between March and September each year represents an additional contribution to potential new production, and was added to that estimated from the seawater nitrate data to produce an estimate of the total annual potential new primary production (Figure 2.18).

Annual atmospheric inputs of oxidised nitrogen (Figure 2.19) have shown a decreasing trend in all areas since 1980. The largest inputs are to the East Scotland Coast and Fladen areas, down-wind of the major centres of population. Inputs between March and September each year represent an additional contribution to potential new production, and were added to that estimated from the seawater nitrate data (Figure 2.18).

The combined results show that the highest rates of annual new primary production are confined to the outer shelf regions (West Shetland, North Scotland Coast and Hebrides). Long-term average potential new primary production declined with distance into the interior of the North Sea (Fladen and Forties), and was lowest in the inshore regions. River inputs during spring and summer had the greatest effect on annual potential new primary production in the East Scotland Coast region (11% of total annual PNP), Moray Firth (9%) and Irish Sea and Clyde region (7%). In all other areas, river inputs contributed less than 2% to total annual potential new primary production which was less than the input from atmospheric deposition (Figure 2.19). Potential new primary production in the northern areas declined through the 1970s from peak values in the 1960s and has been variable but stable thereafter. In the south-western areas, peak primary production was in the 1990s, whilst the North Sea regions showed no significant long term trend.

Discussion

The analysis shows that annual river inputs of oxidised nitrogen to the assessment regions were small compared to, for example the southern North Sea (Figure 2.20). In contrast to the Scottish regions, annual potential new primary production in ICES area IVc (latitude interval 51.00°N to 53.50°N (English Channel – Humber Estuary) since 1960 has been strongly correlated with river inputs, with an increasing trend between 1960 and the mid-1980s, and decreasing thereafter (Figure 2.20). River inputs during the summer were estimated to contribute 20% of annual potential new primary production in ICES area IVc. Evidence from salinity data shows that the high rates of potential new primary production in the outer shelf regions (Hebrides, North Scotland Coast and West Shetland) were sustained by inflows of nutrient rich North Atlantic water from across the continental shelf edge. Without this inflow of nitrate, and inflows from rivers and atmospheric deposition, the shelf waters would become depleted in nitrogen due to the action of denitrifying bacteria which cause the breakdown of nitrate to nitrogen gas and venting to the atmosphere. For this reason, the interior of the central North Sea, which is remote from both ocean and river inputs of nitrate, was characterised by low annual rates of potential new primary production. Atmospheric deposition, rather than river input was the major external

source of nitrate to this region, contributing approximately 3% of annual PNP.

A study of the North Sea indicated that the annual production by plankton eating fish (mainly herring, sprat, sandeel and Norway pout) was approximately 7% of annual potential new primary production. These fish species are a vital link in the food web since they constitute the major food resource for the valuable predatory fish such as cod and whiting and the bird and mammal populations, and hence are referred to as forage fish. On the basis of the North Sea study, the potential new primary production results indicate that, averaged over the period 1960-2003, the potential forage fish production in Scottish waters could be approximately 10.2 million tonnes (wet weight) per annum (Table 2.4). The proportion of annual forage fish production which may be landed by fisheries without risking detrimental effects on high trophic levels will be variable, depending on, for example, the species and age composition of fish in a given area. In the North Sea, approximately 12% of annual forage fish production is landed each year by fisheries, but this includes the industrial fisheries for sandeels which are of minor importance in Scottish waters. Relating potential new primary production to potential landings is the subject of ongoing research.

## Summary Assessment

| Parameter | Geographical region | Key factors & pressures | What the evidence shows | Trend | Status now | Confidence in assessment | Reason for overall status |
|---|---|---|---|---|---|---|---|
| Annual new primary production (PNP) | Hebrides | Climatic factors affecting oceanographic processes | High PNP, supported mainly by nutrient influx from the ocean | ↔ | ■ | II | Data available but models still need refining |
| Annual new primary production | West Shetland | Climatic factors affecting oceanographic processes | High PNP, supported mainly by nutrient influx from the ocean | ↔ | ■ | II | Data available but models still need refining |
| Annual new primary production | North Scotland Coast | Climatic factors affecting oceanographic processes | High PNP, supported mainly by nutrient influx from the ocean | ↔ | ■ | II | Data available but models still need refining |
| Annual new primary production | Fladden | Climatic factors affecting oceanographic processes and atmospheric deposition | Moderate PNP, supported by transport of nutrient from the outer shelf regions and atmospheric deposition | ↔ | ■ | II | Data available but models still need refining |
| Annual new primary production | Irish Sea and Clyde | Climatic factors affecting oceanographic processes and river inputs of nitrate, plus anthropogenic sources of nutrients | Low PNP, supported mainly by transport of nutrient from neighbouring regions and an increasing trend in river nutrients | ↔ | ■ | I | Data available but models still need refining and spatial resolution too coarse to delineate Clyde and inshore details |
| Annual new primary production | East Shetland | Climatic factors affecting oceanographic processes | Moderate PNP, supported mainly by transport of nutrient from the outer shelf regions | ↔ | ■ | II | Data available but models still need refining |
| Annual new primary production | East Scotland Coast | Climatic factors affecting oceanographic processes and river inputs of nitrate, plus anthropogenic sources of nutrients | Low PNP, supported mainly by transport of nutrient from the North Sea regions and inputs of river nutrients | ↔ | ■ | I | Data available but models still need refining and spatial resolution too coarse to delineate inshore details |
| Annual new primary production | Forties | Climatic factors affecting oceanographic processes and atmospheric deposition | Moderate PNP, supported mainly by transport of nutrient from the outer shelf regions and atmospheric deposition | ↔ | ■ | II | Data available but models still need refining |
| Annual new primary production | Minches and Malin Sea | Climatic factors affecting oceanographic processes and river inputs of nitrate and atmospheric deposition, plus anthropogenic sources of nutrients | Low PNP, supported mainly by transport of nutrient from the outer shelf regions, inputs of river nutrients and atmospheric deposition | ↔ | ■ | I | Data available but models still need refining and spatial resolution too coarse to delineate inshore details |
| Annual new primary production | Moray Firth | Climatic factors affecting oceanographic processes and river inputs of nitrate, plus anthropogenic sources of nutrients | Low PNP, supported mainly by transport of nutrient from the North Sea regions and inputs of river nutrients | ↔ | ■ | I | Data available but models still need refining and spatial resolution too coarse to delineate inshore details |

## Table 2.4 Annual potential new primary production

| Region | Sea surface area km² | 1960s PNP | 1970s PNP | 1980s PNP | 1990s PNP | 2000s PNP | 1960-2003 average PNP | 1960-2003 average potential forage fish production x10³ tonnes |
|---|---|---|---|---|---|---|---|---|
| Hebrides | 41,233 | 121.8 | 110.3 | 103.5 | 120.1 | 112.8 | 113.8 | 2,123.4 |
| West Shetland | 34,695 | 166.1 | 114.2 | 98.1 | 89.1 | 105.7 | 115.9 | 1,818.8 |
| North Scotland Coast | 46,056 | 121.6 | 91.7 | 80.8 | 81.5 | 87.8 | 93.4 | 1,945.5 |
| Fladen | 37,036 | 72.0 | 58.0 | 56.0 | 55.4 | 61.4 | 60.4 | 1,012.6 |
| Irish Sea and Clyde | 30,395 | 47.4 | 49.5 | 57.3 | 67.0 | 57.3 | 55.5 | 763.1 |
| East Shetland | 15,038 | 138.8 | 101.5 | 94.1 | 82.9 | 98.9 | 103.8 | 706.4 |
| East Scotland Coast | 38,065 | 45.3 | 39.7 | 40.3 | 42.5 | 42.7 | 42.0 | 723.7 |
| Forties | 24,566 | 56.0 | 51.5 | 53.7 | 56.6 | 59.7 | 54.9 | 610.5 |
| Minches and Malin Sea | 31,338 | 25.8 | 22.0 | 22.6 | 24.6 | 21.0 | 23.5 | 333.5 |
| Moray Firth | 10,127 | 34.2 | 25.4 | 23.4 | 24.8 | 26.3 | 26.9 | 123.2 |
| Combined Scottish Regions | 308,550 | 87.0 | 70.1 | 66.2 | 68.6 | 70.9 | 72.8 | 10,160.8 |

PNP (gC/m²/y) averaged over each reporting region and over decades, together with the implied potential production of forage fish (plankton-eating fish, mainly herring, sprat, sandeel and Norway pout, thousands of tonnes wet weight/year) in each region. Average potential fish production assumed to be 7.3% of PNP.

## Figure 2.17 Spatial distribution of annual PNP

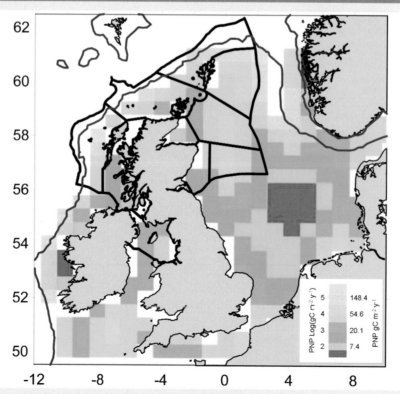

PNP (gC/m²/y) in the year 2000 for shelf waters shallower than 200 m, estimated from the draw-down of nitrate in the water column. Outlines of the reporting regions, as described in Figure 1.7, are overlaid in black and the 200 m depth contour in purple.

## Figure 2.18 Time series of annual PNP (g carbon/m²/year) in each of the Scottish reporting regions

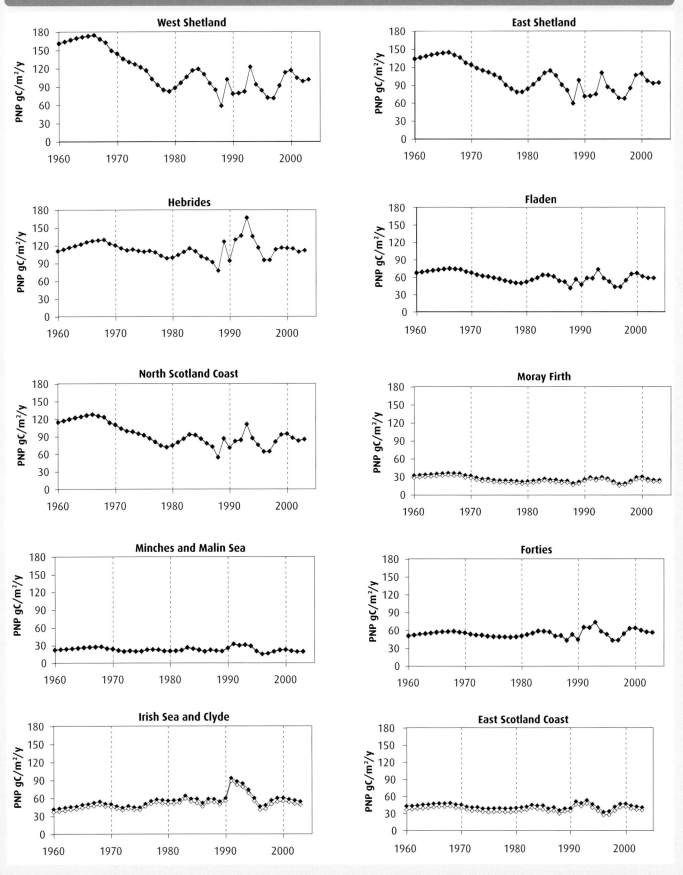

Open symbols, estimates based on water column nitrate draw-down only; filled symbols, estimates including the contribution of river inputs of nitrate during spring and summer. The Irish Sea and Clyde regions have been combined. Panels arranged in approximate geographical order.

## Figure 2.19 Time series of annual inputs of oxidised nitrogen and average proportion of annual new primary production

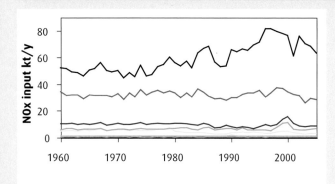

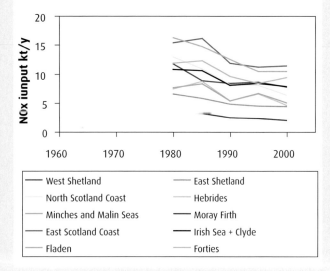

*Upper panel*: time series of annual inputs of oxidised nitrogen (nitrate+nitrite, kt/y) from rivers to each of the reporting regions between 1960 and 2005. The Irish Sea and Clyde regions have been combined, and include inputs from England, Wales and Northern Ireland as well as from Scotland. *Lower left panel*: time series of annual inputs of oxidised nitrogen from river and atmospheric deposition to each region, estimated at 5 year intervals between 1980 and 2000. *Lower right panel*: average (1960-2003) proportion of annual new primary production in each region due to spring and summer (March-September) inputs of oxidized nitrogen from rivers and the atmosphere.

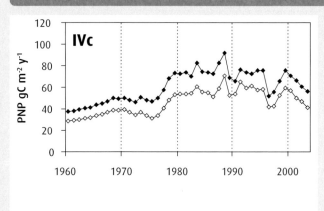

| | |
|---|---|
| — West Shetland | — East Shetland |
| — North Scotland Coast | — Hebrides |
| — Minches and Malin Seas | — Moray Firth |
| — East Scotland Coast | — Irish Sea + Clyde |
| — Fladen | — Forties |

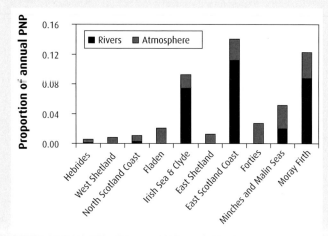

## Figure 2.20 Time series of annual PNP in the southern North Sea and annual inputs of oxidised nitrogen

*Upper panel:* time series of annual PNP (gC/m²/y) in the southern North Sea (ICES area IVc, 51.00°N – 53.50°N (51° 00'N – 53° 30'N)). Open symbols, estimates based on water column nitrate draw-down, filled symbols, estimates including the contribution of river inputs of nitrate during spring and summer. *Lower panel:* Time series of annual inputs of oxidised nitrogen (nitrate+nitrite, kt/y) from rivers to the southern North Sea (ICES area IVc) between 1960 and 2005.

## CONCLUSION

Understanding the physical characteristics of the seas around Scotland, and their link to the wider-scale processes, is fundamental to understanding the state of Scotland's seas. A vast amount of data has been, and continues to be, gathered. However, in order that changes in the physical characteristics of the waters around Scotland can be detected and ascribed a cause, there is a need to continue collecting data and to developing models which can accurately reproduce the current situation as well as predict future trends. In preparing this chapter it is evident that:

> there remain areas of Scotland's waters that have been surveyed by lead line only;

> there is a need to provide a better understanding of the deep waters to the west of Scotland;

> pH is one of the water property measurements requiring increased attention;

> better knowledge of seabed sediments is required; and

> all those involved in the simulation of the waters around Scotland would benefit from a greater sharing of model information and data. In addition, access to information from a common model of Scotland's seas would provide more accurate inputs to smaller-scale local models, benefiting many types of studies.

# Chapter 3
# Clean and Safe Seas

## INTRODUCTION

Scottish coastal seas support some of the most productive marine ecosystems in the world and this reflects, amongst other things, the general high quality of our marine waters. Scotland's low population density and position on the north-western seaboard of Europe have ensured that there has been relatively little contamination of the seas and any contaminants that have been released have an opportunity to dilute and disperse. Inevitably, as in any developed country, Scotland has an industrial history and as could be expected, where industrial development in the central belt was concentrated, some water quality problems remain some of which result from historical contamination.

The sea acts as a sink for virtually all the substances (and hence pollution[A]) that enter fresh waters and also receives chemical contaminants from the atmosphere, some of which may not originate in Scotland. Domestic inputs of contaminants to the seas and estuaries have demonstrably been reduced in the last 30 years as improved legislation and statutory powers, and an understanding of the consequences of pollution, have enabled Scotland increasingly to regulate the discharges from key polluters.

A clean and healthy sea is, of course, not just about chemicals in the water. It also relates to all changes that can affect animal and plant life at any stage in their life cycles. Other significant deterioration in quality can come from a lack of water clarity caused by increased turbidity (see Chapter 2), noise from man-made sources or temperature changes caused by effluents that are significantly warmer or colder than their receiving waters. Intensive agriculture has led to a big increase in very fine soil particles containing nutrients being washed from land to sea. Bottom sediments must also remain healthy as many sites are highly productive or contain unique habitats of conservation interest. Even climate change linked processes, such as acidification of the sea caused by increased concentrations of carbon dioxide in the atmosphere, can affect the survival of some species. Changes in storminess or rainfall have also been linked to climate change and can influence freshwater run-off from land or marine circulation patterns. Bacterial contamination of inshore seas comes from both human derived sewage and diffuse run-off from land with bacteria derived principally from farming of livestock.

As highlighted in Chapter 1, work to maintain and improve the cleanliness of the seas has been greatly helped by a wide range of legislation and conventions, most of which now originate from the EU. Regulating agencies aim to use all available legislation to ensure that Scotland's seas are clean and safe and to meet the OSPAR objective to continually reduce discharges with the ultimate target of achieving concentrations near background values for naturally occurring substances, close to zero for manmade synthetic and radioactive substances, and with no discernable eutrophication attributable to human derived inputs. The recent Marine Strategy Framework Directive (MSFD) adds to this by introducing the concept of achieving good environmental status (GES) (Table 3.1).

| Table 3.1 Qualitative MSFD GES descriptors for clean and safe seas |
| --- |
| **MSFD Annex I GES descriptors** |
| **GES Descriptor 5** - Human-**induced eutrophication** is minimised, especially adverse effects thereof, such as losses in biodiversity, ecosystem degradation, harmful algae blooms and oxygen deficiency in bottom waters |
| **GES Descriptor 8** - **Concentrations of contaminants** are at levels not giving rise to pollution effects |
| **GES Descriptor 9** - **Contaminants in fish and other seafood** for human consumption do not exceed levels established by Community legislation or other relevant standards |
| **GES Descriptor 10** - Properties and quantities of **marine litter** do not cause harm to the coastal and marine environment |
| **GES Descriptor 11** - **Introduction of energy**, including underwater noise, is at levels that do not adversely affect the marine environment |

**EVIDENCE THAT THE SEA IS CLEAN AND SAFE**

As discussed in Chapter 1 the vision of clean and safe was developed in the report *Safeguarding our Seas* and is used to steer one of the evidence groups as part of the UKMMAS. Clean and safe in this context is taken as principally relating to the chemical, eutrophic, bacteriological and litter status of Scottish seas. The chemical status in particular is multi-faceted as it can relate to water concentrations of toxic or hazardous substances or measures of these compounds in sediments or biota as well as covering radioactive substances. For persistent substances, measurement of concentrations in biota or sediments is preferred as they integrate the build up with time. A number of specific programmes are in place to collect evidence each having one or more regulatory or international convention drivers that frame the monitoring programme. The principal programmes are listed in Annex 2. These programmes assess both the risk to humans (e.g. through shellfish consumption, radioactive substances critical dose assessments or bathing water quality), as well as to the marine ecosystem (e.g. by measuring concentrations of nutrients and xenobiotics). The monitoring sites are varied, but many are coastal, with a focus either on areas under pressure or on areas that have had significance to man in terms of waste disposal, industrial development, finfish or shellfish production. Samples are taken from sediments, biota and water depending on the programme. Table 3.2 summarises some of the data available that are used to determine if Scotland's seas are clean and safe.

SEPA collects data on the flow of all major rivers, which are gauged close to their tidal limits (see Figure 2.10). As the concentrations of contaminants and nutrients in these rivers are also measured (see Case Study 3.1), along with all key point source discharges, total loads of pollutants to coastal stretches can be calculated. Information of the pollutant loads entering the sea is essential to help scientists understand the complex relationship between these inputs and the levels found in the marine environment.

*Classification of waters*

Even though the discharge of contaminants into the sea is more under control than it has ever been, it is still necessary to assess environmental quality directly. The search for an overall indicator of marine health is not new and SEPA annually classified the environmental quality of coastal margins and estuaries up until 2006 (see case study 3.2) but this was replaced in 2007 by a more thorough classification using WFD 2000/60/EC methods which are described in Case Study 3.3. The WFD only extends to 3 nautical miles from the Scottish baseline but the new MSFD will operate in a similar manner and cover more offshore seas out to the national territorial limit.

| Table 3.2 Summary of data collected that could indicate whether Scotland's seas are clean and safe | |
|---|---|
| **Indicators of clean and safe seas** | **Principal data collectors** |
| Contaminants in food (excluding phycotoxins) | FSAS, FRS |
| Contaminants in the environment | FRS, SEPA, SMRU, Shetland Oil Terminal Environmental Advisory Group (SOTEAG), Advisory Committee on Protection of the Sea (ACOPS), Defra on behalf of various monitoring authorities |
| Eutrophication | FRS, SEPA, Sir Alister Hardy Foundation for Ocean Science (SAHFOS) |
| Integrated classification | SEPA |
| Litter | Local Authorities International Environmental Organisation (KIMO), Marine Conservation Society, Plymouth University, SEPA |
| Microbiology | SEPA, FSAS, FRS, Shetland Seafood Quality Control |
| Radioactive Substances | SEPA, CEFAS |
| Toxins | FRS, FSAS, SEPA, SAMS |

## CASE STUDY 3.1 Loadings on Riverine Inputs and Direct Discharges (RID)

### Chemical contaminant inputs to the marine environment

Chemical contaminants enter the marine environment by direct or indirect release to rivers, from industrial discharges and from sewage works discharges. SEPA measures the concentrations of a range of contaminants in larger rivers and industrial and other discharges, and these are multiplied by the appropriate flows to give the so-called RID inputs as annual loadings in kilograms or tonnes[1].

These loadings are reported annually to OSPAR, set up to administer the 1992 OSPAR Convention which covers many of the human activities that might adversely affect the marine environment of the North-East Atlantic Ocean.

The substances for which loadings are calculated fall into the following categories:

> metals, including cadmium, mercury, lead, copper and zinc;

> organic compounds, including lindane and polychlorinated biphenyls (PCBs); and

> plant nutrients that may contribute to eutrophication, including compounds of nitrogen and phosphorus.

### How the information is gathered for Scotland

Scotland has been divided into seven areas for the purpose of gathering information on the loadings of the substances listed above. Tables of loadings are collated for the rivers, industrial

discharges and sewage works discharges to each area for each individual substance. These loadings data can be interpreted by area and year to identify where inputs are highest or over time for each area, to assess trends with time.

### Examples of trends in metals inputs over time

The data show steady reductions in cadmium inputs to marine waters in both the rivers Forth and Clyde catchment areas (Figure 3.1a), and for lead in the Clyde catchment area (Figure 3.1b). These figures confirm that the UK has achieved the targets of 50% reductions in the loadings of these List I substances to the marine environment, as it pledged to do under the EU Dangerous Substances Directive.

### Loadings data in relation to the state of the marine environment

Information on loadings of chemical contaminants from rivers, sewage works and direct discharges are important, as they help to determine the current state of Scotland's marine environment. For example, the metal loadings measured can be related to the concentrations of metals in marine mussels, which bio-accumulate these and other contaminants.

### Nutrient inputs in relation to eutrophication

Nutrients data are collected in the same way and discussed separately in Case Study 3.8.

### Figure 3.1a Discharges of metals to Scottish marine waters, 1990-2004

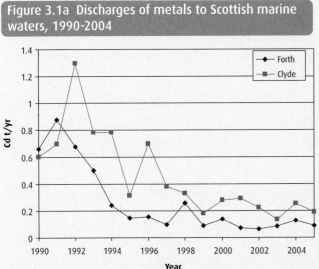

Cadmium in the Forth and Clyde Catchment Areas

### Figure 3.1b Discharges of metals to Scottish marine waters, 1990-2004

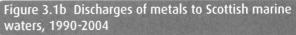

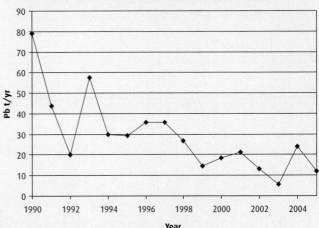

Lead in the Clyde Catchment Area

### Summary Assessment

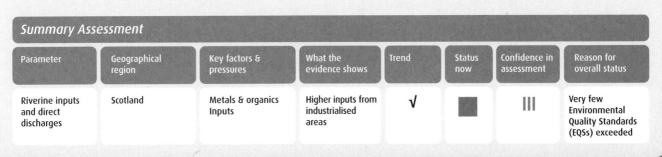

| Parameter | Geographical region | Key factors & pressures | What the evidence shows | Trend | Status now | Confidence in assessment | Reason for overall status |
|---|---|---|---|---|---|---|---|
| Riverine inputs and direct discharges | Scotland | Metals & organics Inputs | Higher inputs from industrialised areas | √ | ■ | III | Very few Environmental Quality Standards (EQSs) exceeded |

## CASE STUDY 3.2    Coastal and estuarine water quality classification

Between 1996 and 2006 SEPA classified Scotland's saline waters using classification systems that are detailed in Annexes 7 and 8 of this report. Four classes were used (A-D) with A listed as excellent and D seriously polluted. This case study summarises the results of water quality assessments up to 2006[2]. In 2006, a new system for assessing water quality was introduced under the WFD and is described in Case Study 3.3.

### Estuarine water quality
SEPA classified over 800 km² of estuaries in Scotland, using seven assessment criteria: aesthetics, fish migration, bottom-dwelling animals, resident fish, persistent substances, dissolved oxygen and dangerous substances. Results are given in area (km²).

Between 2000 and 2006 the area of unsatisfactory or seriously polluted estuarine waters reduced by 2.8 km² (8.6%). This was a lower figure than had been hoped, largely because of the introduction of improved data and assessment methods. For example, the South Esk Estuary (Montrose Basin) had its classification downgraded, although there is no evidence that water quality in Montrose Basin had actually deteriorated.

Weather conditions can also have an impact on annual classifications. For example, wetter weather in 2002 led to higher river flows into the major estuaries, more dilution of pollutants, greater mixing, improved oxygen levels and higher classifications. A clearer overall picture of water quality can be achieved using a three-year average. The three-year average figure of Class C and D estuaries with improved water quality in 2006 (using 2006, 2005 and 2004 totals) was 21 km².

The quality of Forth and Clyde estuaries is especially affected by historically polluted sediments. The majority of the estuaries also continue to be impacted by sewage discharges. Diffuse run-off from urban and agricultural areas can also be significant sources of pollution (i.e. oils and nutrients). Some local issues remain with regards to aesthetics (litter) in estuaries which can draw public complaints.

### Coastal water quality
SEPA classified almost 12,000 km of coastline in Scotland, using four assessment criteria: aesthetics, biological, bacteriological, and chemical condition. Results are given in coastal length (km).

At the end of 2006, Scotland had only 90.5 km of unsatisfactory or seriously polluted coastal waters, a reduction of 72% since 2000. 94% of coastal waters were classified as excellent.

As in the case of the estuaries, coastal waters quality trends are expressed as a three-year rolling average of the total length of Class C and D waters, smoothing out the influence of particularly wet or dry years. As shown in Figure 3.2, the rolling average continued to fall in 2006 as it has done every year since. The amount of unsatisfactory and seriously polluted coastline in Scotland has steadily decreased since 1999. In 1999, the lengths making up the total of 322 km that required improvement were mostly next to significant population centres with inadequate sewage disposal arrangements, or were affected by agricultural or urban diffuse pollution.

## Figure 3.2  Annual totals and three-year rolling average for Classes C and D coastal waters

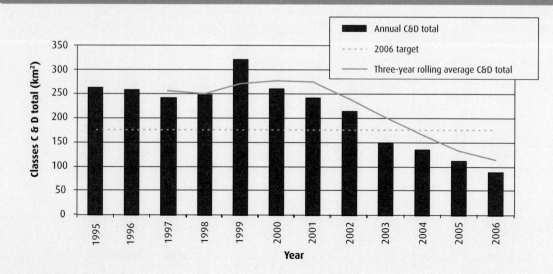

## Reasons for improvement

Continuing investment by both Scottish Water and industry resulted in lower contaminant concentrations in all saline waters. Key polluting industries have been targeted with improvement programmes, partly resulting from the results of the classification of their local waters. The decline of heavy industry, the use of a more integrated pollution control and an increasing environmentally aware public also contribute to a trend of improvement.

## Future developments

A new water quality classification scheme, based on the mandatory requirements of the WFD came into force in 2006, Case Study 3.3.

## Summary Assessment

| Parameter | Geographical region | Key factors & pressures | What the evidence shows | Trend | Status now | Confidence in assessment | Reason for overall status |
|---|---|---|---|---|---|---|---|
| SEPA Estuary Classification- Based on study of aesthetic condition, fish migration, benthic community or bioassay, resident fish, persistent substances (biota) and water chemistry | Scotland | Main pressure comes from industrial and sewage direct and diffuse discharges. Lesser pressure comes from historical contamination of sediments and shipping. | Historical contamination of sediments but continued improvement | √ | ■ | ‖ | Improvement in point sources, drive to control diffuse sources and decline in heavy industry |
| SEPA Coastal Classification- Based on study of aesthetic condition, biological condition, bacteriological condition and chemical condition | Scotland | Main pressure comes from industrial and sewage direct and diffuse discharges. Lesser pressure comes from historical contamination of sediments, atmospheric deposition, shipping and other maritime industries | Steady Improvement in water quality | √ | ■ | ‖ | Improvement in point sources, drive to control diffuse sources and decline in heavy industry |

## CASE STUDY 3.3  Water Framework Directive classification of transitional and coastal waters

The Directive (2000/60/EC) (WFD) establishes a new legal framework for the protection, improvement and sustainable use of surface waters, transitional waters, coastal waters and groundwater across Europe in order to:

> prevent deterioration and enhance status of aquatic ecosystems, including groundwater and saline waters out to 3 nautical miles from baseline (see Figure 3.3);

> promote sustainable water use;

> reduce pollution; and

> contribute to the mitigation of floods and droughts.

In Scotland, this work is being taken forward by SEPA[3], in conjunction with the Scottish Government and other partners in line with the timetable for action set out in the Directive and guidance agreed with other member states.

A classification approach determined by the WFD will be used to assess the ecological and chemical status of Scotland's saline waters which have been divided up into 507 transitional and coastal water bodies (see Figure 3.3). The results of this classification will help identify:

> significant risks to the environment;

> direct action to protect and improve surface waters; and

> assess the success of actions taken.

The first WFD classifications must be published at the end of 2009 and will be much wider ranging than previous SEPA coastal and estuarine classification schemes. Biological tools to carry out this monitoring have been developed by a UK national group and, where required, intercalibrated with similar tools in other Member States to ensure comparability of assessments. Monitoring work in line with WFD criteria began in the 2007 sampling year although not all the appropriate tools were complete at this time. Under the WFD, surface water status is determined by the lower of a water body's 'ecological status' and its 'chemical status'. Ecological status is determined using a number of 'quality elements', which look at biology, chemistry and physical influences on water quality. Table 3.3 lists the key elements that are to be looked at as part of the classification process.

Figure 3.4 shows a simple decision-tree to illustrate the classification process. Ecological status is measured by looking at the present state and comparing it against an ideal or reference condition for that water body.

## Table 3.3  Key elements used in WFD Classification

| Biological quality elements | Transitional (estuaries & lagoons) | Coastal waters | Artifical & heavily modified waters |
|---|---|---|---|
| Phytoplankton | √ | √ | As applicable |
| Other plants | √ | √ | As applicable |
| Invertebrate animals | √ | √ | As applicable |
| Fish | √ | X | As applicable |
| **Supporting elements** | | | |
| Structural features | √ | √ | As applicable |
| Physico-chemical | √ | √ | As applicable |
| Specific pollutants | √ | √ | As applicable |
| Tidal regime | √ | √ | As applicable |

**Figure 3.3   Coastal and transitional water bodies delineated by the Water Framework Directive**

**Legend**

☐ Coastal and transitional waters

## Figure 3.4 Decision-tree illustrating the criteria for determining the different ecological status classes

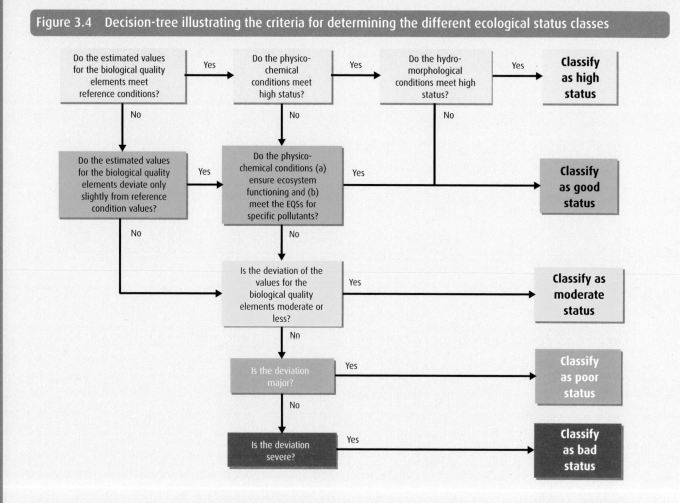

## Summary Assessment

| Parameter | Geographical region | Key factors & pressures | What the evidence shows | Trend | Status now | Confidence in assessment | Reason for overall status |
|---|---|---|---|---|---|---|---|
| WFD Classification using biological, chemical and physical criteria determined by the directive | Scotland | Pollution or physical pressures that reduce the "Health" of the inshore marine environment | Too early to be precise but the majority of Scottish waters are expected to be of High Quality | ? |  | I (Only partial data available at this time) | Risk assessment and existing data though not yet strictly Water Framework Compliant |

## Hazardous substances

Hazardous and persistent substances are of particular environmental concern as by definition they are toxic and/or very resistant to breaking down to safe constituents. Development of regulation correctly reflects our intolerance of these substances. Those of most concern also have the potential to build up in living tissue and the possibility of being concentrated up the food chain (e.g. brominated flame retardants) or follow a number of pathways to end up in the bottom sediments. While FRS and SEPA collect bioaccumulation data from fish, invertebrates and seaweeds, SMRU collect data from larger top predators such as seals who are particularly vulnerable to biomagnification up the food chain as discussed in Case Study 3.4.

In previous decades heavy industry was a serious pollution source for many toxic metals. Although these have largely declined there remain residual problems in historically contaminated sediments especially in the Clyde and Forth estuaries and a few sea lochs. Some removal of this contaminated sediment from, for example, the Clyde Estuary has occurred by natural scouring or dredging of the shipping channel but this has translocated the problem elsewhere. It is not surprising therefore, that there is a noticeable increase in contamination in the area used for dumping dredge spoil at the head of the Firth of Clyde close to the mouth of the Holy Loch. Data collected by BGS on naturally occurring minerals in seabed sediments are an essential aid in helping understand the extent of human derived metal pollution and deriving realistic baseline limits. This is explored in Case Study 3.5.

Despite the overall improvements there are still substances, either in their original state or as breakdown products, that enter saline waters where their fate may not be fully understood. Even the contaminants that are present in seabed sediments have the potential to cause biological harm either by contact with bottom living fauna or by their ingestion of sediment. Our latest regulatory protocols put more emphasis on the need to investigate the potential to cause harm of all new substances before they are released into the natural world. There is an enormous range of substances used in modern industry and new ones coming on line all the time. Very few of the existing chemicals already in use have been properly assessed for risk associated with their release into the marine environment. Trace synthetic substances have no natural background level and many are now becoming detectable in deeper water and even in the polar ice caps.

These observations have led to the discovery of mechanisms such as global distillation and demonstrate the interdependency of the seas with other nations and the folly of assuming the oceans have infinite dilution.

Offshore the main sources of toxic substances (especially oil) are from the dumping or accidental release from ships, waste from oil or gas platforms and atmospheric deposition. Drill cuttings contaminated by oil are present only from historic discharges and, through better treatment processes, the oil in produced water has been reduced even though the volume of produced water has increased. FRS has carried out a study of the effects of hydrocarbon releases on two areas of the North Sea; the Fladen Ground and the East Shetland Basin and these form the basis of Case Study 3.6. Minor oil spills from ships at sea still continue although tanker disasters are thankfully becoming rare worldwide.

Persistent organic pollutants (POPs) include a number of industrial chemicals such as PCBs and chlorinated pesticides. Some of these, such as dichloro diphenyl trichloroethane (DDT) are known to have adverse health effects upon wildlife and man, and they have been found in very high levels in marine mammals, particularly seals. These compounds biomagnify through food chains and concentrate in the fats of seals. Because seals consume food from similar parts of the marine food chains to humans, changes of pollutant levels within seals may indicate possible contamination in the human food chain.

The PCBs in particular have been studied for their potential effect on vertebrate health and studies have found relationships with immune and reproductive dysfunction as well as thyroid activity[4]. The reported threshold for potential adverse health effects in seals is estimated to be approximately 20 mg/kg (ppm) total PCBs in blubber on a lipid weight basis[5]. Although the manufacture and use of PCBs and DDT in European countries have been banned for over 30 years, their legacy persists and POPs are present in harbour seals around the Scottish coast (Figure 3.5). The effects of PCBs on the immune system mean that there is a positive relationship between the severity of disease and the levels of PCBs in seals[6, 7].

Levels of PCBs in Scottish seals have declined over that last two decades (Figure 3.5). However, the most recent survey in 2003 found very high levels in seals captured at haul out sites in south-west Scotland, including in the Special Area of Conservation (SAC) for this species on Islay. Indeed, all the adult males sampled had levels more than twice the threshold for likely effects[8]. The relatively high level of PCBs in south-west Scottish waters may be due to food chain contamination emanating from POP usage in the Clyde where high PCB levels are also still found in the sediments[9]. Although PCBs are no longer in use, newer persistent contaminants with similar structures and effects are taking their place. These include the polybrominated diphenyl ethers (PBDEs) and hexabromocylcododecane (HBCD) which have been used as flame retardants. While many of the PBDE compounds have now also been banned in Europe, HBCD is being used and is increasing in the blubber of UK marine mammals[10]. PCBs remain a useful indicator of contamination and levels in seals correlate with the occurrence and uptake of the newer POPs including the PBDEs (Figure 3.6).

Summary

Seals tend to concentrate POPs across broad spatial scales in the marine environment and for parts of the food chain that are relevant to human health. Seals are also relatively easy to sample as indicators of trends. Across Scotland, results show that POP levels are at or below the threshold at which they are likely to have direct health effects, but in some cases the levels are well above those where an effect upon marine mammal health might be expected.

**Figure 3.6   Relationship between total PCBs and total PBDEs in adult male harbour seals from Scotland**

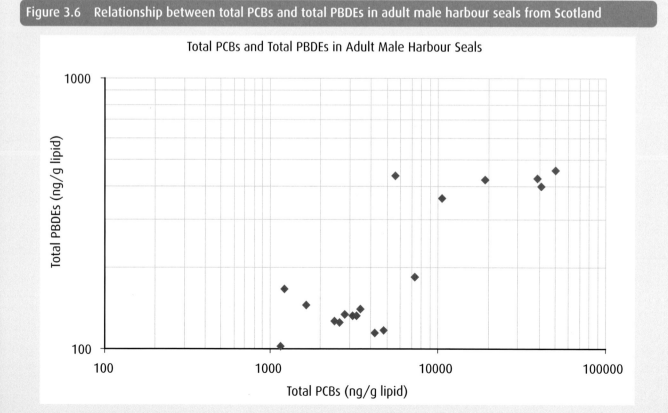

Total PCBs and Total PBDEs in Adult Male Harbour Seals

**Figure 3.5** Geometric mean (± standard deviation) of total PCB concentrations in adult male harbour seals from around Scotland and Northern Ireland in 1989 and 2003

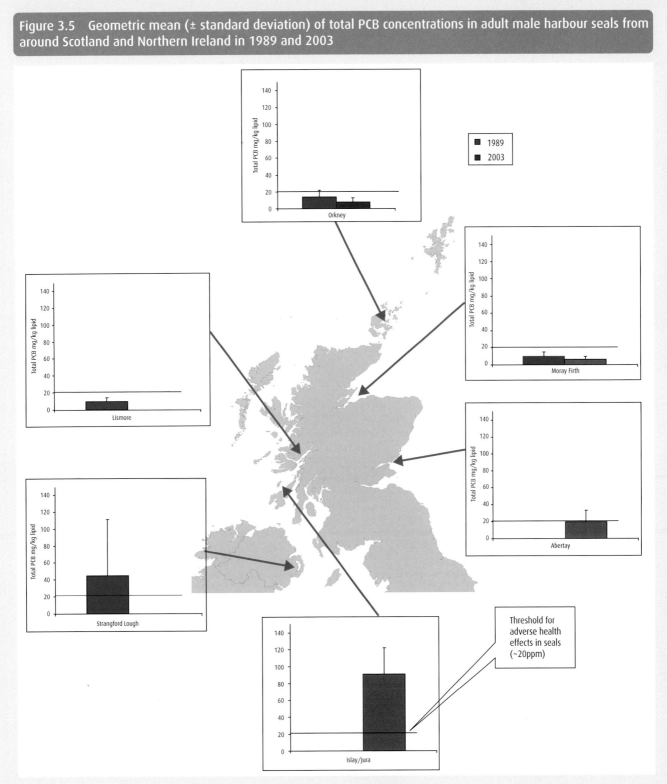

(Concentrations are calculated as Aroclor1254 equivalents for comparison with original data)

Approximately 5,000 samples of sediment collected by the British Geological Survey (BGS) from the sea floor around Scotland have been analysed to measure their concentration of metals. Over 30 metals, including copper (Figure 3.7), lead, zinc and cadmium are available in the BGS database from which geochemical maps, statistical analysis and interpretation of the distribution patterns have been made in relation to the geology of the sea bed. As the samples were collected mainly during the 1970s and 1980s, they provide a useful baseline that predates much of the commercial activity that has taken place offshore of Scotland. In addition, there is a limited amount of inorganic geochemical data from selected estuaries and radioactivity measurements.

Naturally occurring concentrations of metals in seabed sediments are derived from the minerals, rock fragments and organic material (shell debris and vegetation) that comprise the sediments. They are the result of erosion of the underlying rocks or consolidated sediments (e.g. glacial deposits) or by weathering of rocks, soils and sediments on land. Sediment from land areas are supplied to the sea by rivers and winds or by erosion of coastal areas by wave action.

Contaminants entering the sea can also be derived from land by rivers and the atmosphere or from point sources such as ships or offshore installations. The contaminants follow the same processes of transport as naturally occurring metals, either in solution or held in suspension on the surface of fine-grained particles (see Chapter 2), although most contaminants show a stronger affinity for the latter. Much of this suspended material does not accumulate on the sea floor as it remains in the water column to be transported by currents over long distances. Where conditions are favourable, such as in areas with weak current strengths over bathymetric depressions on

the sea bed, sediments may be deposited to form contaminant 'sinks'. Sediment grain-size, particularly the fine-grained component, is therefore an important factor in determining how sediments and metals are transported and deposited in the marine environment.

An important factor in the assessment of contaminant levels in seabed sediments is the establishment of 'background' concentrations. Background can be defined as the concentration that would be found in the environment in the absence of human activity. These values are often defined using, for example, the average abundance of metals in the Earth's crust, although these often do not reflect regional variations or the influence of marine processes. Local assessments of possible contaminants around Scotland using BGS data, which are indicators of the cleanliness of the seas, have produced a representative range of values that can be used to define background concentrations. BGS's shallow cores can also be used to record changes in geochemistry over time.

To further identify areas of the sea floor where metal accumulations are enriched above the concentrations that would be expected to occur naturally, a technique known as 'normalisation' is applied to the data. This method compensates for the influence of grain size on metal distribution to more easily identify areas influenced by human activity. The BGS data are normalised to the element lithium (Li), which not only represents grain-size variation but is also an important constituent of the minerals that make up Scotland's geological formations. Lithium also has the advantage of not being used to any great extent in manufacturing processes and therefore is unlikely to be present due to contamination. Once the grain-size affects have been removed, maps are produced that show areas where metal enrichment can not be explained by natural processes alone (Figure 3.7).

## Summary Assessment

| Parameter | Geographical region | Key factors & pressures | What the evidence shows | Trend | Status now | Confidence in assessment | Reason for overall status |
|---|---|---|---|---|---|---|---|
| Sediment quality/ inorganic geochemistry | All. Some in parts only. | Input from wide range of human activities including commercial/ industrial in both land areas and marine environment | Hotspots of increased metal concentrations above naturally occurring background levels | ? | ▢ | ‖ | Sufficient available for regional baseline assessment. Predates industrial activity during the last 20 years. Quality assured data. |

Figure 3.7 Distribution of copper around the Scottish coast (normalised to lithium)

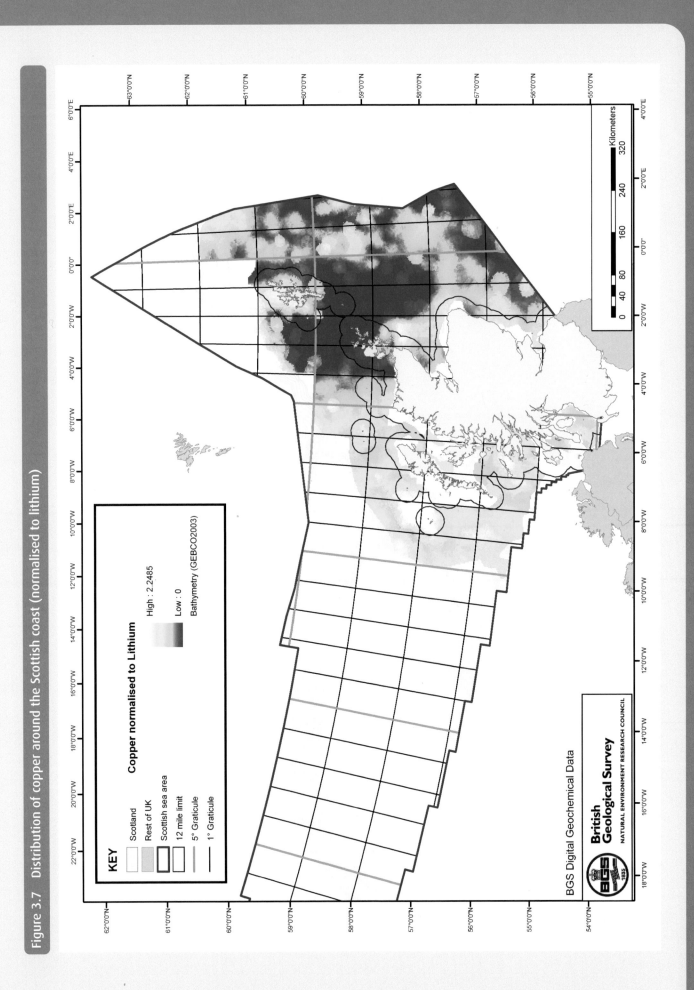

The North Sea has been the focus of offshore oil and gas production over the past 40 years and, as a result, hydrocarbons have been discharged to the area during drilling (via cuttings contaminated with oil-based drill muds), production (via produced water discharges) and via incomplete combustion during flaring operations. Hydrocarbon concentrations in the North Sea have been investigated over a number of years with the aim of assessing the impact of oil exploration and production and to confirm that increased regulatory control has resulted in a decrease in hydrocarbon contamination. FRS has concentrated on two areas of the North Sea; the Fladen Ground and the East Shetland Basin (Figure. 3.8).

A number of sediment surveys have been undertaken in these potentially accumulative areas (Table 3.4) which are also productive fishing areas; results from these samples are discussed below.

**Table 3.4   Details of the sediment surveys undertaken together with the number of samples analysed for oil equivalents and PAHs using both a systematic grid (SG) and stratified random (SR) approach**

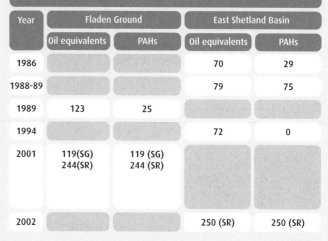

| Year | Fladen Ground | | East Shetland Basin | |
|---|---|---|---|---|
| | Oil equivalents | PAHs | Oil equivalents | PAHs |
| 1986 | | | 70 | 29 |
| 1988-89 | | | 79 | 75 |
| 1989 | 123 | 25 | | |
| 1994 | | | 72 | 0 |
| 2001 | 119(SG) 244(SR) | 119 (SG) 244 (SR) | | |
| 2002 | | | 250 (SR) | 250 (SR) |

**Figure 3.8   Locations of the Fladen Ground and the East Shetland Basin**

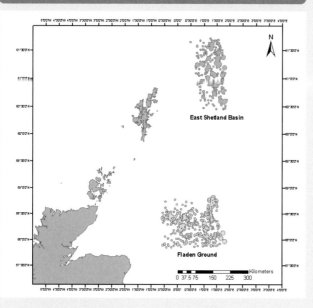

The distribution of oil platforms and single wells are also indicated in both areas.

*Survey design*

Historically, sediment has been sampled using a systematic grid (SG) approach involving several transects across each area being sampled at regular intervals. An alternative approach is the stratified random (SR) survey; this allows a much simpler statistical analysis. In the latter approach, which has been used more recently (Table 3.4), sediment samples are collected at random, with the number of samples per stratum being proportional to the far field area, defined as those areas greater than 5 km from an oil platform and 2 km from a single well. Near field is defined as less than 5 km from an oil platform or 2 km from a single well.

Samples from the historical and recent surveys (Table 3.4) were screened for hydrocarbons by ultraviolet fluorescence (UVF) to give estimates of total hydrocarbon concentrations expressed as crude oil equivalents. Samples were then selected for more detailed analysis.

## Temporal trends in hydrocarbon concentrations

Near field Forties oil equivalent concentrations determined in pre-2000 surveys of both the Fladen Ground (Figure 3.9) and East Shetland Basin (Figure 3.10) were all above background (< 50 µg/g dry weight). Mean Forties oil equivalent concentrations in the far field were lower than in the near field in both areas. The Forties oil equivalent concentrations in sediments collected from the Fladen Ground in 2001 were significantly lower compared to 1989. Both the 2001 near field and far field sediment (systematic grid and stratified random sampling) were below background. Furthermore, 2001 near field sites gave lower concentrations than found in the far field in 1989. East Shetland Basin near field sediments have shown a progressive decrease in mean Forties oil equivalent concentrations with time while in the far field, mean concentrations were above background in both 1986 and 1989 but by 1994 showed a significant decrease (Figure 3.9 and Figure 3.10). The mean oil equivalent concentration determined following the 2002 SR survey was < 50 µg/g dry weight.

**Figure 3.9    Mean Forties oil equivalents and total PAH concentration in the Fladen Ground**

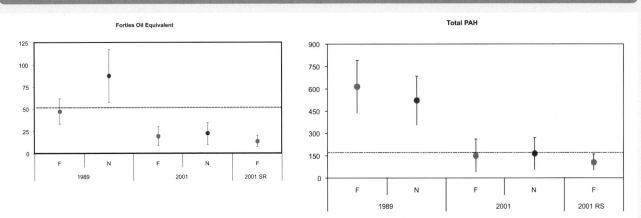

Interval plot showing the mean Forties oil equivalents (µg/g dry weight) and total PAH concentrations (µg/kg dry weight) in the Fladen Ground in 1989 (systematic grid (SG)) and 2001 (SG and stratified random (SR)). Samples from both the near (N, red symbol) and far (F, blue symbol) field were analysed for the grid surveys. Dotted line = assumed background level.

**Figure 3.10    Mean Forties oil equivalents and total PAH concentrations in the East Shetland Basin**

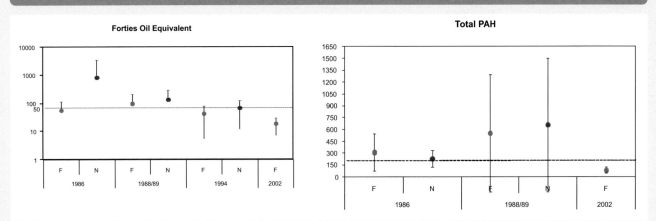

Interval plots of mean Forties oil equivalents (µg/g dry weight) and total PAH concentrations (µg/kg dry weight) in sediment from the East Shetland Basin surveys in both near (N, red symbol) and far (F, blue symbol) field samples.

Fladen Ground sediment PAH concentrations determined following the 2001 SG and SR surveys were generally low (< 150 µg/kg dry weight) and were greatly reduced relative to 1989. In the East Shetland Basin, the 2002 SR survey returned a mean PAH concentration below 150 µg/kg dry weight. In both areas, the PAH distribution profile, and concentration ratios, indicated a predominantly pyrolytic (from combustion), as against petrogenic (from oil), input. In the East Shetland Basin there was some evidence of petrogenic input, but this was of mixed North Sea and Middle Eastern origin. This is typical of input from shipping activity.

## Conclusion

Hydrocarbon concentrations in both the Fladen Ground and East Shetland Basin in 2001 and 2002 can be classed as low or close to background. Furthermore, significant decreases in hydrocarbon concentrations were observed when compared to earlier surveys, it is probable that many will have degraded.

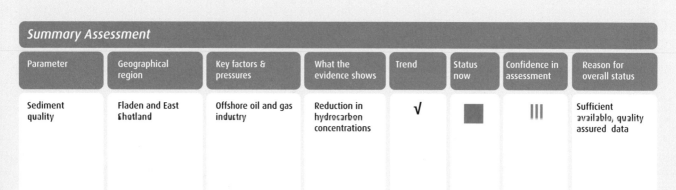

### Summary Assessment

| Parameter | Geographical region | Key factors & pressures | What the evidence shows | Trend | Status now | Confidence in assessment | Reason for overall status |
|---|---|---|---|---|---|---|---|
| Sediment quality | Fladen and East Shetland | Offshore oil and gas industry | Reduction in hydrocarbon concentrations | √ | ■ | III | Sufficient available, quality assured data |

## Monitoring

FRS and SEPA undertake monitoring targeted on understanding the sources of pollutant but they also participate jointly in the UKMMAS Clean Safe seas Environmental Monitoring Programme (CSEMP)[(11)]. Samples are taken from biota, water and sediments (Figures 3.11 and 3.12) to analyse for metals, PCBs, organochlorine pesticides (OCPs), PAHs (both parent and alkylated) and, more recently, PBDEs. Integrated with these chemical analyses are a series of biological effects tests to provide a comprehensive assessment of environmental health. The programme fulfils the UK's commitment to European Directives and its mandatory monitoring requirements under the OSPAR JAMP.

**Figure 3.11    Sampling seabed sediments from the FRV *Scotia* by FRS as part of the CSEMP Programme**

The general aims of CSEMP are to:

> support consistent standards in national and international monitoring programmes for marine environmental quality;

> establish appropriate protective regulatory measures;

> coordinate and optimise marine monitoring in the UK;

> provide a high quality chemical and biological data set from the UK's marine environment; and

> detect long-term spatial and temporal trends in physical, biological and chemical variables at selected estuarine and coastal sites.

To ensure the precision and validity of results produced, all organisations contributing to CSEMP are required to demonstrate a high standard of biological and chemical analytical quality control and to participate in intercalibration testing.

It is important that the level of contaminants accumulated in living things alone is not measured but that the effects of these substances in the survivability and health of the population involved is investigated since, even the contaminants that are present in seabed sediments have the potential to cause biological harm either by contact with bottom living fauna or by their ingestion of sediment. Biological effects testing is used by FRS, SEPA and the academic community (e.g. Glasgow Caledonian University) especially where there are little data available on the effects of a contaminant on living systems. Such testing can yield subtle results that may demonstrate effects in terms of behaviour, cell development or physiology. As an example there are increasing concerns about endocrine disrupting substances and plasticisers such as diethylhexylphthalate (DEHP) which are present even in some treated sewage effluents. Most of the new threats now come from synthetic substances, such as pharmaceuticals. They may be knowingly released into the sea, as when drugs are used under carefully prescribed conditions to treat farmed fish or conversely have unintentional pathways into marine waters via sewage or freshwater run-off as in the case of 17ß-oestradiol (arising from the female contraceptive pill). Traditionally, biological effects measurements have utilised the likes of enzyme activity, concentrations of metabolites or the incidence of externally visible fish diseases. However, more recently there has been an attempt to utilise a genomics approach as illustrated in Case Study 3.7.

Monitoring pollution in the seas is vital but to ensure we have intelligently managed improvements, regulators and politicians must be aware of what is going into the sea and whether there are any significant trends or particular hotspots. To ensure transparency of information SEPA makes all discharge information available in a Web based format outlined in Case Study 3.8. This allows anyone to access information on licensed release of chemicals to all waters including saline ones.

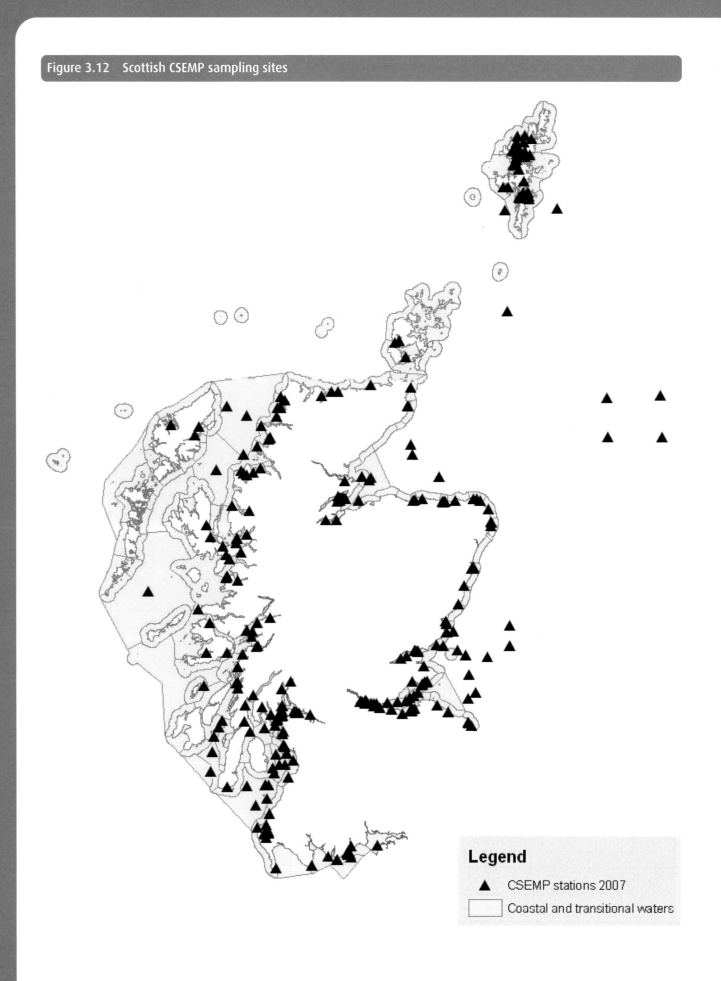

Figure 3.12    Scottish CSEMP sampling sites

Legend

▲    CSEMP stations 2007

☐    Coastal and transitional waters

## CASE STUDY 3.7   Evaluating the effects of environmental stressors on marine wildlife - Emerging techniques and approaches: DNA microarrays and qPCR arrays

### Current biomarkers of environmental stress

Biomarkers provide an indication of the exposure of wildlife to environmental stressors such as exposure to hazardous substances and increasing sea temperatures. Current practice is to assess the altered status of a biological parameter such as an enzyme activity or level of expression (e.g. CYP450) comparing animals from impacted or altered locations to those at locations believed to be unaffected by stressors. Increased expression of CYP450 indicates exposure to, for example, PAH and highlights the potential for adverse effects such as cancer resulting from the exposure. Recent practice does not rely on measurement of a single biomarker but incorporates a suite of measurements. For instance where PAH pollution is suspected (e.g. in the vicinity of oil platforms, oil terminals, harbours) CYP measurement may be combined with measurements of conjugated bile products and induction of other enzymes such as glutathione-S-transferase and UDP-glucuronosyltransferase. Although this approach broadens the data collection it is sampling only a very small proportion of the biological response and has limited power to predict higher order consequences affecting health or reproductive capacity.

### DNA microarrays and qPCR arrays

Techniques developed during the Human Genome Project allow the parallel measurement of thousands of biomarkers in single biological samples. DNA microarrays consist of glass slides on which minute deposits of specific DNA sequences have been printed in a regular matrix (Figure 3.13). Each deposit represents a distinct gene, and is used to measure the level of expression of that gene, and each array has tens of thousands of such deposits. In principle arrays can measure the expression level of every gene in a tissue. Microarrays were originally applied in the area of medicine and enabled the identification of genes whose expression differed between diseased and normal tissue. Other studies investigated the effects of drugs on mammals and found that typically the expression of 50-100 genes would be altered. More recently, microarrays have been used in an environmental context and two types of study have been conducted. The first is where the effect of a stressor is assessed under laboratory conditions while in the second type animals from the environment are profiled. An example of the former type of study includes work conducted by Glasgow Caledonian University, FRS and SEPA which used an array to study the effects of ethinyl oestradiol on plaice. The very first published report of an environmental application used a microarray jointly developed by the University of Stirling and the University of Birmingham and analysed flounder from two UK locations. Arrays are also under development for

invertebrates. Recently an array for mussel has been used to evaluate environmental status of mussel on the west coast of Scotland in work conducted by Glasgow Caledonian University and SEPA. The outputs of array studies provide a wealth of novel data that identifies both general and specific stress responses and these hold the prospect of being diagnostic of both exposure and of potential adverse effects in the future. However, environmental applications of genomic approaches have been limited by the lack of genomic resources (e.g. sequence data, cloned genes) for sentinel species. This problem is becoming less problematic as the number of genome projects increase and with the wider application of the revolutionary approach to sequencing with the ultra-high throughput DNA sequencing systems available today providing a plethora of data on diverse organisms.

There is continuing activity in Scotland in the development of arrays and their application to establishing the state of the marine environment. A consortium consisting of the University of Stirling, Glasgow Caledonian University, FRS, University of Birmingham, University of Exeter and CEFAS are investigating adaptation in fish to stressors using the previously described flounder array and a newly developed stickleback array (Figure 3.13). This Ecotoxicogenomics project is reaching its conclusion and results of laboratory and environmental studies are currently being analysed. It should be noted that the volume of data generated by array experiments is large and dedicated Bioinformatic Scientists are now required to analyse and interpret the data.

In addition to arrays for wildlife others have focussed on applications relevant to aquaculture in the marine environment. The TRAITS project is a collaboration between the Universities of Stirling, Aberdeen and Cardiff, the Roslin Institute and the Norwegian School of Veterinary Science. Project objectives are to identify the genetic basis of commercially important traits in salmon and to develop DNA microarrays to monitor indicators of health and performance. The project has developed a salmon array with 17k spots and results of its use are just appearing in the literature. The University of Aberdeen is also in the process of developing an array for the rainbow trout.

Microarrays are essentially discovery tools and in their current form are unsuitable for routine environmental use. Array experimentation is technically demanding and, as alluded to earlier, the data-analysis process is far from simple. There is a deficit of skilled staff for experimentation and subsequent bioinformatics. However, microarrays are hugely informative in facilitating an alternative method of gene biomarker determination.

Quantitative, Real-time PCR (qPCR) has been introduced over the last decade as a means of measuring biomarker (gene) levels. The method uses fluorescent reagents to follow the progress of PCR reactions on a continuous basis. Equipment for this technique is based on the use of 96 well microtitre plates, every well of which can be optically scanned for fluorescence as individual reactions proceed. The use of qPCR arrays has been pioneered in the medical field and targeted arrays (e.g. drug metabolism, oxidative stress, apoptosis) are commercially available for use on humans (SuperArray). Thus microarray studies lead to the discovery of genes whose expression is altered by exposure to a particular stressor and which will be informative on exposure and effect. This allows the development of a targeted qPCR array. qPCR provides a robust technology and in an array format can achieve the same as a macroarray measuring multiple transcripts simultaneously in a single biological sample.

At the time of writing, qPCR arrays are under development at the University of Stirling for flounder for work in collaboration with FRS and at Glasgow Caledonian University for plaice again in collaboration with FRS.

A bigger study is about to start in which Glasgow Caledonian University is collaborating with SEPA (East Kilbride) in a Knowledge Transfer project that will develop and evaluate qPCR arrays for stickleback and mussel. Each of these developments is made possible by knowledge gained through array experiments in the projects indicated above.

## Conclusion

The application of genomics techniques in environmental studies is in its infancy but is developing rapidly. This summary has only addressed DNA-based techniques but the other 'omics' such as proteomics and metabolomics are likely to be relevant to environmental monitoring in the foreseeable future. In an attempt to share experience, avoid duplication of effort and to agree on international standards the UK (NERC) is funding a national and international Knowledge Transfer projects to consider 'omics' applications in the environment. Partners in these projects include the University of Stirling, Glasgow Caledonian University and FRS. Thus Scotland is well placed to take advantage of the huge benefits resulting from the applications of 'omics' approaches in terms of expertise, resources and global involvement.

### Figure 3.13  Microarray data

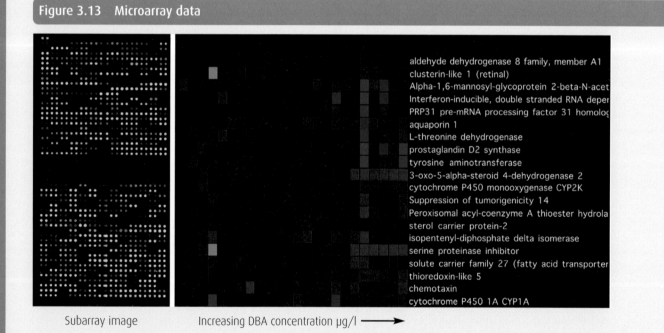

Subarray image          Increasing DBA concentration µg/l ⟶

The figure shows microarray data generated by the NERC-funded Ecotoxicology Consortium from an experiment in which stickleback were exposed to increasing concentrations of dibenzanthracene (DBA). The image on the left shows a portion of a microarray used to test a single sample. Each dot represents an individual DNA sequence and the computer-generated colours indicate if the gene for that sequence has increased (red), decreased (green) or unaltered (yellow) expression relative to an untreated animal.  The image on the right is a 'heat map' that summarises data from multiple microarrays. Each row represents an individual gene and each column a separate microarray test sample with animals exposed to increasing DBA from left to right. The colour coding of the 'heat map' indicates if expression increases (red) or decreases (blue) relative to untreated animals.

## CASE STUDY 3.8    Scottish Pollutant Release Inventory (SPRI)

The Scottish Pollutant Release Inventory (SPRI) is a publicly accessible electronic database of releases of pollutants to air, water and land from licensed sources. Many of the discharges are to estuarine or coastal waters, and knowledge of these discharges is helpful in understanding the state of Scotland's marine environment. The SPRI can be accessed via the SEPA web site[12]. Its aims are to:

> provide data and information to the public and so help facilitate discussion and public participation in environmental issues and decision making;

> provide data and information for policy makers and academics;

> provide information on pollutants to support on-going work to prevent and reduce pollution caused by these substances;

> allow comparison of releases of substances by industry sector; and

> deliver the system by which Scotland will comply with the requirements of an EU Regulation on the implementation of a European Pollutant Release and Transfer Register.

SPRI dischargers are asked to supply information on their total emissions to air or to water as kilograms per year. There are threshold values below which emissions do not need to be reported. The SPRI currently contains information for pollutant releases for 2002, 2004, 2005 and 2006.

### Types of site which report information to the SPRI

Sites reporting to the SPRI include:
> processes covered by the Pollution Prevention and Control Part A regulations – these include many industrial and manufacturing processes;

> sites covered by the Radioactive Substances Act Band A or Band B – these include nuclear power stations, hospitals and universities;

> waste water treatment works;

> waste management site such as industrial or municipal landfill sites; and

> marine caged fish farm sites.

### Substances reported

There are six main sections in the form to be completed. Sections A, B and C require information on emissions to air, discharges to waters and releases to land respectively. These are supplied for individual compounds within each of the broad groupings of:

> inorganics

> organics

> radionuclides

> metals and compounds

> other pollutant groups

These groupings include a total of 129 substances for releases to air and 77 for releases to waters; for some substances, reporting is required to both media.

### How to access the SPRI

To access the site see reference[12]. Searches can then be undertaken by inserting a post code and a distance from it as a search range. Alternatively, the SPRI Emission Data can be accessed directly. If choosing this latter option, searches can be undertaken by postcode, by pollutant or by operator name.

For example, selecting by pollutant, the screen shown below (Figure 3.14) appears which asks for the search to be refined by year, by pollutant, by PPC Code or Industry Sector and by media. A choice is given to see release figures that are below the reporting thresholds for the pollutant selected.

### Figure 3.14    Sample of SPRI web page screen

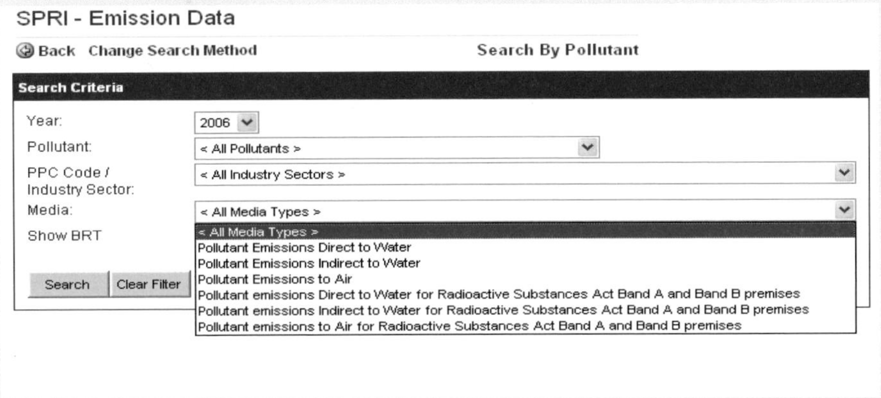

**SPRI - Emission Data**

Back   Change Search Method                    Search By Pollutant

**Search Criteria**

| | |
|---|---|
| Year: | 2006 |
| Pollutant: | < All Pollutants > |
| PPC Code / Industry Sector: | < All Industry Sectors > |
| Media: | < All Media Types > |
| Show BRT | |

< All Media Types >
Pollutant Emissions Direct to Water
Pollutant Emissions Indirect to Water
Pollutant Emissions to Air
Pollutant emissions Direct to Water for Radioactive Substances Act Band A and Band B premises
Pollutant emissions Indirect to Water for Radioactive Substances Act Band A and Band B premises
Pollutant emissions to Air for Radioactive Substances Act Band A and Band B premises

Search    Clear Filter

The SPRI information is presented as a list of companies in alphabetical order. You can then select to view the data supplied by the company and/or to see the location of the company selected on a map.

## Nutrient inputs and eutrophication

The key nutrient in saline waters is normally nitrogen, as this is usually the element limiting the growth of algal blooms. Despite obligations under OSPAR to reduce the input of nutrients, the input of inorganic nitrogen and phosphorous compounds is an example where less success has been achieved in reducing discharges so that loadings have hardly changed in the last 15 years[13] (Figures 3.15 and 3.16).

For Scotland, sewage is a smaller source of nitrogen inputs to the sea than farming, so the implementation of secondary sewage treatment as required by the Urban Waste Water Treatment Directive, has had little influence on the total inorganic load of nutrients that are discharged. Fortunately despite this lack of progress, only a couple of small local areas of the Scottish marine environment are deemed eutrophic and this is explored in more detail in Case Study 3.9.

Nitrogen concentrations in the Firths of Clyde and Forth are elevated above background levels due to their catchments serving high population numbers. However, perhaps surprisingly, more significant concentrations are found in the estuaries of the South Esk and Ythan rivers, where the nitrogen arises mainly from agriculture. Where waters are seen to be at risk, catchment areas may be subject to nitrogen restrictions for farming (nitrogen vulnerable zone) or tertiary treatment for sewage (the removal of nitrogen or phosphorus). Nutrients naturally cycle in the sea and the upwelling of deep, naturally nutrient rich water along the coastal shelf edge is essential for supporting healthy fisheries. Significant shifts in the biomass of phytoplankton is observed in long term data sets collected offshore by continuous plankton recorders towed behind ships. These changes appear to arise from climatic change (sea warming) and trends in the North Atlantic Index, rather than any change in nutrient fluxes. Scotland's requirement to carry out regular eutrophication assessments for OSPAR are expanded in Case Study 3.9.

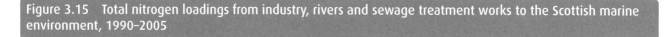

**Figure 3.15  Total nitrogen loadings from industry, rivers and sewage treatment works to the Scottish marine environment, 1990–2005**

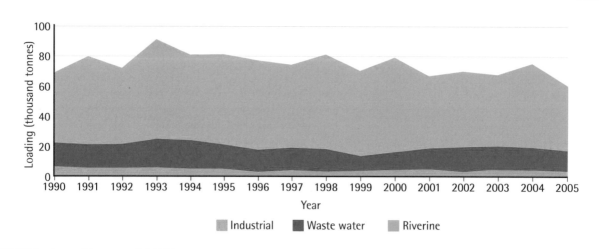

**Figure 3.16  Phosphorus loadings from industry, rivers and sewage treatment works to the Scottish marine environment, 1990–2005**

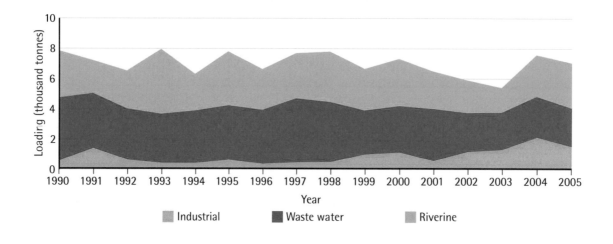

## CASE STUDY 3.9   Eutrophication in Scottish marine waters

### What is eutrophication?

Eutrophication is the enrichment of water by nutrients, especially compounds of nitrogen and/or phosphorus. This causes an accelerated growth of algae and higher forms of plant life, producing an undesirable disturbance to the balance of organisms present in the water and to the quality of the water concerned. Where eutrophication is found, action is needed to restore the ecosystem to full health and ensure that the marine environment can be used sustainably.

### How is eutrophication assessed?

Eutrophication is assessed using criteria set by the OSPAR Common Procedure[14] under which threshold values have been set for:

> causative factors, e.g. nutrient inputs and winter nutrient concentrations, particularly nitrate as this limits algal growth in marine waters;

> direct effects of nutrient enrichment, e.g. summer chlorophyll a levels;

> indirect effects of nutrient enrichment, e.g. oxygen deficiency; and

> other possible effects, e.g. shellfish poisoning.

### What is the state of Scotland's marine waters in relation to eutrophication?

Most of Scotland's marine waters are not at risk of eutrophication, and are designated as non-problem areas. The Ythan Estuary in north-east Scotland, 20 km north of Aberdeen, was identified as a Problem Area (PA). This was because the criteria for winter nutrient concentrations, N:P ratios and macroalgal coverage and biomass were exceeded. The South Esk Estuary, part of Montrose Basin, was identified as a Potential Problem Area (PPA), due to high levels of macroalgal coverage and biomass. Although these sites have been classified in this way the ecosystems still appear healthy and human use is promoted. In Montrose Basin there are internationally important numbers of pink-footed geese, greylag geese and redshank, and nationally important numbers of shelduck, widgeon and eider, and a Visitor Centre and Wildlife Reserve run by the Scottish Wildlife Trust.

Occasional blooms of toxic or non toxic species may occur virtually anywhere for reasons that are not clear and certainly show little relationship with nutrient levels (Figure 3.17).

## Figure 3.17   Red tide on a beach in Skye

How is water quality improved in the impacted areas?
Water quality is improved by identifying the reason for the eutrophication, implementing the relevant legislation and taking appropriate management action. The extensive macroalgal coverage in the Ythan and South Esk Estuaries was due to high loadings of nitrogen, mainly from agricultural sources.

The EU Nitrates Directive seeks to protect waters from pollution caused by nitrates. In 2000, these areas were identified as Nitrate Vulnerable Zones (NVZs) under this Directive, and management measures in terms of improved agricultural practice taken to reduce diffuse inputs of nitrates and improve water quality.

The EU Urban Waste Water Treatment Directive (UWWTD) sets measures to protect the marine environment from the adverse effects of insufficiently treated urban waste water (sewage) discharges. This Directive also requires regular assessment of eutrophication status in a similar way to OSPAR but eutrophic areas are called sensitive waters. Failure of these assessments lead to statutory requirements for improvements.

A note on geographical regions
In Chapter 1, the recently agreed reporting regions are outlined. These include large Regional Sea Areas, and the smaller Water Framework Directive water bodies, the latter having to be reported on for their eutrophication status. These eutrophication assessments describe specific sea areas intermediate in size between these, typically estuaries or coastal waters. These are the geographical regions described in the Summary Assessment.

## Summary Assessment

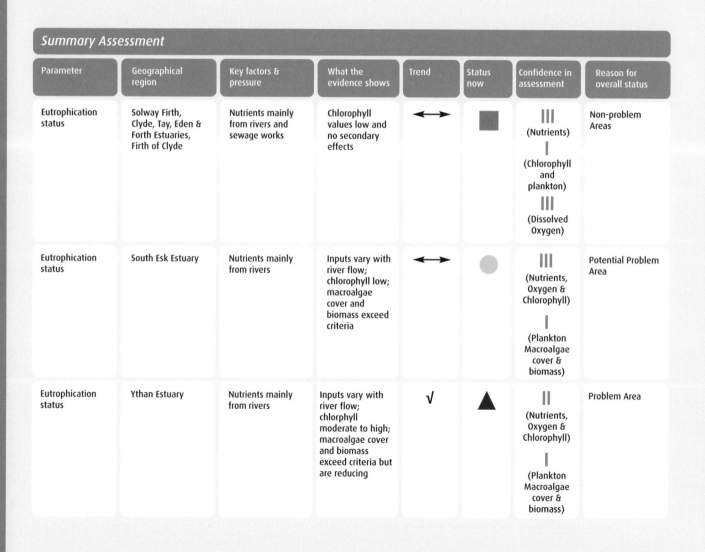

| Parameter | Geographical region | Key factors & pressure | What the evidence shows | Trend | Status now | Confidence in assessment | Reason for overall status |
|---|---|---|---|---|---|---|---|
| Eutrophication status | Solway Firth, Clyde, Tay, Eden & Forth Estuaries, Firth of Clyde | Nutrients mainly from rivers and sewage works | Chlorophyll values low and no secondary effects | ↔ | ■ | III (Nutrients) <br> I (Chlorophyll and plankton) <br> III (Dissolved Oxygen) | Non-problem Areas |
| Eutrophication status | South Esk Estuary | Nutrients mainly from rivers | Inputs vary with river flow; chlorophyll low; macroalgae cover and biomass exceed criteria | ↔ | ● | III (Nutrients, Oxygen & Chlorophyll) <br> I (Plankton Macroalgae cover & biomass) | Potential Problem Area |
| Eutrophication status | Ythan Estuary | Nutrients mainly from rivers | Inputs vary with river flow; chlorphyll moderate to high; macroalgae cover and biomass exceed criteria but are reducing | √ | ▲ | II (Nutrients, Oxygen & Chlorophyll) <br> I (Plankton Macroalgae cover & biomass) | Problem Area |

## Radioactive substances

Radioactive substances, though treated separately by regulation, become distributed in the environment in the same way as any other substance depending on its stability and solubility even though the manner in which they have the potential to cause environmental harm is different. Some radioactive substances, though discharged at very low levels, have half lives of hundreds or even hundreds of thousands of years. Radioactive substances are used in industry for a variety of applications, for example in medicine, nuclear powered submarines and food preservation. These applications result in discharges and emissions of radioactivity into the environment. Radioactivity is also naturally present in the environment, for example in rocks and sediments.

SEPA controls the amount of radioactive wastes that industry is allowed to discharge to the environment. A continual and comprehensive monitoring programme, which includes sampling of a variety of media such as seaweed, water, grass and a large range of seafood and locally grown produce, is undertaken by SEPA.

By researching the people that live in the vicinity of nuclear licensed sites, understanding their habits and what food they eat, the regulator can undertake an assessment of the impact of the discharges to the most exposed individuals to ensure that legal limits of exposure are not breached.

Details of some of the monitoring are explored in Case Study 3.10. The data analysis in this case study did not include sites of known localised contamination, for example at Dalgety Bay, Chapelcross and Dounreay. These sites are subject to a different monitoring strategy and are not suitable for assessing trends in the marine environment but are discussed below.

### Inputs of radionuclides into the environment from Dounreay

Following the discovery of 34 fragments of irradiated nuclear fuel on the seabed near Dounreay in 1997, an order was made under the Food and Environment Protection Act 1985 to ban the harvesting of seafood within a 2 km radius of the discharge pipeline. Regular annual monitoring of Sandside Bay and the Dounreay foreshore has led to the discovery and removal of radioactive particles from these areas. In 2005 a radioactive particle was also found at Dunnet beach. Limited offshore monitoring has also detected hundreds of particles in the marine environment. The particles originate from the historic activities at the Dounreay plant.

A comprehensive scientific assessment showed that the overall current risk of a member of the public encountering a particle on public beaches at Sandside was low.

The Dounreay Particles Advisory Group (DPAG) was set up in 2000[15].

### Radioactive contamination at other sites in Scotland

At Dalgety Bay in Fife radium 226 contamination was first detected in 1990. It is believed to have originated from salvage work involving radium-coated instrumentation at a former military airfield at Dalgety Bay. Some contaminated material has been removed. Although the most recent assessment of the radiological risk showed that there was a realistic chance of encounter, the potential effects on health were considered to be low. It also suggested that further investigation of the extent of the contamination is warranted.

Monitoring in July 2005 confirmed the presence of radioactivity in an area of Aberdeen beach near the harbour. Sampling and analysis has been undertaken to identify potential sources of the radioactivity. Radiation exposure received by members of the public using the beach regularly was negligible.

Some of the nuclear installations in Scotland are approaching the end of their useful operating life and radioactive waste associated with their decommissioning will have to be managed in the future. Accumulations of intermediate and high-level radioactive waste, already stored at some nuclear installations in Scotland, present particularly challenging issues for ensuring safe, long-term disposal[16].

## CASE STUDY 3.10    Radioactive substances

### Introduction

SEPA is responsible for regulating the keeping, use and, if necessary, the disposal of radioactive waste from offshore installations, hospitals, universities and research premises. SEPA also grants authorisations for the disposal of radioactive waste from nuclear licensed sites in Scotland. These permits minimise the impact on human health and the environment by the use of radioactive material and any disposal of radioactive waste The primary objective of protecting human health is achieved through SEPA's legal powers under the Radioactive Substances Act 1993 (RSA 93) and other legal instruments.

SEPA also monitors environmental radioactivity in coastal waters to assess the impacts of these authorised discharges of radioactive wastes. This report summarises monitoring data for 1997-2006. SEPA's environmental radioactivity monitoring programme provides the data needed to assess the detriment (dose) incurred by the most affected members of the public from authorised disposals of radioactive waste. These critical groups are people who, because of what they eat and what they do (work and pastimes), are more likely to have greater exposure than other groups of people. Because of the large numbers of pathways by which radioactive sources can be encountered, it is possible to have more than one critical group per source.

### Major sources of radioactivity in Scotland's marine environment

The major components of man-made (anthropogenic) radioactivity in the marine environment arise from the discharges from nuclear licensed sites and the non-nuclear industry. Discharges from nuclear licensed sites have continued to show a decreasing trend, due to operator process improvements and regulatory involvement. The following list details the key sources of discharges of radioactive waste in each UK maritime region.

### Irish Sea

*Sellafield, Cumbria:*
Situated on the Cumbrian coastline, only a few miles from the Scottish border, Sellafield is the largest nuclear site in the United Kingdom. The regulation of the release of radioactive substances from this site is carried out by the Environment Agency. However, due to the nature of Sellafield discharges, SEPA carries out a programme of environmental monitoring to assess the impact of these discharges on Scotland.

*Chapelcross, Dumfries & Galloway:*
Located within four miles of the Solway Estuary, Chapelcross is a four-reactor station with eight 30 MW turbines. This station ceased electricity power production in 2004 and is now undergoing decommissioning.

### Clyde

*Hunterston A & B Stations, Ayrshire:*
Situated near West Kilbride on the Hunterston Peninsula of the Ayrshire coast.

*Hunterston A*
Powered by twin Magnox reactors, Hunterston A ceased electricity power production at the end of March 1990 and is undergoing decommissioning.

*Hunterston B*
Powered by a pair of Advanced Gas-cooled Reactors, Hunterston B, currently operating at a reduced level of 70% maximum output, is capable of supplying power to over 1 million homes.

*HMNB Clyde, Firth of Clyde:*
Her Majesty's Naval Base (HMNB) Clyde establishment consists of the naval base at Faslane and the arms depot at Coulport.

Babcock Naval Services, a subsidiary of Babcock Support Services Limited, operates at HMNB Clyde in partnership with the Ministry of Defence (MoD). However, the MoD is responsible for the disposal of radioactive waste.

### North Scotland Coast

*UKAEA Dounreay & Vulcan NRTE, Caithness:*
Dounreay (Figure 3.18) was once Britain's centre for fast reactor research and development. Now the 140-acre site in Caithness is the largest nuclear decommissioning project in Scotland and the second largest nuclear licensed site in the UK after Sellafield. It is planned that Dounreay will be fully decommissioned by 2033.

The Vulcan Nuclear Reactor Test Establishment, operated by the MoD (Procurement Executive), is located adjacent to the UKAEA site, and the impact of its discharges is considered along with those from Dounreay.

### Forth

*Torness Station:*
Situated on the east coast, near Dunbar, Torness power station has been in operation since 1988. It is powered by two Advanced Gas-cooled Reactors and, with an electrical output of 1250 MW, is capable of supplying power to over 1.5 million homes.

*Rosyth Royal Dockyard:*
Decommissioning of Rosyth Royal Dockyard in Fife commenced in 2003 following the final refit operations on two Royal Navy nuclear submarines. In addition to carrying out the yard's own clean-up operations, seven of the Royal Navy's eleven decommissioned nuclear submarines are currently stored at Rosyth.

**Figure 3.18    Dounreay fast reactor site in Caithness, north Scotland**

SEPA's marine environmental radioactivity monitoring programme includes analysis of seawater, sediments, seaweed and seafood (fish, crustaceans). As the availability of fish and shellfish samples varies significantly across Scotland there is difficulty in directly comparing the regions against each other. However, overall analysis of monitoring data showed that generally there were no statistical trends and that, importantly, many of the results were at the limits of detection for the radionuclide of concern (i.e. no positive result). The limit of detection will vary for each radionuclide and is dependant on sample size, which can vary due to the availability of marine species (particularly seafood).

Annually, a summary of the results of SEPA's marine and terrestrial programmes is published in Radioactivity in Food and the Environment (RIFE) reports[17]. The reports include an assessment of the impact of discharges on various critical groups.

**Summary Assessment**

| Parameter | Geographical region | Key factors & pressure | What the evidence shows | Trend | Status now | Confidence in assessment | Reason for overall status |
|---|---|---|---|---|---|---|---|
| Radioactive Substances | Sampling locations around Scottish coast | Industrial use especially power generation | Low concentrations (most samples below the limit of detection) and no discernible trend | ↔ | ■ | II | No evidence of risk to human health or the environment at the RIFE sites |

### Radioactivity beyond 12 nautical miles

Monitoring in deeper waters outside of 12 nm is carried out by Cefas and is reported at a UK level as part of the commitment under the OSPAR Radioactive Substances strategy. Particular attention was paid to caesium 137, the bulk of which stems from historic discharges from Sellafield in Cumbria going back to the 1970s. Although these levels have dramatically fallen with time, concentrations measured off the west coast of Scotland were still around one hundred times higher than the global fallout level found in North Atlantic surface waters[18].

Naturally occurring radionuclides, principally uranium 238 and thorium 232, are disturbed when the Earth's crust is drilled to extract oil and gas. They are found around oil and gas platforms and from the scaling removal of equipment brought ashore. The levels are low and even though this waste is not considered to be a hazard, strategies are in place to reduce the amount of waste produced and re-inject as much as possible into the drilled strata[19]. Predictions show a further steady reduction expected over the next 15 years.

### Temperature and noise

Changes in temperature and the creation of artificial noise are two of the most prevalent forms of man derived energy entering the marine environment. Temperature changes can either be hot or cold and are of significance where this is a large difference between the discharged water and the receiving water. Mixing ensures that the area affected is relatively small but can be problematic if it is a narrow estuary with restricted circulation. Hot water is principally found in cooling water from, e.g. power stations or process water, e.g. from distilleries. Standards are still to be decided under WFD but no discharge in Scotland is considered to have more than a small local effect.

Noise is very much a product of the last hundred years and comes from diverse sources such as military activities, shipping, seismic exploration and renewable energy structures. There is little information on the effect of noise on invertebrates, some on fish but the greatest concern is on the disturbance to marine mammals many of which rely on sonar for communication[20]. Some human derived sound, especially from electronic sonar devices, can travel large distances on water. Steps are now being taken to control unnecessary noise so that in the case of seismic surveys JNCC is consulted in every case and has guidelines to cover noise but there are few situations that are unique to Scottish waters.

### Litter and waste

Litter (Figure 3.19) visibly demonstrates the interconnectivity of the seas as even remote beaches far from any centres of human habitation may still have heavy deposits of litter, and discarded waste can be found in the open sea either floating on the surface or sunken to the sea bed depending on its buoyancy. Surveys of both the public and scientist's opinion show a continuing concern about litter and rubbish in the seas and on shorelines. It causes both ecological harm and an aesthetic eyesore.

**Figure 3.19    Beach litter at Helensburgh**

Marine litter has been an ongoing problem for many years and arises from a number of sources including wilful discharge by individuals, fly-tipping and dumping from vessels. Some waste may also arise from accidents, as seen in the south coast of England in 2007 in relation to the grounding of the *Napoli*, or unintentional carelessness. The litter in Scottish seas may be derived locally, or have travelled thousands of miles, from well outside Scotland's direct influence. Some sea lochs act as natural collecting funnels when facing prevailing winds, e.g. the Head of Loch Long at Arrochar in the Clyde Sea area collects large accumulations of litter on the beach even though the local population is very small.

Many surveys have described the problem so that we know that about 80% of marine litter originates from land and up to 90% of the waste consists of plastics which may persist for considerable periods of time[21]. Litter is not only unsightly but large items can strangle animals and small pieces can be ingested by animals sometimes with fatal consequences. Litter has an economic cost in blocking water intakes, getting wrapped round boats propellers or simply the cost of physically removing it from beaches. However, controlling the entry of litter into the environment has proved far more difficult as it originates from so many sources. Education, a general move to reduce packaging and a change to biodegradable materials will all help but the solution does not lie with any agency or even one country. There is no evidence marine litter has declined over the last 20 years and it may still be on the rise.

*Bacterial contamination*
Faecal bacteria originate from human sewage and from animal faeces principally washed into burns from farmland in wet weather. Their presence is monitored via indicator species present in all warm-blooded species, rather than disease causing bacteria themselves which are only present when in large numbers when there is an infection in the source community. Both indicator and pathogenic bacteria have a limited survival rate in saline waters, but if sewage treatment and dispersion are inadequate they may be present at levels high enough to cause illness or infections in humans bathing or in contact with the receiving water. There were 61 EU recognised bathing waters around Scotland's coast in 2006, and it is SEPA's task to ensure that they all meet EU bacterial standards. There has been a significant overall reduction in average bacterial counts over the last 10 years and all identified bathing waters met the EU standards for the first time in 2006. Wet weather remains an influence on bacterial levels as high rainfall inevitably washes more bacteria from pasture land. The 100% record was not maintained in 2007 as the wetter summer led to increased run-off from diffuse rural and urban sources (Figure 3.20). The general reduction in measured faecal coliforms is a result of better sewage treatment, more effective discharge locations and targeted farm inspections and improvement plans.

Shellfish are also monitored for their bacteriological concentration under two EC Directives. SEPA monitors shellfish as part of their assessment of the quality of waters in which shellfish live for the Shellfish Waters Directive 79/923/EEC. The FSAS monitors shellfish to ensure they are safe to go to market for human consumption under EC legislation including EC 2073/2005, EC 2074/2005, EC 852/2004, EC853/2004 and EC 854/2004 (see Case Study 5.1). Under this legislation shellfish production areas are classified as shown in Figure 3.21 but any particular site may have more than one classification for the same production area depending on the time of year.

**Figure 3.20    Annual average faecal coliform concentration for all samples from the 60 continuously designated EU bathing waters: 2000-2007**

(Where three waters were no longer monitored during 2007 concentrations were taken at the 2006 level)

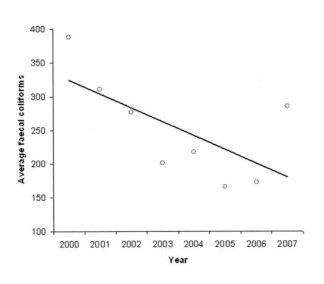

## Figure 3.21 Classification of shellfish production areas

| Production areas are grouped into four different categories: | | |
|---|---|---|
| Category A | Less than 230 E.coli/100 g shellfish flesh | May go for human consumption if End Product Standard * met |
| Category B | Less than 4,600 E.coli/100 g shellfish flesh in 90% of samples | Must be depurated, heat treated or relayed to meet Category A requirement |
| Category C | Less than 46,000 E.coli/100 g shellfish flesh | Must be relayed for long periods (at least two months) whether or not combined with purification, or after intensive purification to meet Category A or B |
| | More than 46,000 E.coli/100 g shellfish flesh | Unsuitable for production |
| * A requirement to be met before a product can be marketed | | |

The results of the classifications are of great significance to the financial viability of the producer. Although there is a general relationship between the amount of bacteria found in shellfish to concentrations found in the water column the relationship is not simple because some bacteria can survive or even multiply within some species of shellfish. This makes it difficult to come up with water standards that will guarantee resident shellfish meeting high classification standards. Where water quality improvements can be justified they will be actioned through the WFD.

### WHAT GAPS ARE THERE IN OUR KNOWLEDGE?

Inevitably our knowledge of what is clean and safe comes from monitoring data which generally are collected on a risk assessed based approach, i.e. the greatest attention is given to areas where problems are already confirmed or at least likely. The WFD and the new MSFD both challenge these assumptions and require monitoring even in areas assumed to be clean. Knowledge of deeper offshore waters is generally much poorer than the inshore coastal zone. Both SEPA and FRS have more recent programmes that are more wide ranging.

For radioactive substances there is little study on the effects of these substances on natural biological communities. The critical path and dose limit calculations for humans may not protect all marine species and more information is required. Much of the regulation that is linked to the measurement of eutrophication assumes a link between human derived nutrients and blooms. However, the sequential growth of marine phytoplantonic algae are still subject to large natural variations that have no known connection to human activities, including the occasional blooms of toxic algae.

As well as via ecosystem assessment methods, any potential adverse impacts of persistent pollutants on biota are monitored by bioaccumulation and biological effects assays. All approaches are needed because contaminant movement pathways and effects are not fully understood, and with new xenobiotic chemicals increasingly present, it is not always clear what will be the most sensitive receptor. Biological effects monitoring methods are varied dependent upon the nature of the threat. They are an important component of the UKMMAS CSEMP monitoring programme. They may comprise study of any impact of the test chemical on a particularly sensitive phase of a marine organism's life cycle (such as the initial development of oyster embryos, or the feeding rate of a bivalve mollusc); the production of a chemical by the test organism in response to contaminant exposure; or an adverse growth development such as 'imposex' in certain (commercial) molluscs exposed to extremely low concentrations of tributyltin (TBT) antifouling compounds. Use of TBT based anti-foulants has been phased out over the last 20 years, but effects can still be seen.

Bioaccumulation studies are well established, and Scotland has some long and growing time series of results. These show a general decline in concentrations of long-lived chemicals whose use was banned years ago (such as DDT and PCBs), but concentrations of other newer chemicals, especially plasticisers and flame retardants, are now present or increasing where they were previously absent. Analysis of modern synthetic chemicals at the low levels found in environmental samples is very expensive and time consuming. It is therefore important that scant resources are targeted at the substances that represent the most genuine risk. More biological effects testing could help by helping screen substances allowing an assessment to be made of which are potentially more problematic. Unfortunately the raft of EU regulations currently determine which substances must be looked for and this may include contaminants not expected in Scottish waters and does not include some that have a high probability of being present.

Much of the assessment of hazardous substances is performed on an individual compound or compound group basis. There is a need to assess the likely impacts of mixtures of hazardous substances in the marine environment, since it is mixtures rather than single compounds to which marine biota are exposed. Climate change is much discussed but it is not yet clear how this will affect water quality although there is some evidence that the seas are likely to become more acidic. Monitoring these small changes is quite difficult and such work has barely begun in Scottish seas (see Chapters 2 and 6). Changes in ocean currents could also affect the temperature of Scottish waters and the recycling of nutrients, both of which could effect primary production and any dependent biota.

# Chapter 4
# Healthy and Biologically Diverse Seas

## INTRODUCTION

Scotland's seas are positioned between subpolar and subtropical influences and support a spectacular and diverse assemblage of habitats and species. The inshore waters (out to 12 nm) cover an area of ~88,600 km², greater than the whole landmass of Scotland and comprise a broad range of habitats. Some of the most characteristic of these include sheltered sea lochs, wave exposed rocky coasts, long sweeping sandy bays, and small and large estuaries and firths. Factors, such as wave exposure, tidal currents, depth, turbidity, and tides influence the nature of the habitats and communities of animals and plants found living there.

There is a long and distinguished history of marine research and survey in Scotland. Two of the oldest marine research laboratories in the world are at Millport on the Clyde and the Gatty Marine Laboratory at the University of St Andrews; both established in 1884, only nine years after the oldest marine laboratory in the world, the Stazione Zoologica in Naples. These laboratories were followed shortly afterwards by the establishment in 1899 of the Fisheries Research Laboratory (now FRS) in Aberdeen. Much invaluable work has been carried out over the years at these institutes together with other groups including the University of Aberdeen, Heriot Watt University and the Scottish Association for Marine Science (SAMS) (Dunstaffnage), which emerged from the original foundation of the Millport Laboratory in 1884. In more recent times, the Marine Nature Conservation Review (MNCR), started by the Nature Conservancy Council in the 1980s and continued until the late 1990s under the auspices of the Joint Nature Conservation Committee (JNCC), together with the targeted surveys and seabed mapping undertaken by SNH, have further contributed to our growing wealth of knowledge about the biological diversity of the seas.

Despite all this interest and research there remains much to be explored and discovered about the marine wildlife of Scotland. The current best estimate of the total number of species of marine plants and animals (including both invertebrates and vertebrates) in Scottish waters is in the order of 6,500. If the microbial flora is included in the total then the number of species in Scottish waters is around 40,000. New species are continually being added to these lists; the majority of these additions are the results of better and more sophisticated survey and sampling and serve to further enhance the biological diversity of our seas, but others are less welcome non-indigenous and invasive species, which become established as a result of being introduced in ballast waters and other human vectors. Global climate change is affecting the distribution of some native marine species and could ultimately result in some species becoming extinct in Scottish waters whilst they may be replaced by other species more adapted to warmer water.

To ensure the long-term health of the marine ecosystem it is essential to maintain the ecological balance of this highly complex and dynamic environment, for example by ensuring sustainable exploitation and stewardship of marine resources and by protecting key biodiversity features.

The concepts of healthy and biologically diverse seas are enshrined in the proposed European MSFD as part of what comprises GES (see Chapter 1). Marine ecosystems are communities of plants and animals interacting with each other and with their environment. A healthy ecosystem is one:

> not suffering any loss of productivity or carrying capacity (i.e. where resources are used within their capacity for regeneration, and where nothing detracts from the overall variety and quality of the natural heritage); and

> fully able to deliver the services that support all life.

Ecosystem health is associated with resilience - being capable of coping with disturbances, such as storms, pollution, or harvesting pressure, without losing overall structure and ability to function. Thus healthy ecosystems can recover from, or adapt to, change. Furthermore, in a healthy ecosystem evolutionary forces may cause some species to decline or become extinct whilst allowing new species to evolve or increase to fill the niche.

Loss of marine ecosystem health may be identified from symptoms such as the build-up of waste material and the proliferation of simpler life forms that thrive on it, or the loss of keystone species unbalancing ecological relationships (as demonstrated by significant and rapid changes in the abundance of a small number of species). Other symptoms of poor ecosystem health include the presence of bioinvaders, the loss of biological diversity or a higher rate of mortality within key species caused by disease rather than predation, climate, or food scarcity.

With such a diverse, and dynamic environment the challenge is in identifying characteristics that are sufficiently generic, but at the same time specific, that can be used to adequately describe the sea as healthy and biologically diverse. On this basis it is proposed to adopt the relevant qualitative descriptors for determining good environmental status as presented in the MSFD (Table 4.1).

In describing the health and biological diversity of the seas it is important to be able to assess if the desired conditions are being met or maintained. In the marine environment it is impossible to aspire to measure everything and it is thus necessary to identify some key indicators that can act as a window to its overall health.

The Scottish Biodiversity Forum coordinated work that led to the publication in 2007 of *Scotland's Biodiversity Indicators*[1] which identified 17 state indicators across the terrestrial, freshwater and marine realms. Of these, five are of particular relevance to the marine environment and report on its health and the continuing biological diversity (Table 4.2). Others are of more marginal relevance, and it is likely that additional indicators will be needed to fully report on the health and state of marine biodiversity.

## EVIDENCE THAT THE SEA IS HEALTHY AND BIOLOGICALLY DIVERSE

Many of the indicators of a clean and safe sea may be used to determine if Scotland's seas are healthy and biologically diverse. For example, the concentration of contaminants in seals is an indicator of both the cleanliness of the marine ecosystem, as well as the health of marine mammals. Many of these data are the result of site condition monitoring, conducted by SNH to fulfil obligations under the EC Habitats Directive and requiring a six-yearly reporting cycle. Fisheries stock assessments are conducted regularly by FRS (see Annex 2). The scale at which species abundance data are collected vary from a small number of select coastal sites, to all of Scotland's coastal and offshore seas. Increasingly, European Directives are paying more attention to the general ecological health of the marine environment. The existing WFD relies heavily on measures aimed at assessing the health of transitional and coastal (TRAC) waters with the forthcoming MSFD following similar lines but extending further off shore to national territorial limits. Results of these WFD assessments will be communicated as a ranking in a classification scheme. Table 4.3 summarises some of the available data that could be used to determine if Scotland's seas are healthy and biologically diverse.

### Table 4.1    Qualitative MSFD GES descriptors for healthy and biologically diverse seas

**MSFD Annex I GES Descriptor**

GES Descriptor 1 - **Biological Diversity** is maintained. The quality and occurrence of habitats and the distribution and abundance of species are in line with prevailing physiographic, geographic and climatic conditions

GES Descriptor 2 - **Non-indigenous species** introduced by human activities are at levels that do not adversely alter the ecosystems

GES Descriptor 3 - Populations of all **commercially exploited fish and shellfish** are within safe biological limits, exhibiting a population age and size distribution that is indicative of a healthy stock

GES Descriptor 4 - All elements of the **marine food webs**, to the extent that they are known, occur at normal abundance and diversity and levels capable of ensuring the long-term abundance of the species and the retention of their full reproductive capacity

### Table 4.2    Scottish Biodiversity Indicators of particular relevance to the marine environment

| Indicator and Code | Evidence Source | Current trend |
| --- | --- | --- |
| Abundance of breeding seabirds (S5) | UK Seabird Monitoring Programme | Deteriorating |
| Marine Plankton (S14) | Data from UK Continuous Plankton Recorder | Divergence |
| Estuarine Fish (S15) | SEPA and FRS monitoring programmes | Improving |
| Marine Fish Stocks within safe limits (S16) | Population estimates from models based on fish landings data | Fluctuating |
| Non-native species (S17) | Geographical distribution of known non-native species | Deteriorating |

Marine biological data are reported under a range of mechanisms. Principal among these is the requirement upon SNH to monitor and report upon the condition of each qualifying feature within the Natura network (i.e. the habitats and species listed under Annexes 1 and 2 of the EC Habitats Directive, for which Special Areas of Conservation (SAC) (Figure 4.1) have been designated (see Tables 4.4 and 4.5), and rare or vulnerable bird species listed under Annex 1 of the EC Wild Birds Directive, for which Special Protection Areas (SPA) have been designated (Figure 4.2)). Information on the condition of each qualifying feature is reported both to the JNCC, to facilitate UK reporting to Europe, and to the Scottish Government[A].

The Natura reporting mechanism records the condition of features within designated sites but not their condition outwith such areas (although JNCC prepares, on a six year cycle, Favourable Conservation Status Assessments of all the habitats and species listed in the Annexes of the EC Habitats Directive, based on best available information). These assessments are based upon species and habitat ranges across the UK rather than in Scotland alone. However, not all the marine habitats and species considered of national importance to Scotland are represented in these European Directives, but instead are contained on the Scottish Biodiversity List which contains 109 marine species and 88 marine habitats in Scotland[B].

Apart from Natura sites, the condition of notified features within all Sites of Special Scientific Interest (SSSI) is also monitored and reported upon by SNH on a six-yearly cycle, though in the marine environment this designation is limited to intertidal areas[C].

Marine biological data, such as species records, collected through the SNH Site Condition Monitoring programme, and other marine surveys that it funds, are uploaded onto a database (Marine Recorder) and forwarded to JNCC for public dissemination via the National Biodiversity Network Gateway[2]. Spatial data, such as habitat maps, collected through such surveys are also forwarded to JNCC for collation and dissemination through the MESH (Mapping European Seabed Habitats) project[3]. All published SNH marine survey reports are also available through the SNH website[4]. To facilitate collaboration on planned marine surveys, as well as exchange of data, scientists from FRS, SEPA, SNH, Scottish Government and academia meet twice yearly through the Marine Biodiversity Research Coordination Group, established in 2006 through the Scottish Biodiversity Strategy.

**Table 4.3    Summary of data collected that could indicate whether Scotland's seas are healthy and biologically diverse seas**

| Indicators of healthy and biologically diverse seas | Data collectors |
| --- | --- |
| Habitat extent and condition | FRS, National Oceanographic Centre (NOC), SAMS, SNH, University of Plymouth |
| Litter | Cefas, Local Authorities International Environmental Organisation (KIMO), Marine Conservation Society, Plymouth University, SEPA, Zoological Society of London |
| Sea temperature | FRS, ICES, Met Office, SAMS, SEPA |
| Seabed erosion and sediment change | SEPA, SNH |
| Species abundance and distribution | FRS, SAMS, Sea Mammal Research Unit (SMRU), SNH |
| Species as indicators of change | British Trust for Ornithology (BTO), FRS, JNCC, Marine Biological Association (MBA), SAMS, SEPA, SMRU, SNH |
| Species or biological communities as indicators of pollution | FRS, SEPA, SMRU, SOTEAG, SNH, University of Aberdeen, Glasgow Caledonian University, University of Stirling |

## Figure 4.1 Marine Special Areas of Conservation in Scotland

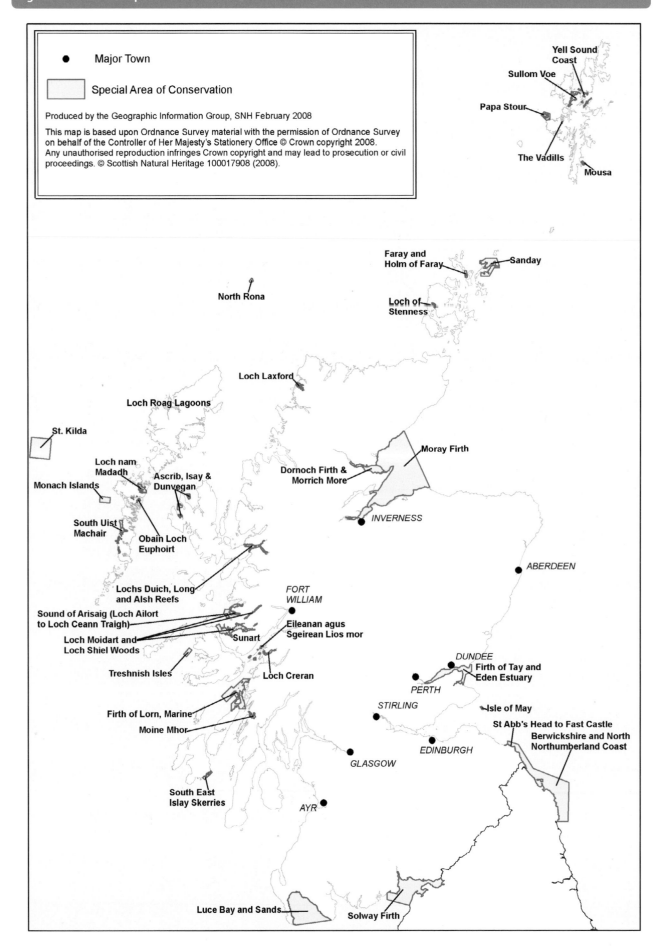

## Figure 4.2   Coastal Special Protection Areas in Scotland

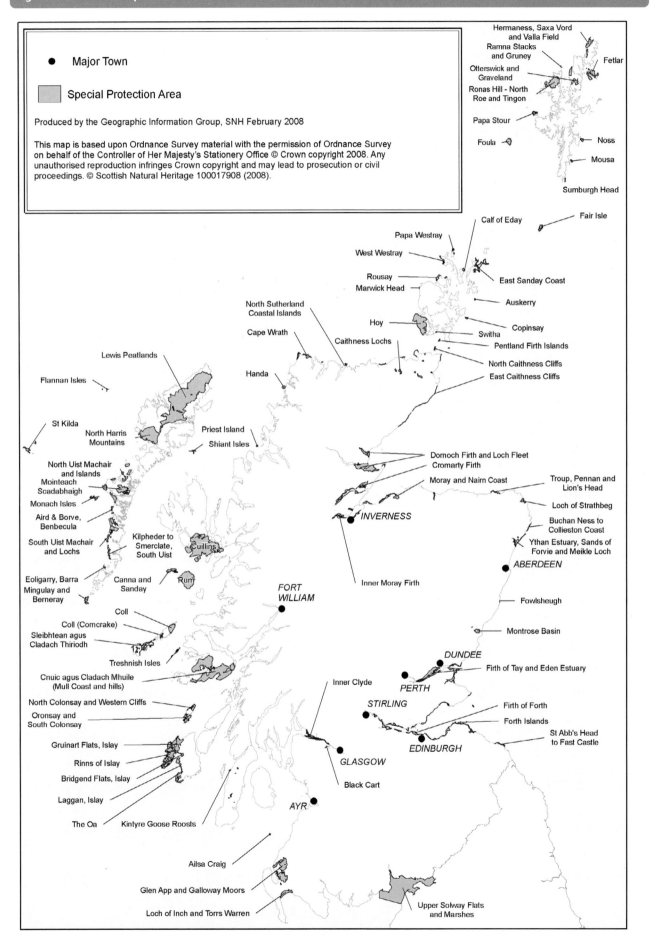

- Major Town
- Special Protection Area

Produced by the Geographic Information Group, SNH February 2008

This map is based upon Ordnance Survey material with the permission of Ordnance Survey on behalf of the Controller of Her Majesty's Stationery Office © Crown copyright 2008. Any unauthorised reproduction infringes Crown copyright and may lead to prosecution or civil proceedings. © Scottish Natural Heritage 100017908 (2008).

Hermaness, Saxa Vord and Valla Field
Ramna Stacks and Gruney
Fetlar
Otterswick and Graveland
Ronas Hill - North Roe and Tingon
Papa Stour
Noss
Foula
Mousa
Sumburgh Head

Calf of Eday
Fair Isle
Papa Westray
West Westray
Rousay
East Sanday Coast
Marwick Head
Auskerry
North Sutherland Coastal Islands
Hoy
Copinsay
Cape Wrath
Switha
Caithness Lochs
Pentland Firth Islands
Lewis Peatlands
North Caithness Cliffs
Handa
East Caithness Cliffs
Flannan Isles
St Kilda
Priest Island
North Harris Mountains
Shiant Isles
Dornoch Firth and Loch Fleet
Cromarty Firth
North Uist Machair and Islands
Moray and Nairn Coast
Troup, Pennan and Lion's Head
Mointeach Scadabhaigh
Loch of Strathbeg
Monach Isles
Buchan Ness to Collieston Coast
Aird & Borve, Benbecula
INVERNESS
Ythan Estuary, Sands of Forvie and Meikle Loch
South Uist Machair and Lochs
Kilpheder to Smerclate, South Uist
Cuillins
ABERDEEN
Eoligarry, Barra Mingulay and Berneray
Canna and Sanday
Rum
FORT WILLIAM
Inner Moray Firth
Fowlsheugh
Coll
Coll (Corncrake)
Montrose Basin
Sleibhtean agus Cladach Thiriodh
Treshnish Isles
DUNDEE
Cnuic agus Cladach Mhuile (Mull Coast and hills)
Inner Clyde
Firth of Tay and Eden Estuary
PERTH
North Colonsay and Western Cliffs
STIRLING
Firth of Forth
Oronsay and South Colonsay
Forth Islands
St Abb's Head to Fast Castle
Gruinart Flats, Islay
EDINBURGH
Rinns of Islay
GLASGOW
Bridgend Flats, Islay
Black Cart
Laggan, Islay
The Oa
Kintyre Goose Roosts
AYR
Ailsa Craig
Glen App and Galloway Moors
Upper Solway Flats and Marshes
Loch of Inch and Torrs Warren

**Table 4.4  Marine habitats listed under Annex 1 of the Habitats Directive for which Scottish SACs have been designated**

Sandbanks which are slightly covered by sea water all the time

Submerged or partially submerged sea caves

Estuaries

Mudflats and sandflats not covered by seawater at low tide

Coastal lagoons

Large shallow inlets and bays

Reefs

**Table 4.5  Marine species listed under Annex 2 of the Habitats Directive for which Scottish SACs have been designated**

Bottlenose dolphin

Grey seal

Common seal

*Plankton*

Plankton are the microscopic plants and animals that inhabit the pelagic zone and are typically free-floating, although many are capable of independent vertical movement and can swim up and down in the water several hundred metres per day. They are widely recognised to be some of the most important organisms on Earth. Both phytoplankton (Figure 4.3) (microscopic plants) and zooplankton (microscopic animals) are at the lowest levels of the food chain in all marine ecosystems and constitute a vital food-source for many higher level animals. A number of aspects of marine environmental and ecosystem health can be measured by looking at different components of plankton abundance: for example a measure of phytoplankton colour index (PCI) is an indicator of phytoplankton biomass, whilst the relative abundances of two closely related zooplankton copepods influenced by sea-water temperature provides evidence of climate change effects. In Scotland long-term records from the Continuous Plankton Recorder (CPR) (Figure 4.4) are available (Case Study 4.1).

**Figure 4.3   Diverse diatoms from Scottish waters (phytoplankton)**

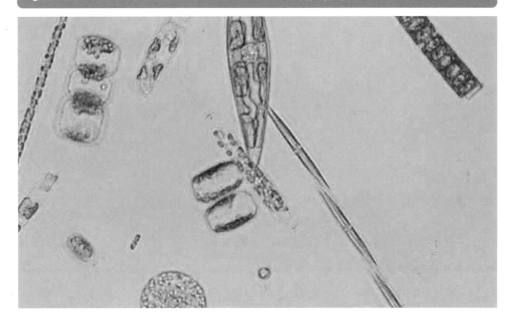

**Figure 4.4   Continuous Plankton Recorder being deployed**

The CPR is a high-speed plankton sampler, designed to be towed by merchant ships, which collects plankton for later examination in the laboratory. Starting in the 1930s, and especially since 1946, the CPR has been used on a changing network of routes across the North Sea and North Atlantic, and has provided a unique long-term set of biological data covering large parts of the UK seas. Four of the current (2006) survey routes pass through Scottish waters (Figure 4.5), providing a record of the species encountered and their abundance along the ship's regular sailing route[5].

The 'A' route, from Shetland to Aberdeen, is one of the longest continuously sampled routes in the CPR survey, with more than 60 years worth of data available. The route passes through an important area where oceanic water from the Atlantic Ocean enters the North Sea (Figure 4.6). A variety of ecological changes in the North Sea have been attributed to variations in this inflow. Analysis of CPR data from this route are investigating the changes that have taken place in this area and how they relate to broader scale changes[D].

### Figure 4.5   CPR survey routes in Scottish waters in 2006

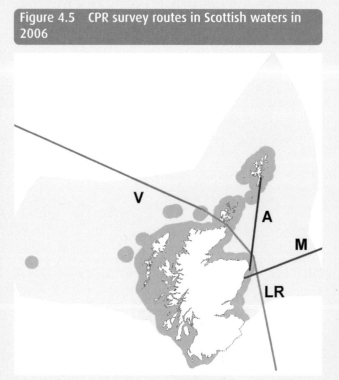

Lerwick to Aberdeen (A); Humber to Sule Skerry (LR); Aberdeen to Norway (M); and Iceland to Sule Skerry (V)

### Figure 4.6   Atlantic inflow to the north-western North Sea

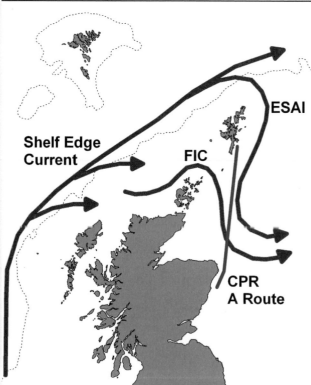

The approximate paths of the Shelf Edge Current, Fair Isle Current (FIC) and East Shetland Atlantic Inflow (ESAI), in relation to the CPR A-route from Shetland to Aberdeen. The 200 m depth contour is also shown.

The occurrence in the North Sea of certain Atlantic plankton 'indicator species' has long been used as an indirect index of the strength of the Atlantic inflow. Figure 4.7 shows one such index which indicates that there was a period of relatively strong inflow around 1960, followed by a lengthy period from about 1965 to 1985 during which inflow was relatively low. Since 1985 there have been more peaks and troughs in the index, suggesting greater variability in the inflow.

Figure 4.7    Atlantic Inflow Index from CPR 'A' route samples, 1946-2005

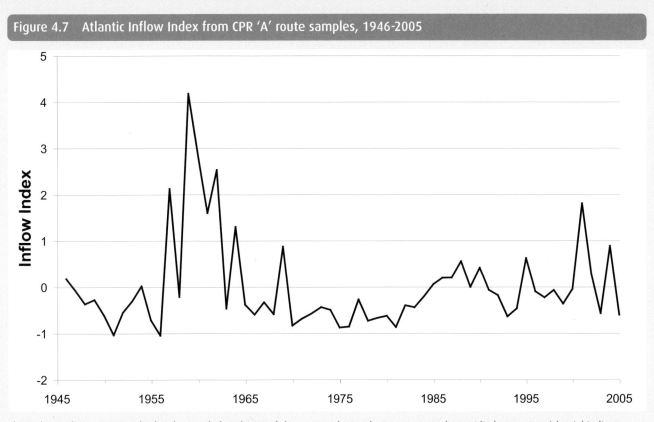

The index is the mean standardised annual abundance of the copepods *Candacia armata* and *Metridia lucens*, two 'classic' indicator species[6].

### Warm water plankton

Figure 4.8 shows the abundance of *Euchaeta hebes*, a species that originates from the Bay of Biscay area (south of 50°N) and is associated with the inflow of warmer Atlantic water to the North Sea. *E. hebes* was almost entirely absent from the 'A' route samples prior to the mid-1980s, but has since increased dramatically in abundance. Influxes of this species to the North Sea about 1990 and 1997 have been reported previously[6,7] but there was a further dramatic increase after 2000, peaking in 2004. This is consistent with the known northwards shift in the distribution of warm water plankton, although it provides more detail of the timing and variability of the shift. There are indications that seabird breeding success in Shetland was lower in years when there were more warm water plankton. It may not be a coincidence that 2004, which saw unprecedented numbers of *E. hebes* and other warm water species, was the worst year on record for seabird breeding success in the North Sea[8].

### Cold water plankton

In contrast, the abundance in 'A' route samples of *Calanus finmarchicus*, a species associated with colder more northerly waters, has changed little over the past few decades (Figure 4.8). This does not appear to be consistent with the general decline in the abundance of this species in the North Sea in recent decades, or with reported northwards retreat in the distribution of colder water plankton. The reasons for this remain unclear.

### Conclusions

The CPR survey data have revealed major biological changes in the plankton in the seas around the UK over the last few decades[9,10]. As well as a 'regime shift' in the North Sea in the mid-1980s, there has been a pronounced general northwards shift in the distribution of warm water plankton (by about 10° of latitude), and a parallel retreat to the north in the distribution of cold water plankton. These changes are associated with increasing sea temperatures, and have been linked to global warming.

While the broad picture of such changes across the North Sea and North-East Atlantic has already been described, patterns of change may be more varied on a smaller scale. Further analysis of these, and other, CPR data in Scottish waters could provide more detailed information on changes over smaller geographical areas and of the impact that these changes have on other components of the marine ecosystem.

**Figure 4.8   Abundances of *Euchaeta hebes* (warm water) and *Calanus finmarchicus* (cold water) in CPR 'A' route samples from 1946 to 2005 (mean annual abundance per sample)**

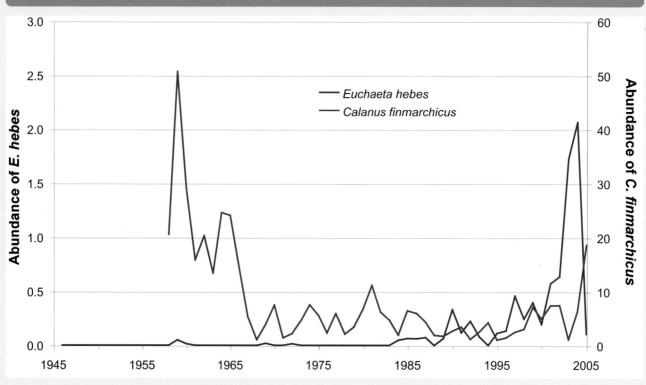

## Phytoplankton

Phytoplankton are the microscopic plants at the base of all food chains. They live in the surface waters where there is sufficient light to support photosynthesis and include diatoms, cyanobacteria and dinoflagellates. In normal circumstances phytoplankton are considered beneficial and essential to marine life, but a small number of species produce highly potent toxins that can accumulate in filter-feeding shellfish, such as mussels and scallops, destined for human consumption. In such circumstances fisheries have to be closed and fishermen suffer through loss of earnings. Algal blooms (Figure 4.9) may have other harmful effects including causing mass kills of marine fauna, mild toxicity to bathers as well as reduced aesthetic quality of affected waters. The number of species of phytoplankton in Scottish waters has been estimated at around 2,150 but new species are continually being recorded including some harmful non-native species that have been introduced through ballast waters and other human sources. A coastal ecosystem monitoring site was therefore established off Stonehaven in 1997 to monitor the state of the marine ecosystem in the north-east of Scotland. These data are currently allowing an assessment of the phytoplankton community, as well as identifying changes in phytoplankton diversity and abundance that occurs over time. Analysis of ten years of data from this site has revealed important variations in the phytoplankton community, see Case Study 4.2.

## Zooplankton

Zooplankton are typically microscopic or small protozoans and metazoans (e.g. copepods and amphipods), but also include much larger organisms such as jellyfish. Also included in the zooplankton are the free-floating eggs and larvae of a wide range of larger animals including fish, crustaceans and molluscs. Zooplankton are a major component of the diet of many fish and birds, and are therefore an essential link between the base of the food web (primary producers) and higher level consumers. Detectable changes in the abundance or species composition of zooplankton may therefore reflect fundamental changes in the ocean environment, including providing early indications of imminent changes in food availability for fish, birds and mammals. Because many zooplankton are relatively short-lived and are capable of high growth rates, they respond quickly to environmental perturbations that influence diversity, such as point-source pollution and predation pressure. Growth and development rates are well known to depend strongly on water temperature, thus changes in zooplankton may provide an early warning of temperature increases in the ocean, see Case Study 4.3.

**Figure 4.9** *Chaetomorpha* **bloom in the Ythan Estuary**

## CASE STUDY 4.2  Stonehaven ecosystem monitoring site – Phytoplankton

### Phytoplankton biomass

The algal pigment chlorophyll a is used as a proxy to estimate phytoplankton biomass in the system. The annual chlorophyll a cycle at this site is shown in Figure 4.10a. The concentrations are typical for northern North Sea regions with low winter concentrations (< 1.0 µg. l⁻¹) from November to March, usually rising to the highest levels during the rapid phytoplankton growth period from April – June. Chlorophyll a concentrations show extreme variability from year to year during the spring and summer months. Individual years fall into two categories. First, a group comprising 1997-2000, 2005 and 2006, (Figure 4.10b) which exhibited a peak in concentration during May/June followed by declining values towards minima in November/December. Second, a group comprising 2001-2004 (Figure 4.10c) during which the May/June peak was absent and instead, maximum values occurred during August/September.

### Phytoplankton abundance and diversity

Phytoplankton show considerable seasonal and interannual diversity at the Stonehaven site with different genera dominating the community at different times of year. Diatoms tend to be more abundant in the spring and autumn. A marked shift can be observed in the data from 2002 (Figure 4.11a). The main diatom bloom in May/June, dominated by the genus *Chaetoceros* from 1998–2001, has disappeared. Since 2002 this spring diatom bloom is now dominated by the genus *Skeletonema* which is observed earlier in the year. Dinoflagellates show periods of maximum abundance during the summer months. A period of low dinoflagellate cell density was observed from 2001–2004 (Figure 4.11b) with previously dominant genera such as *Ceratium* and *Dinophysis* showing decreased abundance. Potential toxin producing genera are routinely observed as part of the phytoplankton community at this site.

### Figure 4.10  Monthly averaged chlorophyll 'a' values over the annual cycle

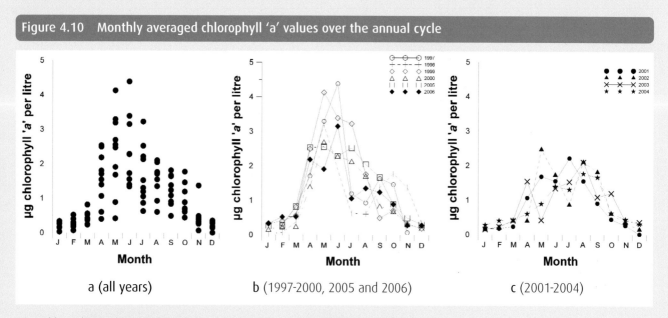

a (all years)  b (1997-2000, 2005 and 2006)  c (2001-2004)

a Monthly midpoint chlorophyll a values.
b Midmonth values of chlorophyll a during years where spring concentrations exceeding 2.5 µg chl'a'.l⁻¹
c Midmonth values of chlorophyll a during years where spring concentrations did not exceed 2.5 µg chl'a'.l⁻¹

## Figure 4.11 Monthly average observations of (a) diatoms and (b) dinoflagellates at Stonehaven over 1997-2007

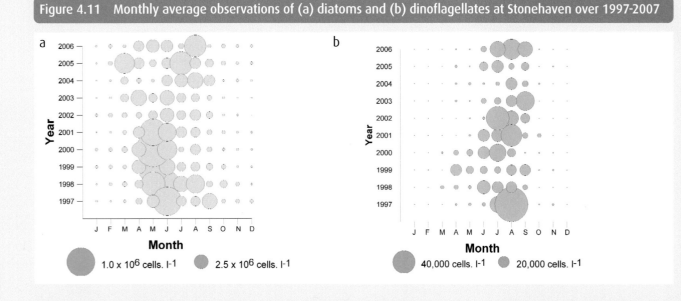

## Conclusions

Considerable variation has been observed in the biomass and abundance of phytoplankton at this site over the last 10 years. The short duration of this time series makes it difficult to determine if these changes will become established in the system or are part of a multi-annual cycle. In future years, as this time series increases in duration, it will provide valuable data which will improve our understanding of the dynamics of the phytoplankton community in Scottish waters as well as their response to environmental drivers such as climate change.

## Summary Assessment

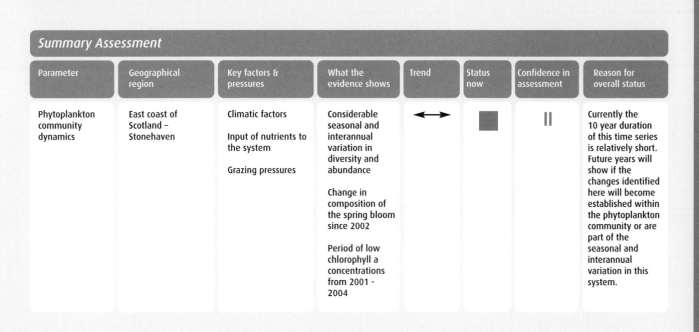

| Parameter | Geographical region | Key factors & pressures | What the evidence shows | Trend | Status now | Confidence in assessment | Reason for overall status |
|---|---|---|---|---|---|---|---|
| Phytoplankton community dynamics | East coast of Scotland – Stonehaven | Climatic factors<br><br>Input of nutrients to the system<br><br>Grazing pressures | Considerable seasonal and interannual variation in diversity and abundance<br><br>Change in composition of the spring bloom since 2002<br><br>Period of low chlorophyll a concentrations from 2001 - 2004 | ⟷ | ■ | ‖ | Currently the 10 year duration of this time series is relatively short. Future years will show if the changes identified here will become established within the phytoplankton community or are part of the seasonal and interannual variation in this system. |

A wide range of samples of small, medium and large zooplankton have been collected on a weekly basis at the Stonehaven ecosystem monitoring site (c.f. Case Study 4.2), established in January 1997. The sampling routine has remained consistent over the past decade with only minor modifications to sampling equipment having been necessary.

Taxonomic analysis of zooplankton is time consuming; with >250 species and developmental stages routinely identified. The species with highest abundances and biomasses are mostly crustaceans and of these most are copepods with *Acartia clausii, Temora longicornis, Pseudocalanus elongatus* and *Calanus* being most common. Other highly abundant non-crustacean species include larval stages of several kinds of benthic invertebrates, along with hard shelled molluscs such as the pteropod *Limacina retroversa* and soft-bodied predators such as the arrow worms *Sagitta* spp. (Table 4.6 and Figure 4.12).

**Figure 4.12   Some of the commonly occurring species of zooplankton at the Stonehaven ecosystem monitoring site**

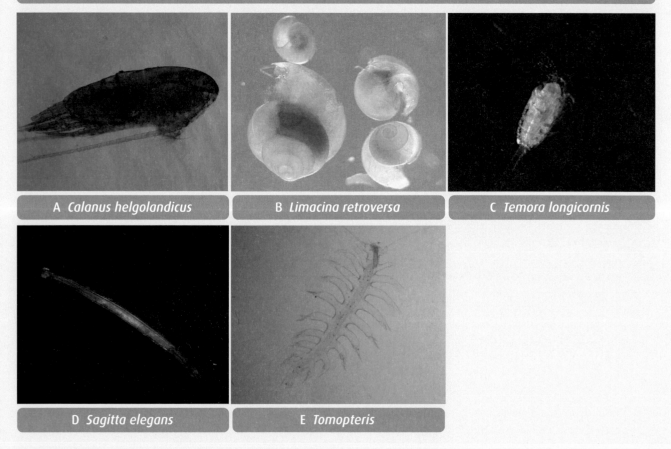

A  *Calanus helgolandicus*   B  *Limacina retroversa*   C  *Temora longicornis*

D  *Sagitta elegans*   E  *Tomopteris*

The results for abundance (both density and standing stock) and biomass are aggregated on a monthly and annual basis. This shows that the 10 most frequent species always account for more than 90% of the total abundance of all recorded species. There are inter-annual differences in total abundance and biomass of zooplankton between 1999 and 2006 (Figures 4.13 and 4.14). These fluctuations are strongly linked with the mean sea temperature. By examining the monthly means an exponential relationship appears between the monthly mean temperatures and the zooplankton abundance and biomass.

These broad analyses indicate that the annual seasonal cycles of the zooplankton assemblage off the east coast of Scotland clearly respond to changes in sea temperature and food availability (Figure 4.15), and are thus potentially vulnerable to climatic changes. Given that the detailed analysis is currently limited to eight years (1999 – 2006) it is not yet possible to determine if these observed changes are part of long-term cycles and trends (e.g. decadal) or are responses to anthropogenic effects.

The underlying detailed species occurrences, compositions and succession of individual species are now being analysed to consider their seasonal fluctuations in relation to the environmental variations, and in comparisons with other observations.

**Figure 4.13   The annual totals of zooplankton species abundances found in the 200 µm-mesh samples**

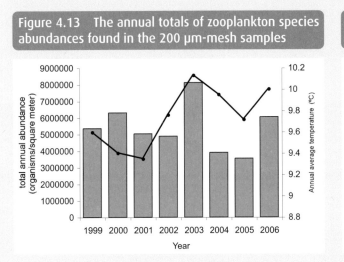

The black lines show the average annual temperature measured at 1m depth (values on the right-hand axis).

**Figure 4.14   The annual totals of estimated biomass (dry weight) found in the 200 µm-mesh samples**

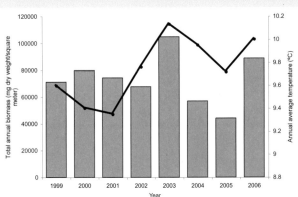

The black lines show the average annual temperature measured at 1m depth (values on the right-hand axis).

**Figure 4.15   Time series of three important elements in the ecosystem productivity, nitrate, chlorophyll (phytoplankton) and copepod abundance**

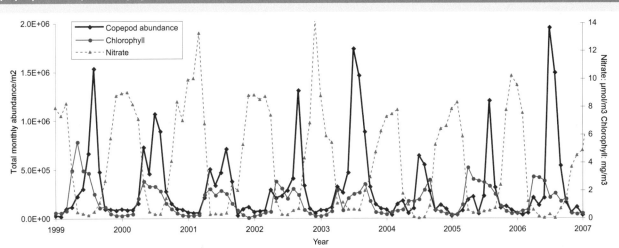

**Table 4.6  Species and groups occurring in the 10 highest ranks of aggregated annual abundance and biomass between 1997 and 2006**

| Groups | Species | Abundance | Biomass |
|---|---|---|---|
| Copepods | *Acartia clausii* | Y (30.4%) | Y (10.9%) |
| | *Calanus helgolandicus* (Late stage and adults) | Y (0.8%) | Y (7.5%) |
| | *Calanus* spp. (Younger stages) | Y (1.2%) | Y (1.7%) |
| | *Centropages hamatus* | Y (1.4%) | Y (1.2%) |
| | *Oithona* spp. | Y (10.4%) | Y (5.9%) |
| | *Paracalanus parvus* | Y (2.2%) | Y (0.9%) |
| | *Pseudocalanus elongatus minutus* | Y (10.7%) | Y (4.5%) |
| | *Temora longicornis* | Y (6.2%) | Y (5.1%) |
| | *Calanus finmarchicus* (Late stage and adults) | N | Y (0.9%) |
| Other crustaceans | *Podon* spp. | Y (1.4%) | Y (1.5%) |
| | *Parathemisto* spp. | N | Y (0.6%) |
| | Decapod larvae | N | Y (5.6%) |
| | Cirripeds | Y (2.3%) | N |
| | *Evadne nordmanii* | Y (0.9%) | N |
| Hard shelled | *Limacina retroversa* | Y (0.9%) | Y (0.6%) |
| | Lamellibranch larvae | Y (4.4%) | N |
| | Echinoderm larvae | Y (2.2%) | N |
| Worm-like | *Appendicularia* | Y (6.5%) | Y (20.2%) |
| | *Phoroni* spp. | N | Y (0.2%) |
| | *Poychaeta* larvae | Y (2.8%) | Y (1.1%) |
| | *Sagitta* spp. | Y (1%) | Y (1.3%) |
| Jellyfish | Coelenterates | N | Y (9.8%) |
| | *Pleurobrachia pileus* | N | Y (1.4%) |
| Other | Cyphonautes larvae | Y (2.2%) | N |

Percentages are overall values for the full time series. The **Y** indicates a species that has occurred in the top 10 ranking. The **N** indicates that it has not been among the 10 highest ranked for either biomass or abundance. *(Some smaller organisms like small hard shelled larvae only rank in abundance, but make up little biomass, while larger organisms like jellyfish make up a significant proportion of the biomass while only consisting of relatively few individuals.)*

## Summary Assessment

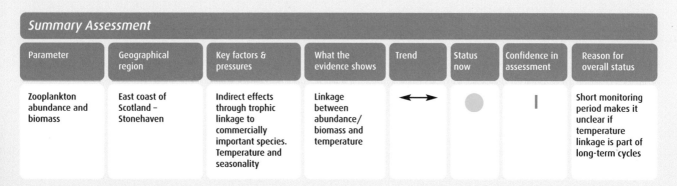

| Parameter | Geographical region | Key factors & pressures | What the evidence shows | Trend | Status now | Confidence in assessment | Reason for overall status |
|---|---|---|---|---|---|---|---|
| Zooplankton abundance and biomass | East coast of Scotland – Stonehaven | Indirect effects through trophic linkage to commercially important species. Temperature and seasonality | Linkage between abundance/ biomass and temperature | ⟷ | ● | I | Short monitoring period makes it unclear if temperature linkage is part of long-term cycles |

Many plankton species are sensitive to climate change, with increasing temperature, changes in nutrient fluxes and ocean acidification. Many zooplankton, particularly larval forms and those with calcareous skeletons or components, are sensitive to increasing acidification. Long-term changes in plankton communities and productivity are serious. Major producers of oxygen and $CO_2$ absorbers, plankton critically mediate Earth's major biogeochemical cycles.

### Habitats and benthos

Some of the finest marine habitats in Europe can be found within Scottish waters, including rugged rocky reefs carpeted in soft corals, sea fans and sponges; shallow beds of pink maerl (Figure 4.16) - a delicate coralline seaweed; beds of gaping file shells; saline lagoons; deep mud habitats with burrowing anemones and tall seapens; and fragile and extremely rare tubeworm reefs (found at only a handful of localities in the world) (Figure 4.17). In the deep waters to the east of Mingulay in the Western Isles, there are coldwater coral reefs with remarkably rich associated animal communities (the only known example within UK 12 nm territorial waters). These diverse assemblages of animals and plants living within or on the sea-floor are important both in their own right, providing resources for humans, and as a vital component of the marine food web providing habitat and food for other marine species[11].

Knowledge of the distribution of habitats and species within Scottish territorial waters has improved considerably over recent years, initially through the work of the MNCR and more recently due to the commissioning of marine survey programmes and reviews partly to help support the selection and designation of SACs. Even so, the coverage is widely dispersed and patchy, with substantial sections of the north and east coasts of Scotland remaining especially poorly surveyed[12].

**Figure 4.16   Maerl**

**Figure 4.17   Tubeworm reefs**

The status of benthic communities and their associated habitats is a function of both natural change and their level of exposure to the wide range of human activities the productive seas support. An overview of these activities is provided in the next chapter and further details on the direct and/or indirect impacts on benthic biodiversity is provided in the supporting documentation to the Scottish Biodiversity Strategy[13].

The adoption of the EC Habitats Directive and the subsequent establishment of a Europe-wide network of high-quality conservation sites, SACs enabled parts of the underwater component of Scotland's natural heritage to be protected from potentially damaging activities for the first time. To date 29 SACs (Figure 4.1) with marine habitat features (and 45 SSSIs with primarily intertidal features) have been identified in Scotland. The important benthic components of these sites are subject to an ongoing programme of cyclical assessment to determine their status via SNH's marine Site Condition Monitoring (SCM) programme, which started in 2002. A process is currently underway to identify areas that would qualify for designation as SAC in Scottish offshore (i.e. >12 nm <200 nm) waters, thus enhancing further the Natura 2000 network.

SNH assessed the condition of 20 SAC habitat features (approx. 36% of the total number of SAC habitat features (56) from 29 sites) in the first six-yearly monitoring cycle (1998-2004). SNH's programme of broad-scale mapping, undertaken as a pre-cursor to SCM to inform site management needs, underpinned reporting on an additional 16 features. Of the total 36 features assessed thus far, 97% (Figure 4.18) were deemed to be in favourable condition (well above the UK average of ~74%[14]) and this work continues[E].

Two marine SACs have been deemed to be in unfavourable condition as a result of the condition monitoring work. A significant decline in the density of horse mussels was recorded in 2004 from a bed within the Lochs Duich, Long and Alsh Reefs SAC. The cause for the decline was not entirely clear-cut but the survey team witnessed a group of scuba divers loading several large sacks of live horse mussels into a van. It is not known whether this was a commercial operation or an isolated incident. The serpulid worm reefs within Loch Creran SAC have been partially destroyed with the damage attributed to a range of fish farming, vessel mooring and historical fisheries activities (see Case Study 5.5). Given the importance and rarity of the serpulid reefs feature, within Loch Creran there is now a statutory provision under Scottish inshore fisheries legislation to afford the features the highest possible level of protection, prohibiting fishing completely from the areas within the loch where the reefs are located.

Whilst the results of the SCM work generally indicate that Scotland's coastal benthos and habitats (<12 nm) are healthy and biologically diverse, many unknowns remain and the presence of clear evidence of anthropogenic damage to internationally important habitats within the most closely watched inshore areas (which represent a tiny fraction of Scotland's marine environment) raises questions about the long-term sustainability of a number of current activities.

The status of Scotland's benthos cannot be determined solely from the observations of condition within a small number of coastal protected areas, and the distribution and extent of habitats in the wider Scottish marine environment should be considered. However, there are, as yet, no systematic surveys or monitoring programmes to inform this bigger picture assessment. Limited additional contextual information is available through the UK *Biodiversity Action Plan* (UK BAP) and the *Scottish Biodiversity Strategy* (SBS). The former lists priority species and habitats, as well as action plans, to achieve our commitment of a significant reduction in the current rate of biodiversity loss by 2010 under the international Convention on Biological Diversity. Of the 605 priority species and 60 priority habitats listed that are found in Scotland, 74 and 22, respectively, are marine (Tables 4.7 and 4.8). Experts have identified the top priority actions for at least half of these species to be further research and/or monitoring, without which their protection cannot be ensured. (Table 4.9). More information can be obtained from http://www.ukbap.org.uk/

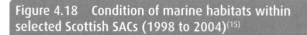

**Figure 4.18 Condition of marine habitats within selected Scottish SACs (1998 to 2004)[15]**

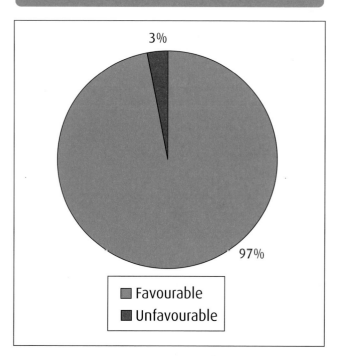

3%

97%

■ Favourable
■ Unfavourable

Figure 4.19   *Fucus distichus*

Figure 4.20   Basking shark

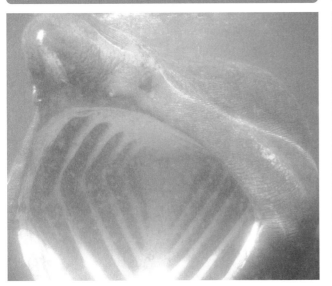

Figure 4.21   Mackerel

## Table 4.7  Priority marine species found in Scotland

| Scientific Name | Common Name |
| --- | --- |
| *Ascophyllum nodosum ecad mackii* | Wig wrack or Sea-loch egg wrack |
| *Cruoria cruoriaeformis* | a red seaweed |
| *Dermocorynus montagnei* | a red seaweed |
| *Fucus distichus* | Brown alga (Figure 4.19) |
| *Lithothamnion coralloides* | Coral maerl |
| *Phymatolithon calcareum* | Common maerl |
| *Ammodytes marinus* | Lesser sandeel |
| *Aphanopus carbo* | Black scabbardfish |
| *Centrophorus granulosus* | Gulper shark |
| *Centrophorus squamosus* | Leafscraper shark |
| *Centroscymnus coelolepsis* | Portuguese dogfish |
| *Cetorhinus maximus* | Basking shark (Figure 4.20) |
| *Clupea harengus* | Herring |
| *Coryphaenoides rupestris* | Roundnose grenadier |
| *Dalatias licha* | Kitefin shark |
| *Dipturus batis* | Common skate |
| *Gadus morhua* | Cod |
| *Galeorhinus galeus* | Tope shark |
| *Hippocampus guttulatus* | Long-snouted seahorse |
| *Hippoglossus hippoglossus* | Atlantic halibut |
| *Hoplostethus atlanticus* | Orange roughy |
| *Lamna nasus* | Porbeagle shark |
| *Leucoraja circularis* | Sandy ray |
| *Lophius piscatorius* | Sea monkfish |
| *Merlangius merlangus* | Whiting |
| *Merluccius merluccius* | European hake |
| *Micromesistius poutassiou* | Blue whiting |
| *Molva dypterygia* | Blue ling |
| *Molva molva* | Ling |
| *Pleuronectes platessa* | Plaice |
| *Prionace glauca* | Blue shark |
| *Reinhardtius hippoglossoides* | Greenland halibut |
| *Scomber scombrus* | Mackerel (Figure 4.21) |
| *Solea vulgaris* | Sole |
| *Squalus acanthias* | Spiny dogfish |
| *Squatina squatina* | Angel shark |
| *Thunnus thynnus* | Blue-fin tuna |
| *Amphianthus dohrnii* | Sea-fan anemone |
| *Arachnanthus sarsi* | Scarce tube-dwelling anemone |
| *Arrhis phyllonyx* | a deep-sea shrimp |

## Table 4.7   Priority marine species found in Scotland (cont'd)

| Scientific Name | Common Name |
| --- | --- |
| *Atrina fragilis* | Fan mussel |
| *Eunicella verrucosa* | Pink sea fan |
| *Funiculina quadrangularis* | Tall sea pen |
| *Gitanopsis bispinosa* | an amphipod shrimp |
| *Haliclystus auricula* | a stalked jellyfish |
| *Lucernariopsis campanulata* | a stalked jellyfish |
| *Ostrea edulis* | Native oyster |
| *Pachycerianthus multiplicatus* | Fireworks anemone (Figure 4.23) |
| *Palinurus elephas* | Crayfish, crawfish or spiny lobster (Figure 4.24) |
| *Styela gelatinosa* | Loch Goil sea squirt |
| *Swiftia pallida* | Northern sea fan |
| *Balaenoptera acutorostrata* | Minke whale |
| *Balaenoptera borealis* | Sei whale |
| *Balaenoptera musculus* | Blue whale |
| *Balaenoptera physalus* | Fin whale |
| *Delphinus delphis* | Common dolphin |
| *Eubalaena glacialis* | Northern right whale |
| *Globicephala melas (melaena)* | Long-finned pilot whale |
| *Grampus griseus* | Risso's dolphin |
| *Hyperoodon ampullatus* | Northern bottlenose whale |
| *Lagenorhynchus acutus* | Atlantic white-sided dolphin |
| *Lagenorhynchus albirostris* | White-beaked dolphin |
| *Megaptera novaeangliae* | Humpback whale |
| *Mesoplodon bidens* | Sowerby's beaked whale |
| *Mesoplodon mirus* | True's beaked whale |
| *Orcinus orca* | Killer whale |
| *Phoca vitulina* | Harbour seal/common seal |
| *Phocoena phocoena* | Harbour porpoise |
| *Physeter macrocephalus* | Sperm whale |
| *Stenella coeruleoalba* | Striped dolphin |
| *Tursiops truncatus* | Bottlenose dolphin (Figure 4.33) |
| *Ziphius cavirostris* | Cuvier's beaked whale |
| *Caretta caretta* | Loggerhead turtle |
| *Dermochelys coriacea* | Leatherback turtle |

## Table 4.8    Priority marine habitats found in Scotland

Intertidal boulder communities

*Sabellaria alveolata* reefs

Coastal saltmarsh

Intertidal mudflats

Seagrass beds

Sheltered muddy gravels

Tide-swept channels

Fragile sponge & anthozoan communities on subtidal rocky habitats (Figure 4.22)

Estuarine rocky habitats

Seamount communities

Carbonate mounds

Cold-water coral reefs

Deep-sea sponge communities

*Sabellaria spinulosa* reefs

Subtidal sands and gravels

Horse mussel beds

Mud habitats in deep water

File shell beds

Maerl beds

Serpulid reefs

Blue mussel beds

Saline lagoons

Figure 4.22  Fragile sponge

Figure 4.23  Fireworks anemone

## Table 4.9 Species for which the priority action is more research and/or monitoring

| Common name | Survey for new sites and/or monitoring known sites | Research into ecological requirements, conservation action, or into other impacts |
| --- | --- | --- |
| **Algae** | | |
| Wig wrack or Sea-loch egg wrack | √ | |
| Red seaweed | √ | |
| Brown alga | √ | |
| Coral maerl | | √ |
| **Invertebrates** | | |
| Sea-fan anemone | √ | √ |
| Scarce tube-dwelling anemone | √ | |
| Deep-sea shrimp | √ | |
| Fan mussel | √ | √ |
| Pink sea fan | | √ |
| Tall sea pen | | √ |
| Amphipod shrimp | √ | |
| Stalked Jellyfish | √ | √ |
| Fireworks anemone (Figure 4.23) | √ | |
| Crayfish or spiny lobster (Figure 4.24) | √ | √ |
| Loch Goil sea squirt | √ | |
| Northern sea fan | √ | √ |
| **Fish** | | |
| Basking shark | | √ |
| Long-snouted seahorse | | √ |
| Porbeagle shark | | √ |
| Blue shark | | √ |
| **Reptiles** | | |
| Loggerhead turtle | √ | |
| Leatherback turtle | √ | |
| **Mammals** | | |
| Common dolphin | √ | |
| Long-finned pilot whale | √ | |
| Risso's dolphin | √ | |
| Northern bottlenose whale | √ | |
| Atlantic white-sided dolphin | √ | |
| Harbour porpoise | √ | |
| Striped dolphin | √ | |
| Bottlenose dolphin | √ | |

The Scottish Biodiversity Strategy forms the foundation for Scotland's international obligations under the international Convention on Biological Diversity and sets out a 25-year vision to "conserve biodiversity for the health, enjoyment and well being of the people of Scotland now and in the future."[F]

Biodiversity indicators describe change over time in the variety, quantity or distribution of aspects of the natural world and are thus an effective way to measure progress in the delivery of policy commitments. In the recently published *Scotland's Biodiversity Indicators*, of the five most relevant to the marine environment (Table 4.2) two (breeding seabird abundance, and non-native species) were deteriorating, marine plankton was showing divergence, marine fish stocks within safe limits were fluctuating and estuarine fish were improving.

Work is ongoing to coordinate research, survey and marine data management activities within Scotland. This is essential if understanding is to be improved and the future of these hidden assets is to be safeguarded.

Even less is known about the composition and distribution of offshore and deeper seabed communities largely due to the technological constraints and financial implication of sampling in these waters. Information is slowly becoming available as remote survey techniques improve and there is a greater sharing of data and information collected by commercial operations. What work has been done has revealed an amazing wealth of biodiversity that survives in these deep areas, see Case Study 4.4.

### Figure 4.24   Spiny Lobster

## CASE STUDY 4.4   Deep sea biodiversity around Scotland

The deep waters around Scotland are really the birthplace of deep sea research starting in the late 1860s by Charles Wyville-Thomson. The area of interest stretches from the Faroe-Shetland Channel in the north out to Hatton Bank in the west and into the Rockall Trough in the south (Figure 4.25).

Numerous different deep water habitats are found in this area ranging from continental margins to deep water troughs and channels through to seamounts and banks. The Faroe-Shetland Channel is probably the most extensively studied deep water area in Europe, and is particularly important as common approaches and sampling techniques have been used throughout the area.

Investigation into the hydrography of the Faroe-Shetland Channel is conducted primarily by FRS in collaboration with researchers from SAMS. The Faroe-Shetland Channel has an unusual and highly dynamic physical environment as a result of a number of water masses converging in this confined channel[16]. The water masses flow in different directions; north Atlantic water which is warm and saline flows in a north-easterly direction whilst cold, dense Norwegian Sea water underlies this and flows towards the south-west. Of most interest is the boundary between the warm and cold water masses which occurs at a depth of about 350 – 600 m. At this boundary the temperature of

the bottom water can change dramatically over short periods of time, e.g. 7°C in 1 hour.

Biological research, particularly of macrofauna (animals >0.25 mm but < ~3 cm), in the region started again in the mid 1990s as a result of development of the deep water oil industry, with large-scale regional surveys of the west of Shetland sea floor conducted in 1996, 1998, 2000, 2002 and 2006. These have shown that the exponential decline of macrofauna with increasing depth that is often observed in deep water areas, was not seen in the Faroe-Shetland Channel. In fact there was an overall increase in macrofauna abundance with depth in this area.

The macrofaunal diversity patterns were also unusual: there was a peak in diversity and species richness at depths of about 300 – 500 m. This appears to coincide with the warm-cold-water boundary and thus the rapid change in temperature (see Figure 4.26). Peaks in diversity at a mid-depth are also seen in other regions of the deep sea, however they all tend to be at depths greater than those in the Faroe-Shetland Channel. Other factors that appear to influence the macrofauna diversity in the region are sediment grain size, organic matter and especially sea temperature. It is possible that longer term changes in water temperature at intermediate depths influences the faunal community composition.

### Figure 4.25   Deep water areas around Scotland

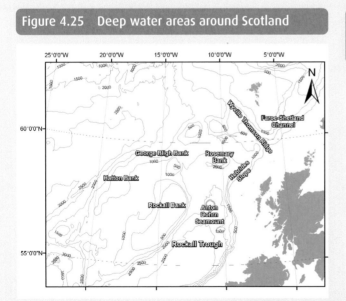

### Figure 4.26   Comparison of variation in macrofaunal species diversity and habitat temperature regime in the Faroe-Shetland Channel

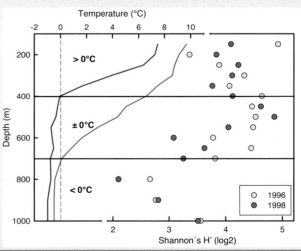

### Summary Assessment

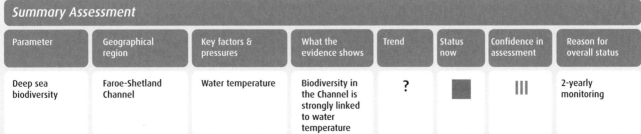

| Parameter | Geographical region | Key factors & pressures | What the evidence shows | Trend | Status now | Confidence in assessment | Reason for overall status |
|---|---|---|---|---|---|---|---|
| Deep sea biodiversity | Faroe-Shetland Channel | Water temperature | Biodiversity in the Channel is strongly linked to water temperature | ? | ▓ | III | 2-yearly monitoring |

*Non-native species*

Invasive non-native species are the second greatest threat to global biodiversity (after habitat destruction) and the greatest threat to fragile ecosystems such as small islands. Apart from the cost in biodiversity terms, invasive non-native species can also create a huge economic cost to a very wide range of sectors, probably of the order of several billion pounds annually in the United Kingdom.

It is estimated that there are around 79 marine and brackish non-native species present in Britain[17] and around 24 of these are present in Scotland. Recent introductions into the marine environment include the large brown seaweed, also known as wireweed (Figure 4.27), into Loch Ryan in 2004 and subsequently into Loch Fyne in 2006 and which has now been recorded as far north as the Firth of Lorn, and the skeleton shrimp which has been found on sites all round Scotland after first being reported in 2004[18]. There are a wide range of vectors that can transport non-native species and for marine species the most important vectors are shipping and aquaculture (Figure 4.29). Shipping can transport species either in ballast water and sediments or as biofouling i.e. attached to the hull (Figure 4.28), anchor chains or other niches around the vessel's hull.

**Figure 4.27   Wireweed**

**Figure 4.28   Heavily bio-fouled ship hull**

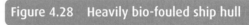

**Figure 4.29   Vectors associated with the introduction of non-native species into British waters[19]**

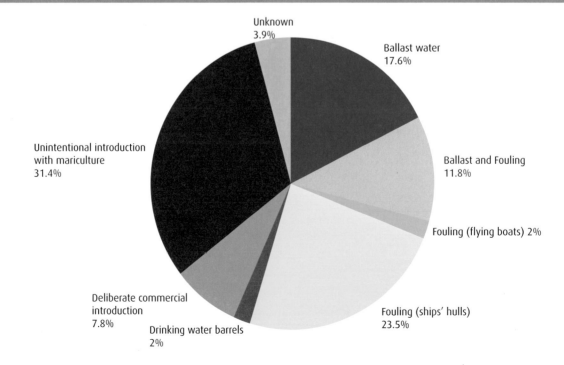

In recognition of this risk of introducing species via shipping the International Maritime Organization (IMO) adopted an International Convention for the Control and Management of Ships' Ballast Water and Sediments in 2004. The Convention has yet to be ratified but aims to have all vessels treating or managing their ballast water to a specific discharge standard, which will be phased in over time depending on the age and size of the vessel. The IMO has now started discussions on the issue of biofouling and will work towards adopting measures to reduce the risk of introducing non native species *via* this vector. A working group of ICES has produced a Code of Practice for the Introduction and Transfer of Marine Organisms[20], which aims to reduce the risk of introducing non-native species via aquaculture.

These measures will all reduce the risk of introducing non-native species into the marine environment and will also help reduce the spread of species that are already present. However, there is a need for monitoring and port surveys to be undertaken to ensure that the information regarding non-native species is up to date. This is important for providing information for a wide variety of purposes such as risk assessment and updating Scotland's Biodiversity Indicators as for some groups such as invertebrates there is not adequate information available to establish any trends in range expansion[1].

A Great Britain Programme Board was established in March 2005 to deliver strategic consideration of the threat of invasive non-native species across Scotland, Wales and England. A draft *Strategy on Invasive Non-Native Species* has been developed and aims to minimise the risk posed and reduce the negative impacts caused by invasive non-native species in Great Britain. The final Strategy is expected to be launched by Ministers in spring 2008.

In Scotland, a Scottish Working Group on invasive non-native species provides a forum within which the development of coherent cross-cutting policy on invasive non-natives in Scotland can be pursued and lead responsibilities agreed, and contributes to and supports the effectiveness of wider action on invasive non-native species at the GB level.

*Fish*

The fish fauna in Scottish waters is diverse and, in terms of abundance alone, one of the most important components of the marine ecosystem. It is estimated that Scotland has a total of 250 fish species[21]. There is one species of hagfish, two species of lamprey and 40 cartilaginous fish (sharks, skates and rays). However, by far the largest group is the bony fish (species such as herring and cod) with around 207 species.

There is a substantial scientific literature on the biology and ecology of fish in Scotland but for obvious reasons this literature is dominated by commercial fish species[22]. Indeed it is probably true to say that the longest time-series of data in the Scottish marine environment is that collected to support the management of fisheries, see Case Study 4.5. However, for non-commercial fish our understanding of population sizes and trends is relatively limited.

Over the course of the year there is a significant fluctuation in the total biomass of fish found in Scottish waters. Biomass is generally higher in the summer than in winter due to seasonal movements of fish for feeding and/or spawning. Pelagic species (e.g. mackerel (Figure 4.21)) are primarily responsible for this fluctuation as demersal species tend to be less transient.

**Figure 4.30 Puffins feeding on sandeels**

Fish play a vital role in the marine ecosystem and are the primary prey for Scotland's internationally important populations of marine mammals and seabirds. The relationships between fish populations and their predators are highly complex but research over the past three decades has provided valuable insights[23,24] and further studies are underway to better understand the relationships. Other work has focussed on the importance of sandeels (Figure 4.30) as a keystone prey species for other fish, marine mammals and seabirds[25].

Research projects such as these (frequently driven by the need to understand the interactions between fisheries, fish stocks and their predators) apply an ecosystem-based approach to management. Indeed, among the variety of human activities that may have an impact on fish populations the most pervasive is likely to be fishing; studies have shown that fishing has led to reductions in the diversity of fish communities in the north-east Atlantic[26].

Another factor with increasing relevance to the status of Scottish fish populations is climate change. A number of species are at the southern or northern extremes of their distribution; certain boreal or Arctic species, such as the Greenland shark, may venture into the northern North Sea and conversely species of a southern character, such as the red mullet, reach the northern limit of their distribution in Scotland. Consequently, sea temperature rise is likely to lead to changes in Scottish fish fauna, with some species moving in and others moving out. While the full implications of climate change for fish stocks are far from certain there is evidence for change in other components of the ecosystem that are likely to have repercussions for fish stocks. For example, a distinct northward shift in the distribution of plankton communities has been recorded since the 1950s: warmer water plankton species are not replacing the colder water species in similar abundances and this is potentially detrimental to the fish larvae for which these plankton are essential prey[27].

## CASE STUDY 4.5   Commercially exploited fish stocks

Populations of fish and shellfish species which are commercially exploited in Scottish and adjacent waters are amongst the most comprehensively monitored and managed components of the marine ecosystem.

For example, FRS conducts 19 regular, repeated annual research vessel surveys targeting different species and different areas during the course of each year. Different survey methods are used depending on the biology and life history of the species under consideration. Surveys using standard fishing trawls are used for demersal fish species such as cod, haddock, whiting, saithe and monkfish. Acoustic surveys contribute to assessing the health of herring stocks, while surveys of egg abundance are used to provide estimates of the size of mackerel stocks. Dredges are used during surveys to assess scallop stocks, and underwater television surveys are used to assess the size of *Nephrops* (langoustine) populations.

Data from these surveys, combined with data obtained by FRS scientists on commercial fishing boats and at fish markets, undergo rigorous quality checking and are then used in various quantitative methods to assess the size of each targeted stock of fish or shellfish. Since many stocks, such as all of the North Sea stocks, are located in waters shared with other countries and fished by a number of different fleets, data from all the countries involved need to be pooled together before a stock assessment can be performed. The process of data collation and assessment is carried out by the ICES[G]. FRS scientists play a major role in ICES.

Data for each species are grouped across particular areas, depending on what is known about the distribution and life histories of the species. For example, mackerel are assessed across the North-East Atlantic as a whole, as they are widely distributed and undergo significant migrations during their life cycle. Species such as herring, haddock, cod and whiting are assessed for the west of Scotland and the North Sea separately, as it is believed the fish stocks in these two areas are separate. Saithe and monkfish are considered to be single stocks crossing the northern shelf, from the west of Scotland to the North Sea via the north of Scotland. Typically, assessments provide information on the rate that fish are removed from the sea (the fishing mortality rate, F), the size of population capable of reproducing (the spawning stock biomass, SSB) and the number of young fish entering the fishery (recruitment).

Various criteria are used to judge the health of each stock, dependent on the biology and life-history of each species, but also on the quality and type of data available.

Mackerel, herring, haddock, cod, whiting and saithe are judged against quite rigid criteria developed by ICES within a Precautionary Approach framework. This defines reference points against which the assessments are compared. In terms of the size of the stock in relation to its ability to maintain stock size through reproduction, three terms are used. Either a stock is at full reproductive capacity, suffering reduced reproductive capacity or somewhere in between these two states and at risk of suffering reduced reproductive capacity. Similarly, in relation to the rate of removal of fish, a stock that is overfished is defined as being harvested unsustainably, while a stock that is being fished at an acceptable level is being harvested sustainably. Owing to uncertainty in the data, a stock can be at an intermediate state and at risk of being harvested unsustainably.

Figure 4.31 shows these terms and how they relate to a traffic-light system of judging the health of a commercially exploited fish stock. Figure 4.32 shows the results of applying the traffic light method to the different stocks of mackerel, North Sea herring, haddock, cod, and saithe.

Unfortunately for herring west of Scotland, whiting in the North Sea and west of Scotland and monkfish on the northern shelf, fishery scientists consider that the existing information they have is not enough to establish where these stocks lie in the traffic-light health system. More work is underway in order to try and fill these gaps. *Nephrops* (langoustine) are not judged using the same system. However, North Sea Nephrops stocks, in the Fladen Ground, Firth of Forth and Moray Firth, have increased since 1996, are now stable and are probably being exploited sustainably. West of Scotland, in the North Minch, South Minch and Firth of Clyde, stocks are stable or increasing.

Scottish scallop stocks are generally healthy at present, but work is underway towards a quantitative indicator of their health and sustainability.

**Figure 4.31   Definition of terms used in the traffic-light method of assessing the health of commercially exploited fish stocks**

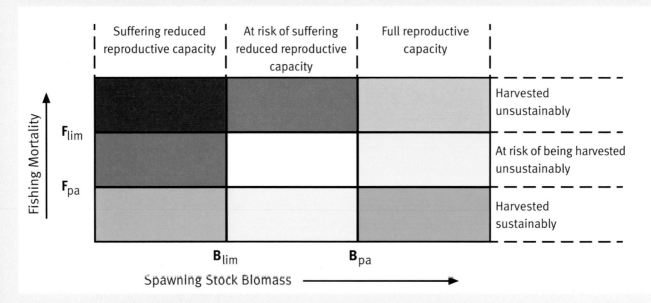

Source: FRS Fish and Nephrops Stocks Information: 2008 http://www.frs-scotland.gov.uk/

**Figure 4.32   The traffic-light method of assessing the health of commercially exploited fish stocks**

| Stock | ICES Reference Points | | | | Current Assessment | | Council Outcome | |
|---|---|---|---|---|---|---|---|---|
| | $B_{lim}(t)$ | $B_{pa}(t)$ | $F_{lim}$ | $F_{pa}$ | F 2006 | SSB (t) 2006 | TAC (t) | UK Quota (t) |
| Makerel – North East Atlantic | ND | 2,300,000 | 0.26 | 0.17 | 0.26 | 2,231,313 | 385,366 | 136,984 |
| Herring – North Sea | 800,000 | 1,300,000 | ND | 0.12(1) 0.25(2) | 0.08(1) 0.35(2) | 1,207,822 | 201,227 | 30,025 |
| Herring – West of Scotland | 50,000 | ND | ND | ND | 0.28 | 77,787 | 28,000 | 16,836 |
| Haddock – North Sea | 100,000 | 140,000 | 1.0 | 0.70 | 0.49 | 237,940 | 46,444 | 31,672 |
| Haddock – West of Scotland | 22,000 | 30,000 | ND | 0.50 | 0.59 | 33,020 | 6,120(3) | 4,743(3) |
| Haddock – Rockall | 6,000 | 9,000 | ND | 0.40 | 0.15 | 19,214 | 6,916 | 5,574 |
| Cod – North Sea | 70,000 | 150,000 | 0.86 | 0.65 | 0.63 | 28,481 | 22,152 | 8,628 |
| Cod – West of Scotland | 14,000 | 22,000 | 0.8 | 0.60 | uncertain | low | 402 | 241 |
| Whiting – North Sea | 225,000 | 315,000 | 0.90 | 0.65 | uncertain | low | 17,850 | 9,336 |
| Whiting – West of Scotland | 16,000 | 22,000 | 1.0 | 0.60 | uncertain | low | 765 | 438 |
| Saithe – Northern shelf | 106,000 | 200,000 | 0.6 | 0.40 | 0.25 | 298,300 | 150,000 | 14,619 |
| Monkfish – Northern shelf | ND | ND | ND | 0.30 | uncertain | uncertain | 18,110 | 11,108 |

Colours refer to those categories shown by Figure 4.31. No colour indicates that data are insufficient to allocate a health category.
Source FRS Fish and Nephrops Stocks Information: 2008 http://www.frs-scotland.gov.uk
(1) For juvenile North Sea herring – ages 0-1
(2) For adult North Sea herring – ages 2-6
(3) Including Clyde
ND = not defined
(t) = metric tonnes

## Marine mammals

Many species of whales, dolphins and porpoises, collectively known as cetaceans, migrate through Scottish waters or are mainly present offshore, towards the edge of the continental shelf. Estimating the distribution and abundance of cetaceans involves considerable expense and expertise and to date there have been only two comprehensive surveys carried out; the status of offshore cetacean populations have recently been estimated[28], whilst trends in abundance remain unknown for most cetacean species in Scottish coastal waters. The abundance of two species, harbour porpoise and minke whale did not change significantly between surveys in 1994 and 2005, although the distributions of both species changed over this period and there is some evidence that the coastal bottlenose dolphin population (Figure 4.33), associated with the Moray Firth SAC, may have declined slightly between 1990 and 2005[29]. A third survey covering regions around the continental shelf edge is currently under way and is due to report in 2008. A significant increase in investment will be required if there is to be an improvement in the overall knowledge base in the near future.

Much more information exists for the two species of seals resident within Scottish waters[30]. Scotland holds about 90% of the seals within the UK. Grey seals (Figure 4.34) have shown a steady increase in population size since records began in the early 1960s but there are now strong indicators that the population is beginning to level off (Figure 4.35). About 40% of the world population of grey seals is present in Scottish waters and about 28% of the European population of common (harbour) seals.

Less detailed information is available for common seals, however, declines of over 40% have been observed in Orkney (Figure 4.35) and Shetland since 2001. Common seal numbers may also be declining in other regions of the Scottish east coast[31], especially the Firth of Tay. To date, population indicators suggest that this decline is not present on the west coast and the Hebrides. However, declines on this scale are of significant concern because they could indicate changes in general environmental conditions.

**Figure 4.34  Grey seal haul-out site**

**Figure 4.33  Bottlenose dolphin**

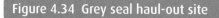

**Figure 4.35  Changes in grey seal pup population in Scotland (green) and the number of common seals counted in Orkney (red)**

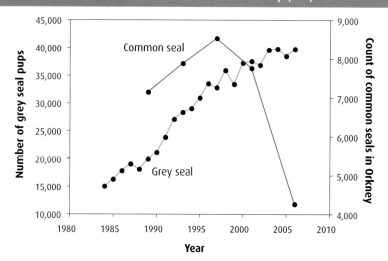

## Summary Assessment

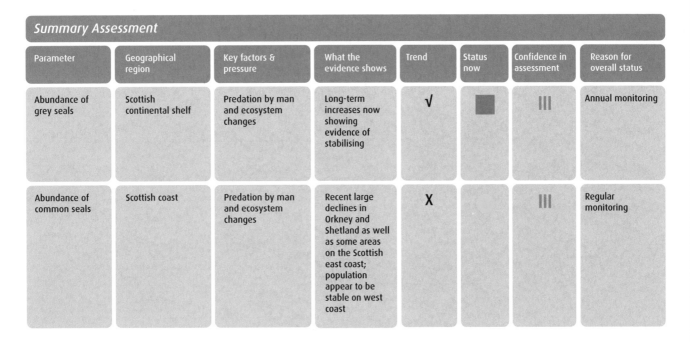

| Parameter | Geographical region | Key factors & pressure | What the evidence shows | Trend | Status now | Confidence in assessment | Reason for overall status |
|---|---|---|---|---|---|---|---|
| Abundance of grey seals | Scottish continental shelf | Predation by man and ecosystem changes | Long-term increases now showing evidence of stabilising | √ | ■ | III | Annual monitoring |
| Abundance of common seals | Scottish coast | Predation by man and ecosystem changes | Recent large declines in Orkney and Shetland as well as some areas on the Scottish east coast; population appear to be stable on west coast | X | ● | III | Regular monitoring |

### Marine turtles

The collation of UK and Republic of Ireland marine turtle records is undertaken by Marine Environmental Monitoring on behalf of the Turtle Implementation Group (TIG), funded by SNH and the other country agencies. The key output is TURTLE a database which, as of February 2007, held 2,304 records, 343 of which were from Scotland[32]. The leatherback turtle is the most commonly reported species, (98 records out of 144 turtle records from Scotland between 1997-2007), most frequently off the west and north coasts, with sightings peaking in late summer and early autumn.

It is extremely difficult to identify trends in marine turtle numbers. Although numbers of records have risen dramatically in recent years (Figure 4.36), this is likely to be due in large part to new and concerted effort in encouraging the submission of marine turtle records (e.g. through the targeted distribution of the UK Marine Turtle Code).

### Figure 4.36 Marine turtles: All species sightings and strandings 1997-2007[33]

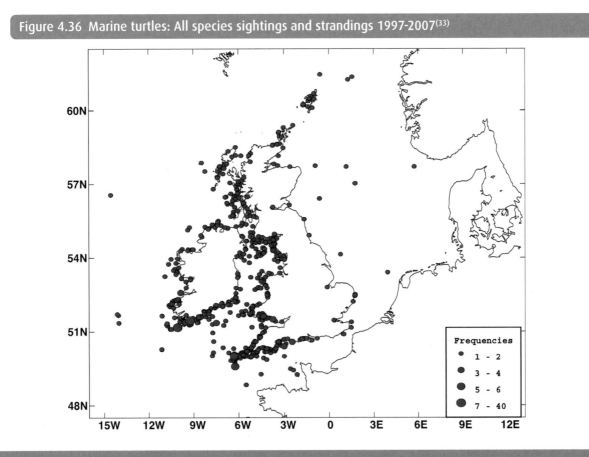

### Seabirds

Scotland holds internationally important populations of a large number of species of seabirds[34]. Seabirds are generally long-lived and changes within the marine environment that affect adult bird survival become evident in the size of the breeding population. Impacts on breeding success, or on the survival of young birds to maturity, also become evident in the breeding population but only several years later[35]. The trends in abundance and productivity are based on data for 13 and 16 species respectively (where data are sufficient) out of a total of 24 breeding seabird species derived from counts from a sample of colonies around Scotland as part of the UK Seabird Monitoring Programme (SMP), coordinated by JNCC, with partner organisations; see for example[36], which commenced in 1986, with data held by RSPB. The trend for the period 1986 – 2004 is shown in Figure 4.39 and illustrates a 30% decline in seabird abundance between 1992 and 2004 compared with the start of the monitoring period. At the last national census (Seabird 2000) 2.8 million pairs of 24 species of seabird were breeding in Scotland, being 75% of the seabird population of the UK.

The SMP collects and collates data on breeding numbers, demographic parameters, including productivity, and diet from a sample of colonies from around the UK. The trend in breeding success for the period 1986 – 2006 is shown in Figure 4.40. Seabirds showed a marked decline in productivity from 2002-2004 and remained low in 2005-2006. The breeding success of some species (fulmar, European shag and great skua) increased in 2006 after a period of very low success. These increases represent only partial recoveries towards average levels over the time series. Common guillemot populations were stable until 1996 and then declined until 2006 and black-legged kittiwake populations have shown a steady decline in breeding success since 1986.

The results of this work show that there are considerable differences in population trends among the 13 seabird species monitored, (Figure 4.41). The overall decline is accounted for by declines among relatively abundant species: notably Arctic tern, Arctic skua and black-legged kittiwake (Figure 4.37). The abundance of these species has been strongly affected by reduced sandeel availability in the waters around Orkney and Shetland and off the east coast of Scotland (Case Study 4.6). Six species decreased in abundance (the Arctic tern by as much as 95%), whereas seven of the 13 species increased in abundance between 1986 and 2004. For example, the northern gannet increased by 85% in this period.

The data provide evidence of an overall decrease in the breeding success of seabirds in Scotland. While the exact timing and geographical component of the decline varied from species to species, the pattern is indicative of a significant and widespread change in one or more factors that affect productivity. The main factors are food availability, weather conditions and predation. Poor food availability can result in starvation of chicks and can force adults to spend longer foraging and less time attending chicks, leaving them susceptible to chilling and predation. Poor weather conditions can inhibit foraging by adults and thereby have a similar impact on chicks as a poor food supply, as well as having more direct impacts such as chilling or washing nests away during storms. Predation of eggs or chicks and, sometimes, breeding adults by other seabirds or by mammals can significantly reduce productivity of a colony, sometimes leading to complete breeding failures[37].

| Figure 4.37   Kittiwake |
|---|

| Figure 4.38   Guillemot with a meal of sprat |
|---|

**Figure 4.39 Abundance of breeding seabirds in Scotland (1986-2004)**

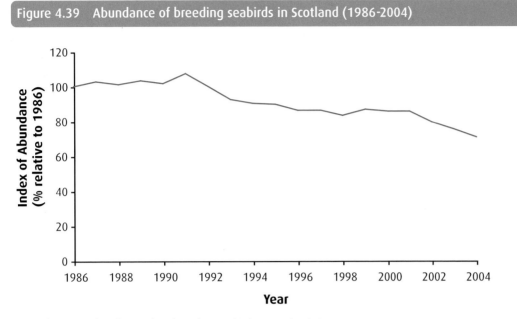

Index change in abundance of 13 breeding seabirds in Scotland since 1986

**Figure 4.40 Breeding success of seabirds in Scotland (1986-2006)**

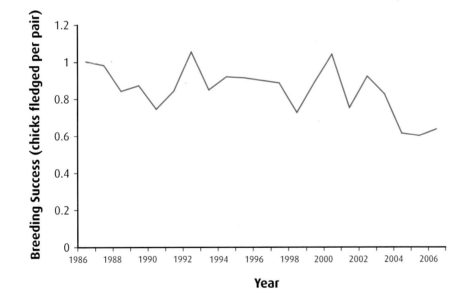

Index change in breeding success of 16 breeding seabirds in Scotland since 1986

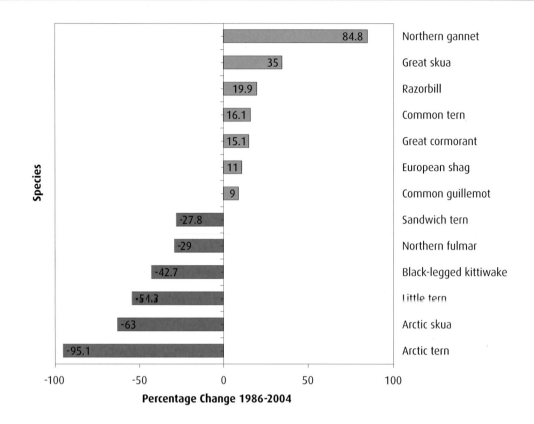

**Figure 4.41   The percentage change in abundance of selected seabird species between 1986 and 2004**

Northern gannet — 84.8
Great skua — 35
Razorbill — 19.9
Common tern — 16.1
Great cormorant — 15.1
European shag — 11
Common guillemot — 9
Sandwich tern — -27.8
Northern fulmar — -29
Black-legged kittiwake — -42.7
Little tern — -51.3
Arctic skua — -63
Arctic tern — -95.1

*Species* (y-axis)

*Percentage Change 1986-2004* (x-axis: -100, -50, 0, 50, 100)

**WHAT GAPS ARE THERE IN OUR KNOWLEDGE?**

There is an increasing demand for all advisers, such as FRS, SEPA and SNH, to provide high quality advice and support in protecting Scotland's natural heritage to underpin social and economic wellbeing. Scotland will increasingly rely on its coasts and seas to provide marine resources (e.g. energy generation, fisheries and transport) to fuel this development. It is essential that this growth is sustainable and that the health and biodiversity of Scotland's seas are not sacrificed.

It is widely acknowledged that there has been, and continues to be, a major investment shortfall in the monitoring of the marine environment. If sustainable development is the aim then sufficient investment of resources is needed in research, survey and monitoring to allow the natural fluctuations in species and habitat distribution and abundance to be separated from that of human influence and climate change, i.e. it is important to develop an understanding of how marine ecosystems function and the consequences of human activities upon them.

The current focus on designated areas and the associated monitoring effort and reporting precludes programmes that could provide crucial long-term, time-series data needed to identify and assess trends essential for providing sound

advice to both the Government and users of the marine environment. The data gathered from the designated sites monitoring programme is, in itself, insufficient to provide a reliable assessment of the state of Scotland's seas, because designated sites cover less than 0.5% of Scotland's territorial waters. Thus, it is outside the SACs, that the gaps in data, information and knowledge are most apparent.

The requirements for more information on the structure and function of habitats and species to fill these knowledge gaps, within a resource tight arena, will require a move towards predictive assessments that can be validated through ground-truthing and the selection of indicators to measure cause and effect. In order to achieve this in a cost-effective manner all agencies and other interested parties (e.g. FRS, SEPA, SNH, BGS, SAMS, universities, etc.) must improve their partnership working and data sharing so that opportunities to collaborate are maximised. Monitoring and survey activities should be set up so that individuals from sister agencies are able to take advantage of field survey opportunities, whilst at the same time promoting more flexible cross-team working (for example, SNH is planning to collect rock samples for BGS during a planned broad scale survey of North Rona). The cost savings throughout the marine sector are potentially enormous as are the opportunities for staff development an raising Scotland's scientific skills base.

## CASE STUDY 4.6   Implications of climate change for Scottish seabirds

Climate change will likely affect seabirds in two major ways: either directly through an increased frequency of very severe weather events resulting in nests being washed off cliffs, breeding burrows becoming flooded etc., or indirectly through changes in prey availability. While instances of the former have been reported, it is the latter effect that is generally considered to be the more important. Thus, how climate change affects seabirds will, to a large extent, be determined by how sensitive their preferred prey is to changes in temperature, salinity, etc., and whether alternative prey available.

In the North-East Atlantic, particularly northern parts of the North Sea, the lesser sandeel is a key prey of many seabirds during the breeding season. The main way climate change is expected to affect seabirds in this region is through climate-induced changes in sandeel availability. Elucidating the detail of such relationships is complicated by the fact that sandeels have been the target of a major fishery. Long-term research on the seabird community on the Isle of May (Figure 4.42), off the south-east coast of Scotland, has shown that both adult survival and breeding success of the black-legged kittiwake, were significantly reduced in the year following a winter with higher than usual sea surface temperature (SST) which resulted in a poor sandeel recruitment[38,39]. In addition, birds bred less successfully and survived less well in years when a sandeel fishery was operating within 50 km of the colony. The results also indicated that the breeding success/ temperature relationship was mediated mainly through one-year old fish while that for adult survival was mediated by the availability of juvenile sandeels. Thus the analysis highlighted the additive negative effects of rising sea temperatures and a local sandeel fishery on kittiwakes and additional analyses using data on kittiwake breeding success for other Scottish east coast colonies have also revealed the possibility of additive effects of climate and sandeel fisheries[40].

Although surface-feeding species such as kittiwake and terns have generally been regarded as being the most sensitive to changes in prey, particularly sandeel, availability[41], recently diving species such as the common guillemot that bring back single items of food for their young, have also started to have bad breeding seasons. Long-term data from the Isle of May showed the average length of sandeels in the early 2000s was only 60% of that 30 years ago[42]. The situation was particularly extreme in 2004 when mean sandeel length was the lowest recorded over a 30-year period. In 2004, sandeels were mainly replaced in guillemot diets by sprat (Figure 4.38), another lipid-rich pelagic fish that should have provided sufficient energy for normal chick growth and fledging success. However, analyses of the energy content of fish brought in for the chicks revealed that values were lower than expected and thus chicks were being fed a low-lipid rather than a high-lipid diet[43].

There is thus good evidence that breeding failures of seabirds at Scottish North Sea colonies in 2004 stemmed from problems lower down the food web. Sea temperatures in the northern North Sea have been rising since the mid-1980s and the abundance and species composition of the plankton, particularly the copepod community, has changed[44]. Such conditions appear unfavourable for sandeel recruitment[38] and also for the survival and/or breeding of a wide range of seabirds[39, 45, 46, 47].

The evidence to date suggests that conditions in the seas around Scotland are becoming less favourable for sandeels and thus for species such as seabirds that depend on them for food. However, it remains possible that the conditions will favour other prey species and that at least some seabirds may be able to take advantage of this. Recent surveys have indeed suggested that a new potential prey species is now available, with an increase in the abundance of the snake pipefish being recorded since 2003[48,49]. The cause of this increase is currently unknown, although it seems to be part of a general spread of Atlantic shelf species into the North Sea. Many seabird species have been recorded bringing snake pipefish to their chicks at Scottish seabird colonies, particularly those in the Northern Isles and St Kilda, and sightings of seabirds feeding on pipefish outside the breeding season are becoming common. However, compared to other potential prey, the energy content of snake pipefish is very low and thus it seems highly unlikely that snake pipefish are a viable alternative food source for seabirds[50].

### Figure 4.42   Researchers catching birds on the Isle of May

# Chapter 5
# Productive Seas

## INTRODUCTION

The seas around Scotland support a wide range of human activity most of which has an economic value. The productive seas part of the Scottish Government's vision is to recognise this activity, through its value to the economy and its associated employment whilst also recognising any associated impacts the activity might have on the state of the seas. In short, there is the overall aim of using the seas sustainably.

There are a number of questions that can be asked:

> **Are our seas being used productively?** To answer this requires data about the actual levels of production or activity and possible assessment of these against targets based upon assessments of potential production. Such data are mostly collected by government with often more detailed data available from industry.

> **Are our seas being used sustainably?** This requires a detailed knowledge of the amount of the resource, its rate of consumption compared with its rate of renewal (if any) and the environmental effects of its use. Overall, levels of a resource are not always known, whilst rate of consumption is covered by statistics about industrial and other types of production. The effects of such use on the environment are sometimes covered by monitoring programmes but not for all uses.

> **What is the value of the seas to the economy?** Economic value by industry (in the form of Gross Domestic Product (GDP) at basic prices) is published by the Scottish Government in the Input-Output tables[1] which are compiled using the European System of Accounts (1995); see The Input-Output Approach section. This Input-Approach framework covers all economic activity in Scotland and uses Standard Industrial Classification (SIC03) codes to detail 128 different industry groups across the whole of the Scottish economy. The tables represent the most detailed cash value GDP breakdowns that are available.

The Input-Output tables also provide detailed information about the flows of products and services between industries. Using this information it is possible to identify industries in other areas of the economy that supply those industries that rely on the sea, as well as industries that buy products from the industries that rely on the sea and add further economic value.

Further to the Input-Output approach to estimating the economic value of specific industries, some industries undertake their own detailed studies to estimate the wider economic contribution of their industry and often include all other linked industrial activity, which can overstate the economic value. As such, Input-Output figures are often lower than specific industry studies.

This report presents an initial analysis from both approaches, first of the Input-Output analysis and, in the sections that follow, more descriptive information about the main marine industries in Scotland, which may include some figures that do not necessarily compare exactly. Data are presented in these two ways to build up an initial evidence base as an overview of marine and marine related activity. A detailed analysis is required to have a full picture. Similarly, a fully integrated assessment of the seas requires the evidence base for both the economic benefits and environmental impacts of the activities. Such an assessment would integrate data from across all parts of a report such as this. It is hoped that the *State of Scotland's Seas 2010* can move towards a more complete assessment.

Understanding the impacts of human activities in an ecosystem context will be integral to future marine assessments. Some of the emerging descriptors of good environmental status (GES) from the Marine Strategy Framework Directive (MSFD) will be helpful. The relevant ones are shown in Table 5.1.

| Table 5.1 Qualitative MSFD GES descriptors for productive seas |
| --- |
| **MSFD Annex I GES descriptor** |
| GES Descriptor 3 - Populations of all **commercially exploited fish and shellfish** are within safe biological limits, exhibiting a population age and size distribution that is indicative of a healthy stock |
| GES Descriptor 6 - **Sea-floor integrity** is at a level that ensures that the structure and functions of the ecosystems are safeguarded and benthic ecosystems, in particular, are not adversely affected |
| GES Descriptor 7 - Permanent **alteration of hydrographical conditions** does not adversely affect marine ecosystems |

The MSFD also states the need to have productive seas that are managed sustainably. Thresholds of "what level of activity represents sustainability" or "what is considered an adequate level of productivity" need to be agreed and indicators established. This has not been undertaken yet, although the Scottish Government's National Targets include increasing to 70% key commercial fish stocks at full reproductive capacity and ensuring they are harvested sustainably by 2015.

Data on economic benefits or economic use have been traditionally collected by way of Government statistics related to particular activities. Data are not collected in similar ways nor are data available for some activities where they form sub sets of larger-scale activities. For example, in Government statistics, port turnover and employment are sub sets of business activity although tonnage throughput is collected for each port.

To support the emerging UKMMAS Productive Seas Evidence Group (PSEG) evidence base, a report entitled *Socio-economic indicators of marine-related activities in the UK economy*[2] is being prepared to provide economic data on a UK basis. This builds on a previous report, *A new analysis of marine-related activities in the UK economy with supporting science and technology*[3]. Both of these reports gather data from Input-Output Tables and industry.

## THE INPUT-OUTPUT APPROACH
### Identification of the core marine environment industries

In order to estimate the value of the seas to the Scottish economy it has been necessary to decide which Scottish industries rely on the seas (or are marine related) in order to produce their output. No attempt has been made to discriminate between activities occurring in Scottish or non-Scottish waters. This initial identification of marine related industries was done using the UK Standard Industrial Classifications (2003)[4].

When deciding which industries represent a broad group definition such as marine-related (Table 5.2), care must be taken to ensure that non-marine industries that buy marine industry products are not included. However, it can be difficult to draw this distinction. An example in this case would be the fish processing industry. It buys 56% of all the Scottish domestic sea fishing industry output. It could be argued that if the fishing industry ceased to exist, the fish processing industry would import fish and continue to function. In such a scenario, it is also possible that much of the fish would still be caught in Scottish territorial waters by foreign boats. Further down the route to the final consumer it is easier to distinguish 'non-marine industries'. These will include packagers, wholesalers and retailers, as well as the restaurants that cook and serve the fish to the final consumer. Whilst they all add value, and therefore contribute to the economy, it could not be said that they would not continue to operate if there were no Scottish fishing industry.

Another example is the 'services ancillary to the oil and gas extraction industries'. It may be reasonable to assume that these mainland industries serving offshore oil and gas extraction activities (see North Sea oil below) would not exist in Scotland if oil had never been discovered in the North Sea. As such it could therefore be considered to rely on the (Scottish) sea and therefore classed as marine-related. However, now the industry and its offshore expertise is here, it is entirely possible that it would continue to operate elsewhere in the world (i.e. export) after North Sea extraction ceases. It therefore follows that it may not be possible to assume that the industry relies solely on the North Sea oil extraction industry.

It is therefore very difficult to know if an industry would continue to operate in the absence of a domestic (i.e. Scottish) supplier or customer and also whether the industry relies on Scottish seas or the sea in general. This analysis has assumed that the fish processing and services ancillary to the oil and gas extraction industries are core 'marine-related' industries rather than non-marine purchases of sea fishing and oil and gas extraction industry output.

| Table 5.2 | List of core marine-related industries | |
|---|---|---|
| Input-Output category[1] | Industry description | Standard Industrial Classification 2003[2] |
| IOC 3.1 | Sea fishing | (SIC 05.01) |
| IOC 3.2 | Fish farming | (SIC 05.02) |
| IOC 5 | Service activities incidental to oil and gas extraction | (SIC 11.2 & 12) |
| IOC 9 (part) | Processing and preserving of fish and fish products | (SIC 15.2) |
| IOC 78 | Building and repairing of ships and boats | (SIC 35.1) |
| IOC 88 (part) | Construction of water projects | (SIC 45.24) |
| IOC 95 (part) | Sea and coastal water transport | (SIC 61.1) |

## Economic value – industry contribution to overall Scottish GDP

The economic value is taken as the contribution of the identified core marine-related industries to the overall Scottish Gross Domestic Product at basic prices (Gross Value Added (GVA)). These are detailed in the Input-Output tables. Employment data for these industries are estimated using the Office for National Statistics Annual Business Inquiry.

Further to this initial value, it is possible to use the Input-Output analytical tables to estimate the economic value generated by non-marine-related industries supplying those identified as marine-related. These are the indirect effects and can be added into the core marine economic value because without the core industry demand, the economic value of these non-core industries would be affected.

For each of the identified core 'marine-related' industries the Input-Output tables have been used to calculate a proxy estimate of the GDP and employment created by other, non-marine-related industries that buy marine-related products. This is supported upstream output, related to the purchase of marine products and is not considered to be marine-related. This is because it is assumed that these industries would import the necessary products and would therefore continue to operate in the absence of the core domestic (Scottish) marine-related industries. The non-marine analysis is included because it can be useful to see which industries buy products from the core marine-related industries and the further economic value generated.

### North Sea oil

In accounting for oil and gas activity in the North Sea, North Sea output is not included in Scotland's official GDP estimates. North Sea activity is instead included in the Extra Regio GDP data in the UK regional accounts, and not attributed to any specific UK region. Official GDP statistics for Scotland similarly exclude North Sea GDP. As such, the Input-Output model of the Scottish economy used to estimate core marine industry GVA and its associated upstream GVA does not take into account North Sea oil extraction activity. It does include all on-shore oil-related activity (Standard Industrial Classification (SIC03) 11.2 "service activities incidental to oil and gas extraction excluding surveying").

Analysis was recently undertaken by the Scottish Government to estimate a realistic, notional share of Scottish North Sea output. The approximate estimate for 2005 was in the order of £20 billion of additional GDP (at market prices) as compared to total Scottish GDP (at market prices, excluding oil) of £98 billion in 2005.

Since the Input-Output model does not include North Sea Output, it is not possible to model any wider effects which might be concomitant with the transfer of a share of North Sea output to Scotland. Any wider effects might serve to increase or decrease Scotland's GVA.

### Methodology summary

The value of the seas is taken to mean the contribution of the identified core marine environment industries to the overall Scottish GVA estimate plus the contribution of the upstream suppliers to the core marine environment industries.

The supported upstream analysis is included to show which industries buy products from the core marine-related industries and the further economic value they generate. This economic activity cannot be considered marine related. A fuller description of the methodologies used is in Annex 4.

### Results

Table 5.3 shows the overall economic value (in terms of GVA and employment) for each of the identified core marine-related industries. As explained, this is in terms of the value of the identified industry category as detailed in the Input-Output tables, plus any indirect economic value associated with their purchase of products from other industries.

**Table 5.3 Summary of marine-related industry GVA (£ million at 2004 prices) and employment (2004)[A]**

| Marine related industry | Core industry | | Indirect | | Total | | Support upstream (proxy) | |
|---|---|---|---|---|---|---|---|---|
| | GVA (£m) | Employment (FTE) | GVA (£m) | Employment (FTE) | GVA (£m) | Employment (FTE) | GVA (£m) | Employment (FTE) |
| Sea fishing | 134.1 | 2,327 | 15.4 | 357 | 149.5 | 2,684 | 123.1 | 5,001 |
| Fish farming | 72.3 | 1,492 | 49.4 | 976 | 121.7 | 2,468 | 6.0 | 213 |
| Service activities incidental to oil and gas extraction | 592.3 | 10,928 | 419.3 | 8,733 | 1,011.6 | 19,661 | 138.5 | 2,528 |
| Processing and preserving of fish and fish products | 228.0 | 8,813 | 253.4 | 5,291 | 481.4 | 14,104 | 25.1 | 842 |
| Building and repairing of ships and boats | 244.7 | 5,849 | 68.1 | 1,367 | 312.9 | 7,216 | 47.9 | 1,073 |
| Construction of water projects | 3.0 | 70 | 1.2 | 24 | 4.2 | 94 | 2.7 | 30 |
| Sea and coastal water transport | 134.7 | 2,312 | 25.9 | 584 | 160.6 | 2,896 | 34.2 | 769 |
| All marine sector | 1,409.0 | 31,790 | 746.9 | 15,793 | 2,155.9 | 47,583 | 284.1 | 7,441 |

Source: Input-Output tables for Scotland 2004

Partial Input-Output category core employment figures are based upon estimated output share applied to employment figures for the whole Input-Output category. Indirect and supported upstream figures are estimated using the Input-Output model. Each of the identified marine industries indirect and supported upstream effects will include activity between other marine industries. To prevent double counting, this activity is not included for the marine sector as a whole. As a result, the all marine sector totals will always be lower than the sum of the identified industries, except for the core industry columns.

FTE = Full Time Equivalent

In 2004, the total value of the marine-related sector was estimated to be £2.2 billion, and was estimated to support around 50,000 full-time equivalent employees. This represents 2.6% of the total Scottish GVA (£83 billion) and 2.4% of total Scottish full-time equivalent employment (around 2 million).

Within this overall figure, roughly half of the economic value is generated within the 'services incidental to oil and gas extraction' industry group, and roughly a quarter within the fish processing industry, followed by shipbuilding and repair, sea and coastal water transport, sea-fishing, fish farming and finally construction of water projects with an estimated economic value of £4.2 million.

The supported upstream analyses shows that almost as much economic value is generated by other industries with purchases from the sea fishing industry, as by the sea fishing industry itself. The majority of this is within the fish processing and hotels and catering sectors. Tables detailing the indirect and supported upstream industries for each of the identified core marine-related industries are in Annex 4.

The detailed indirect and supported upstream analysis shows that, of the overall economic value for the marine sector as a whole, 35% of this or £750 million (and 33% of employment or 16,000 full-time equivalent jobs) is generated indirectly by other industries who supply the marine-related industries. £100 million is generated within the banking sector, £70 million in renting of machinery industries and £60 million in the wholesale distribution industry.

Supported upstream analyses suggest that hotels, catering and pubs generate the most economic value from marine sector products (mainly from purchases from the sea fishing industry), followed by the oil processing industry (mainly from purchases from the services incidental to oil and gas industry) and public administration and defence (mainly from purchases from the ship building and repair industry).

## EVIDENCE THAT THE SEA IS PRODUCTIVE

Table 5.4 shows an initial analysis of the distribution of responsibility between different organisations for the collection of data about the productivity of Scotland's seas. In addition to those listed other groups collect data, in particular specific industries may collect data that can be used to augment and support that collected by departmental or agency responsibilities.

It is too early for this interim assessment to draw firm conclusions about the overall productive state of Scotland's seas, especially with regard to sustainability. However, it is clear from the statistics for the various activities that the seas are well used as a resource. The questions remain, "to what degree of productivity are the seas used?" and "is it sustainable?". Different activities will be productive or sustainable to different extents. Some of the established activities, such as fisheries, will be "productively" exploiting resources with some stocks possibly within sustainable limits (or safe biological limits) while other activities that are comparatively new, such as renewable energy, will still be relatively "unproductive" when compared with the potential resource. At this stage of

| Table 5.4 Summary of data collected that could indicate whether Scotland's seas are productive | |
|---|---|
| **Indicators of productive seas** | **Data collectors** |
| Marine fisheries | Scottish Government, Scottish Fisheries Protection Agency, FRS |
| Coastal salmon fishing | Scottish Government, FRS |
| Aquaculture (fin fish & shellfish) | Scottish Government, FRS, Crown Estate |
| Shellfish stock assessment | FRS, Shetland Shellfish Management Organisation |
| Oil and gas | Department for Business, Enterprise and Regulatory Reform, Scottish Government |
| Ports | Scottish Government, Department for Transport |
| Leisure and recreation | No coastal/marine data collected except for specific studies or industry bodies, e.g. British Marine Federation |
| Historic heritage | Historic Scotland |
| Renewable energy | Scottish Government |
| Dredge spoil disposal | FRS |
| Oil spills | Advisory Committee on Protection of the Sea (ACOPS) on behalf of the Maritime and Coastguard Agency |
| Aggregate extraction | Crown Estate |

assessing Scotland's seas the approach adopted is to provide an introduction to the key individual industries including general assessments, together with some case studies which highlight relevant detail.

An important aspect of resource management is evaluation of the available resource. This allows sustainable levels of production to be determined and allows productivity targets to be set. A tool developed for the Shetland shellfish fishery (see Case Study 5.2) demonstrates one way that this can be achieved. However, it should be noted that the assessment itself is resource intensive and it is not possible to replicate such detailed assessments for all shellfish fisheries nor indeed all marine resources.

## Fishing

The Scottish fishing industry holds a key role in our nation's maritime history. Sea fishing has always been a part of Scottish life. For port communities such as Fraserburgh and Lerwick, it has provided the main source of employment for centuries and continues to do so in whitefish, pelagic and shellfish fisheries.

In recent years the industry has experienced alternating periods of prosperity and hardship, which has created irregular supplies of stock and instability in both the fish processing sector and the markets. Unsustainably high fishing mortality rates in the 1970s-1990s contributed to reducing population sizes, and the process of setting total allowable catch quotas through a series of negotiations between member states and the difficulties inherent in the Common Fishery Policy (CFP) with regards to mixed fisheries have further contributed to the instability.

The Scottish Government's vision is for a Scottish seafishing industry which is sustainable, profitable, supportive of strong local communities and managed effectively as an integral part of coherent policy for Scotland's marine environment. Fish stocks at risk (such as cod) will be allowed to recover, stock management policies will aim to ensure that the industry avoids 'boom and bust' fluctuations. The quality of our marine environment will be safeguarded whilst the long term viability of the industry is assured. The newly-established Scottish Fisheries Council will provide a forum to bring scientists, stakeholders and policy-makers together to develop and implement marine fisheries policies that promote the industry and its communities whilst protecting the stocks and the marine environment.

## Scottish fishing fleets

There are four broad types of fishing fleet which make up the Scottish fishing industry:

> *The pelagic fleet* mainly targets herring and mackerel. It is comprised of a relatively small number of large,

profitable vessels, working usually out of Fraserburgh, Peterhead and Lerwick.

> *The demersal or whitefish fleet* targets bottom-dwelling fish in two types of fishery: the roundfish fishery in the North Sea and west of Scotland (which comprises cod, haddock, whiting and saithe) and the species found in the deeper water to the north and west of Scotland.

> *The mixed demersal and shellfish fleet* are the boats from the whitefish fleet which move between whitefish and *Nephrops* fisheries (prawn, or langoustine, fisheries).

> *The shellfish fleet* is those vessels that specialise in shellfish and *Nephrops*. They are mainly smaller than the pelagic fleet boats and operate within the inshore waters of the west coast, east coast, Borders, Fife, and south west of Scotland. A high proportion of these vessels are under 10 m.

## Fishing ports and vessels

At the end of 2006, there were 2,224 active vessels based in Scotland. Stornoway had the largest number (303), followed by Fraserburgh (221) and Shetland (185). Lochinver had the smallest number (18), followed by Kinlochbervie (26) and Ullapool (67). This represents a net reduction of 62 vessels (or 3% of the fleet) since the end of 2005. In 2006, the segment of the fleet comprising vessels under 10 m in length (inshore and small shellfish vessels) decreased by 49 vessels (or 3%) to 1,518 vessels. The over 10 m fleet segment (pelagic, demersal and mixed demersal/shellfish vessels) decreased by 13 vessels (or 2%) to 706 vessels.

In recent years fishing vessel decommissioning, introduced as a conservation measure to bring the fishing fleet into line with available fishing opportunities, has resulted in a significant decrease in overall fishing capacity. The decommissioning schemes of 2001-2002 and 2003-2004 reduced the size of the whitefish fleet by 165 vessels. It is now thought that the size of the Scottish fishing fleet is in line with catching opportunities.

## Employment in the Scottish fishing industry

In 2006, 4,109 people were regularly employed on Scottish-based vessels across all districts, with a further 999 irregularly employed and 97 crofters[B]. The total number of people employed in sea fishing (5,205 people) represents 0.2% of the total Scottish labour force.

Fraserburgh had the highest number of regularly employed fishermen (614), followed by Ayr (507) and Peterhead (412). Shetland and Stornoway had the highest number of irregularly-employed fishermen (156 and 152 respectively).

## Landings and value of key stocks

The total quantity of fish landed by Scottish vessels has fallen by 15% since 2002. This is mainly due to reductions in the landings of demersal and pelagic fish (29% and 14% respectively). Shellfish landings actually increased by 14% over the same period. In 2006, 379,200 tonnes of live weight catch was landed by Scottish-based vessels. Of this total, 60% was pelagic species, 25% was demersal, and the remainder was shellfish. Figure 5.1 shows the estimated distribution of where the main commercial species (Table 5.5) are caught. The total combined value of these landings was £368.5 million, representing a 3% increase in value despite a decrease in live weight landed. For the first time, shellfish was the most valuable sector to the Scottish fleet, with shellfish landings representing 38% of total value despite its relatively small contribution in weight. Trends in the value of landings are shown in Figure 5.2. Based on 2006 prices, the value of demersal stocks has shown a noticeable decline since 1990. The value of pelagic stocks increased early in the period but has since fluctuated without obvious trend, while for shellfish the value was relatively stable until 2003 but has increased since. Landings made by Scottish vessels into Scottish ports in 2006 accounted for 83% of the total value of landings by Scottish-based vessels (including landings into foreign ports).

Information on landings and value is collected by the Scottish Fisheries Protection Agency and collated by statisticians in the Scottish Government Marine Directorate (SGMD). FRS maintains an ongoing programme of research and monitoring to support fisheries management, which involves examination of the biology and state of commercially important fish stocks (see Case Study 4.5), and research into how changes in the marine environment affect fish stocks.

## Impacts on fisheries

Scottish fisheries are potentially impacted by both environmental and anthropogenic factors. In recent years the seas around Scotland have been warming and there have been observed changes in plankton communities. The incidence of more southerly fish species migrating northwards has also increased. The relationships between these phenomena and the various species of commercial interest are complex and not fully understood. It does, however, appear that environmental conditions for species such as cod are less favourable at the present time. The implications for industry appear to be a reduced opportunity of some key species but there is no indication that stocks will be imminently reduced to the extent they are not commercially important.

Anthropogenic effects on fisheries include permanent structures, dumping at sea, oil and chemical spillages and fisheries themselves. These effects are sometimes relatively localised (for example the Braer oil spill[5]) and affect fisheries in the immediate vicinity but rarely affect entire stocks. Solid structures (for example oil platforms in the North Sea) potentially impede fishing activity but so far have a relatively small footprint compared to available fishing area. Furthermore these can sometimes provide beneficial effects as fish refugia or sites which favour recruitment.

One fishery can potentially impact on another through interaction between the targeted species. Pelagic species take food from the water column; demersal species and crustaceans living on the sea bed ultimately rely on material which comes down through the water column. Fishery induced disturbance to the balance of these processes may adversely affect one or more of the components. There is no evidence that the different types of fishery in Scotland have severely impacted each other but this needs to be carefully monitored. Historically, smaller species of fish such as sandeels have been exploited for the production of fish meal. These species are potential food items for larger human consumption species, although the latter typically take a variety of food. In the absence of a clear understanding of the contribution of small fish, care is also required in their exploitation.

## Table 5.5   Seven commercial fish and shellfish species of major interest to Scotland

| Demersal | Pelagic | Shellfish |
| --- | --- | --- |
| Cod | herring | *Nephrops* (Norway lobster or langoustines) |
| Haddock | mackerel | scallops (or 'clams') |
| Monkfish (or angler fish) | | |

### Fisheries impacts on the marine environment

Fishing activities impact on other components of the marine environment, the important question relates to whether the effects are short-term and reversible and, at the same time, do not compromise biodiversity. Potential impacts involving interaction with other species include unwanted bycatch. Monitoring of Scottish pelagic fisheries suggests that cetacean bycatch is very low. On the other hand discards of unwanted commercial and non-commercial fish and invertebrates remain unacceptably high in some demersal trawl fisheries. Scotland has taken a lead in tackling this through the use of gear technical measures (such as square-meshed escape panels) and the encouragement of behaviour which reduces unwanted catches (for example, real-time closures to avoid juvenile cod). The first voluntary real-time closure of a cod spawning ground was announced in the Scottish Parliament in January 2008.

Towed gears in particular have a physical impact on seabed features. Research suggests that in highly dynamic environments with mobile sediments (e.g. Solway Firth) the effects are not lasting, but in low energy environments (e.g. Loch Creran) this may not be the case. Under the Inshore Fishing Scotland Act 1984 some inshore and sea loch areas are closed to mobile gears to avoid disturbance to deep mud sediments. Open structured seabed features supporting complex communities (e.g. *Lithothamnion* or 'maerl' beds) are also known to be vulnerable to dredging and offshore, slow-growing deepwater corals areas have exhibited trawl damage. Scotland has been active in establishing closed areas to protect these features (for example, through a SAC to protect maerl near Arisaig and the announcement in January 2008 of a consultation to establish a marine conservation area at Lamlash Bay, Arran) and has been supportive of EU efforts to protect deepwater habitats. Areas frequently trawled may suffer damage to less exotic species of bivalve molluscs, sea urchins and polychaetes. Secondary and less obvious effects of different patterns of fishing might be expected to have a secondary and less obvious affect on the balance of predators and prey but this appears not to have been studied to any great extent.

While closed areas or MPAs play an important role in conserving sensitive marine environments and can be important in protecting key life stages of commercial species, reliance on them as a principal fisheries management measure is more questionable. Simulation studies suggest such areas would require to be very large and be accompanied by significant effort reductions to avoid the potentially deleterious effects of effort transfer. In recent years Scotland has undertaken major decommissioning schemes and has observed days at sea regulations in order to reduce fishing activity. This potentially benefits commercial species, other components of the ecosystems in which they live, and habitats.

Summary Assessments for the state of the seven commercial species of major interest to Scotland are included in chapter 4. This report has not attempted to assess the productivity of the fisheries in economic terms.

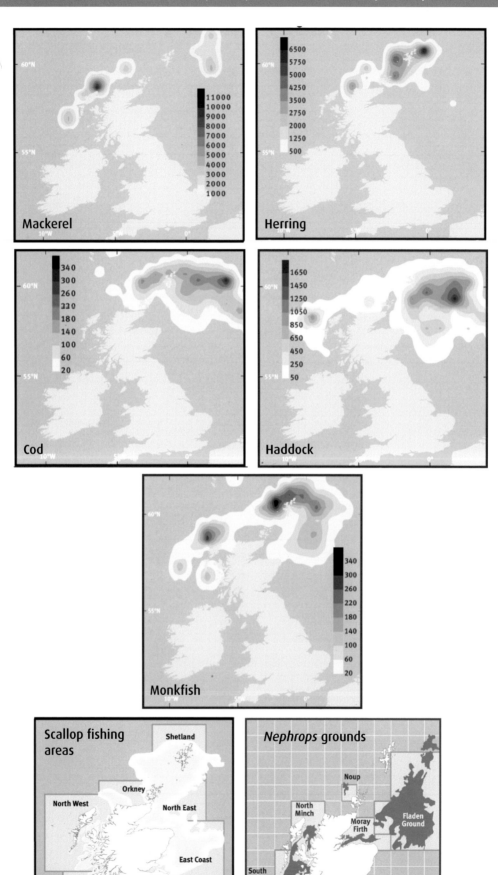

**Figure 5.2    Value[c] of landings at 2006 prices by Scottish-based vessels by species type, 1990 to 2006**

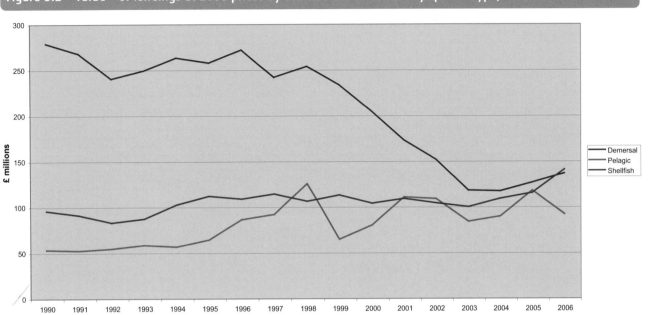

Legend:
— Demersal
— Pelagic
— Shellfish

*Coastal salmon fishing*

The Salmon and Freshwater Fisheries (Consolidation) (Scotland) Act 2003 states the use of rod and line (rarely used), net and coble (limited to the inner Moray Firth and some west coast sea lochs) and bag net, fly net or other stake net as the only lawful methods outside estuary limits of catching salmon.

Coastal salmon fishing uses net fisheries, known as fixed engines (Figure 5.3), which are set in positions which have been determined by generations of fishers. The rights to fish are held as private, heritable titles either by individuals, companies or the Crown. Fixed engines comprise a curtain of netting extending up to 300 m seawards from the shore and up to 4 m deep. A trap at the seaward end catches the salmon. Netting is highly regulated including a minimum mesh size and closure periods. In 2006, 4,169 kg of salmon and sea trout were caught using fixed engines[6].

Fishing effort now is about 10% of that in 1952[7] mainly due to reduced catches making this method of fishing uneconomic. Only the more productive fisheries remain in operation.

Salmon fishing is very seasonal, generally from mid February to late August. The number of netsmen employed varies throughout the season, depends upon the number of gear units deployed and can range from 1 to 6 per station. There are 45 fishing stations in mainland Scotland (east coast (22), north coast (5) and west coast and islands (18)). The value of this coastal activity to the economy is not known, however, it can be very valuable at an individual fisher level. An overall productivity assessment is not considered appropriate here.

The fixed engines have a limited impact on the seabed, being held in place by anchors and chains. Bycatch is negligible.

**Figure 5.3    Fixed engine salmon net**

## Aquaculture – finfish and shellfish

Commercial aquaculture began in Scotland in the mid 1970s, and became well established in the 1980s and 1990s. In 2006, Scottish production of marine finfish represented >99% of UK culture marine finfish and shellfish or some 150,000 tonnes. This production is dominated by Atlantic salmon at 131,847 tonnes (Figure 5.4); Scotland is the largest producer in the EU and the third largest producer in the world, behind Norway and Chile. This is followed by rainbow trout. Increasing numbers of alternative species are being produced including trout, cod and halibut, with some 1,050 tonnes of these species produced during 2006. Shellfish – Pacific oyster, native oyster, common mussel, scallop and queen scallops - accounts for 4,594 tonnes in 2006. Aquaculture is a vitally important industry, in terms of the geographic locations in which it operates, predominantly the west, north west, Western Isles and Northern Isles (Figure 5.5). Many communities are sustained by the employment provided, particularly salmon farming.

The Scottish Government's vision for aquaculture (finfish and shellfish) is set out in its **Strategic Framework for Scottish Aquaculture**[8], first published in 2003. Its vision is that "Scotland will have a sustainable, diverse, competitive and economically viable aquaculture industry, of which its people can be justifiably proud. It will deliver high quality, healthy food to consumers at home and abroad, and social and economic benefits to communities, particularly in rural and remote areas. It will operate responsibly, working within the carrying capacity of the environment, both locally and nationally and throughout its supply chain." The Strategy has four principles: economic; environmental; social; and stewardship. The Scottish Government works closely with the industry and other key stakeholders, and others who operate in the freshwater and marine environment.

### Finfish production

#### Salmon

In 2006 marine production was undertaken by 44 companies farming 252 active sites. Production showed an increase of 2% over the 2005 figure, which reverses a downward trend since a peak production in 2003 of 169,736 tonnes. Production is undertaken by means of seawater tanks and seawater cages, with the majority being undertaken in the latter. Overall, production was dominated by 11 companies in 2006, producing over 90% of the salmon.

| Figure 5.4 The trend in annual production of Atlantic salmon |

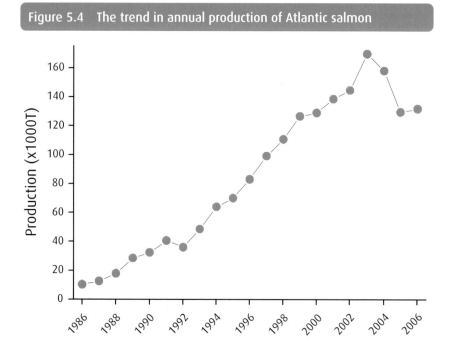

## Figure 5.5   Active seawater fish and shellfish farms in Scotland

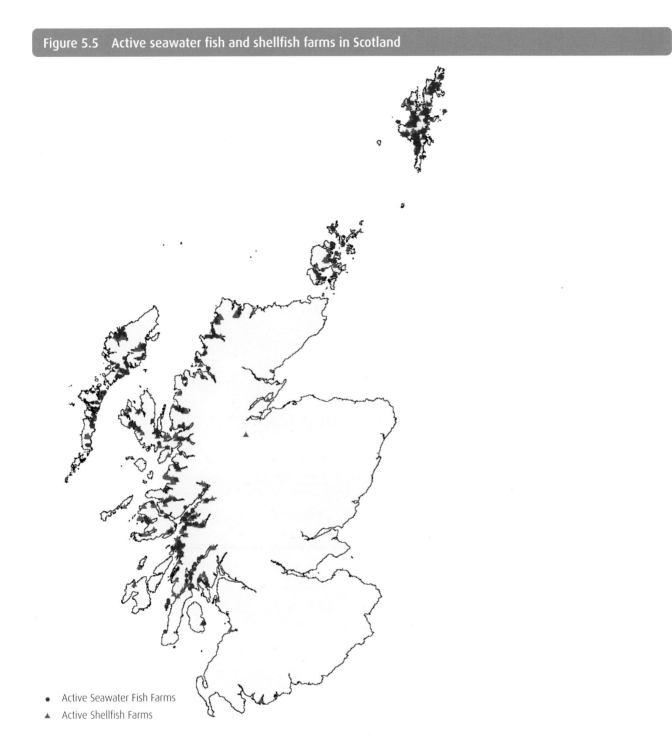

● Active Seawater Fish Farms
▲ Active Shellfish Farms

### Rainbow trout
Farming of rainbow trout is undertaken on both freshwater and seawater sites. A total of 7,492 tonnes of rainbow trout were produced in 2006, of which some 31% or 2,341 tonnes was produced in 10 saltwater sites. Rearing took place in cages.

### Other species
There has been continued interest in the farming of other species – brown trout/sea trout, cod and halibut. Production totals 1,046.5 tonnes between 47 companies.

The largest expansion is within the cod sector which produced 543 tonnes in 2006 and is estimated will produce 2,902 tonnes in 2007. These species provide diversification from the production of rainbow trout and Atlantic salmon. They allow some of the smaller companies to remain within the aquaculture sector and for the larger companies to broaden their production base.

## Shellfish production

One hundred and seventy three companies were active in shellfish production in 2006, operating on 327 active sites, of which 156 (44%) placed shellfish on the market. In this year 4,219 tonnes of shellfish were produced. Suitability of shellfish for human consumption is critical to the market's success. Case Study 5.1, shows how regular monitoring is important to have early warning of any potential problems. Mussels dominated production (4,287 tonnes), followed by Pacific oyster (251 tonnes), queen scallops (60 tonnes), scallops (40 tonnes) and native oyster (24 tonnes). Production of these species is being maintained, though that of farmed scallops increased more than three-fold in 2006. The major areas of production are Shetland and Argyll and Bute. The industry is dominated by small-scale producers, though there is a continued trend towards large companies contributing significantly to the production of all species. Case Study 5.2 demonstrates the importance of resource evaluation as a management tool.

## Data Collection

FRS carries out annual production surveys on behalf of the Scottish Government which collates annual production data from registered fish farm sites. The last full year of data available is 2006[9].

## Employment in the aquaculture sector

Salmon production directly employs 1,142 employees and is the most important economic sector in the Highlands and Islands, a mainly rural area. The rainbow trout sector (both freshwater and saltwater) directly employs 143 employees; other species 92 full-time employees and 17 part-time employees. The shellfish sector directly employs 160 full-time employees, 160 part-time employees, and 80 casual workers. Processing also employs large numbers of workers, though their current numbers are not known. While employment figures continue to decline as a whole throughout the aquaculture sector, the mean productivity per person is increasing throughout the fin fish sector. For Atlantic salmon production, this increased from 132.4 tonnes per person in 2005 to 151.4 tonnes in 2006.

Aquaculture has an annual turnover of over £280 million (2005); made up of £260 million (farmed salmon), about £10 million (rainbow, brown and sea trout), about £2 million (halibut and cod) and about £6 million (shellfish). The value of all fish exports (including aquaculture) from Scotland in 2005, (the most recent figures) was £420 million, which accounts for 60% of all food exports.

## Impacts

The Scottish Government is committed to a sustainable, diverse, competitive and economically viable aquaculture industry that operates within its environmental carrying capacity. Case Study 5.3 discusses the environmental impacts further. A number of initiatives are in place to complement existing legislation to provide protection for the environment. These include a working group to examine the siting of facilities; the publication of the *Environmental Impact Assessment Practical Guidelines Toolkit for Marine Fish Farming* in September 2007[10], providing guidance for planners, applicants and stakeholders and the industry prepared *Code of Good Practice for Scottish Finfish Aquaculture*[11]. In addition, the Aquaculture and Fisheries (Scotland) Act 2007, *inter alia*, underpins the industry Code of Good Practice and makes relevant legal powers and provisions in relation to containment and sea lice. *The Strategic Framework for Scottish Aquaculture* is being reviewed with the aim of maximising benefits from the industry in a sustainable way.

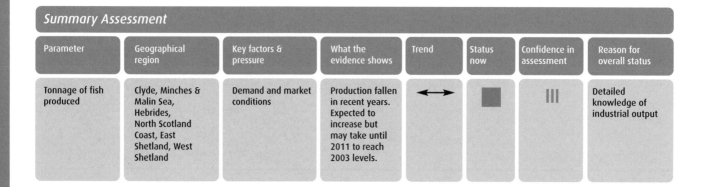

### Summary Assessment

| Parameter | Geographical region | Key factors & pressure | What the evidence shows | Trend | Status now | Confidence in assessment | Reason for overall status |
|---|---|---|---|---|---|---|---|
| Tonnage of fish produced | Clyde, Minches & Malin Sea, Hebrides, North Scotland Coast, East Shetland, West Shetland | Demand and market conditions | Production fallen in recent years. Expected to increase but may take until 2011 to reach 2003 levels. | ↔ | ■ | III | Detailed knowledge of industrial output |

## CASE STUDY 5.1   Safeguarding shellfish quality

The cultivation, harvesting and sale of bivalve molluscs are important to the Scottish economy. Marine phytoplankton is the food source for these filter-feeding organisms.

The vast majority of marine phytoplankton are benign. However, under certain conditions, a relatively few species produce toxins, some of which can accumulate within filter-feeding shellfish.

The perception exists that harmful or toxin-producing phytoplankton is increasing worldwide. It remains unclear whether this is because of improved monitoring and detection, climate change, ballast water transfer or the activity of humans in the coastal zone. However, in Scottish waters a number of independent reviews have found no evidence to link harmful phytoplankton with anthropogenic activity.

Although the shellfish themselves may not be affected, the concentration of the toxin in the shellfish flesh could cause humans ingesting affected shellfish to suffer subsequent ill health.

The Food Standards Agency Scotland (FSAS) is required, under Regulation (EC) No 854/2004 to monitor shellfish harvesting areas around Scotland for the occurrence of toxic phytoplankton, and for the presence of their toxins in shellfish. Monitoring and analysis of phytoplankton and

toxins is conducted by SAMS, Integrin Advanced Biosystems Ltd and Cefas.

Three main groups of toxins are routinely monitored. These are: the domoic acid group, responsible for Amnesic Shellfish Poisoning (ASP), generated by diatoms of the genus *Pseudo-nitzschia*; the lipophillic shellfish toxins including compounds that cause Diarrhetic Shellfish Poisoning (DSP), mostly generated by the genus *Dinophysis*; and the saxitoxins, which lead to Paralytic Shellfish Poisoning (PSP), generated by the genus *Alexandrium* (Figure 5.6). Shellfish harvesting areas will experience temporary closures due to the detection of ASP, DSP and PSP toxins in shellfish at levels that exceed the EU regulatory limits.

Shellfish are sampled from around 100 commercial harvesting areas for the presence of ASP, DSP and PSP toxins. Toxin-producing phytoplankton is also monitored in 41 coastal sites.

Enumeration of phytoplankton species has the potential to be used as an early warning of the possible occurrence of shellfish biotoxin events. To facilitate this, threshold concentrations of the main genera of phytoplankton have been determined by comparing phytoplankton counts with the presence of these toxins in shellfish.

### Figure 5.6   Main genus of toxin-producing phytoplankton monitored in Scottish waters

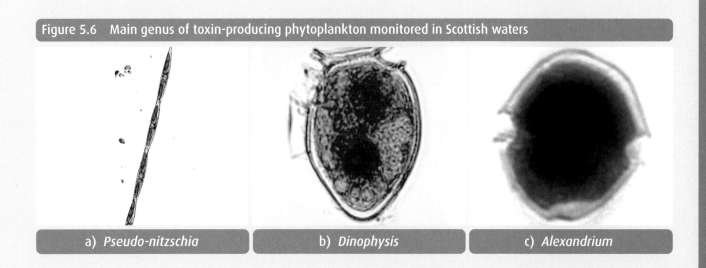

a) *Pseudo-nitzschia*     b) *Dinophysis*     c) *Alexandrium*

Phytoplankton monitoring conducted since 2005 has detected one or more toxic species of phytoplankton at concentrations exceeding the threshold levels in all of the locations sampled (Table 5.6), highlighting the potential impact of toxin events on the shellfish industry.

Waters around Shetland are particularly susceptible to toxic phytoplankton events. Between 1 April 2006 and 31 March 2007, the monitoring programme detected DSP in 11 harvesting areas and PSP in 15 harvesting areas.

Monitoring in Shetland has confirmed the importance of regular water sampling in the early detection of toxic phytoplankton blooms and prediction of biotoxin events in shellfish. Figure 5.7 illustrates the evolution of toxin events in shellfish harvesting areas in Vaila Sound, Shetland during 2006. Increasing numbers of phytoplankton (blue line on the graphs) were identified in advance of elevated biotoxin levels in mussels (bars on the graphs) providing an early warning of the event.

| Table 5.6 Phytoplankton monitoring conducted in Scotland from September 2005 - October 2007 | | | | |
|---|---|---|---|---|
| Location | Number of phytoplankton samples collected | Percentage of samples with *Pseudo-nitzschia* spp. above threshold | Percentage of samples with *Alexandrium* spp. above threshold | Percentage of samples with *Dinophysis* spp. above threshold |
| Argyll | 783 | 4 | 14 | 6 |
| Dumfries & Galloway | 35 | 0 | 31 | 0 |
| Fife | 52 | 0 | 23 | 0 |
| Lochaber | 27 | 2 | 30 | 11 |
| Sutherland | 89 | 7 | 21 | 10 |
| Western Isles | 188 | 13 | 34 | 21 |
| Ross & Cromarty | 67 | 15 | 19 | 12 |
| Borders | 16 | 0 | 19 | 25 |
| Shetland | 596 | 14 | 45 | 23 |
| Skye & Lochalsh | 113 | 8 | 24 | 27 |
| Orkney | 93 | 18 | 47 | 15 |

Source FSAS. Thresholds are *Pseudo-nitzschia* - 50,000 cells/litre; *Alexandrium* – presence; *Dinophysis* – 100 cells/litre.

**Figure 5.7   Evolution of DSP and PSP toxin events at Vaila Sound: Riskaness (A), Linga (B), and East of Linga (C) from June-September 2006**

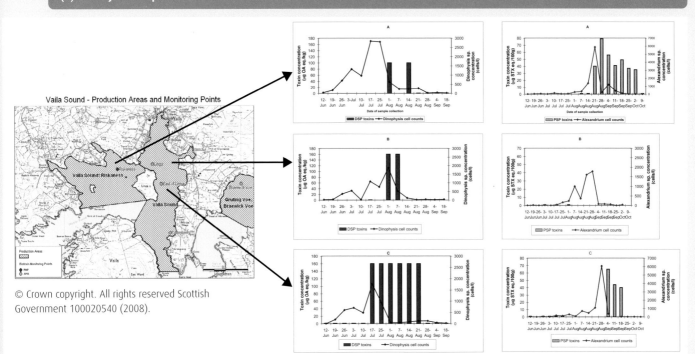

Cultivation of bivalve molluscs is an environmentally sustainable form of farming. However unregulated production or consumption of this natural product has inherent health risks from naturally occurring marine biotoxins. Regular and intensive monitoring of toxins in shellfish and the causative phytoplankton in water, combined with closures of harvesting areas that are experiencing toxic events are essential in protecting public health and in maintaining consumer confidence in this resource.

## Summary Assessment

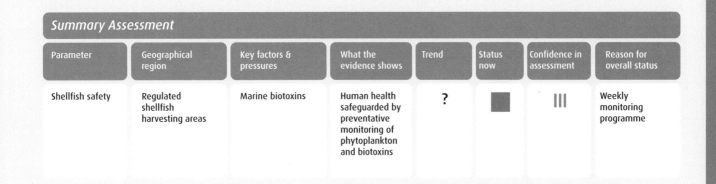

| Parameter | Geographical region | Key factors & pressures | What the evidence shows | Trend | Status now | Confidence in assessment | Reason for overall status |
|---|---|---|---|---|---|---|---|
| Shellfish safety | Regulated shellfish harvesting areas | Marine biotoxins | Human health safeguarded by preventative monitoring of phytoplankton and biotoxins | ? | ▨ | ||| | Weekly monitoring programme |

## CASE STUDY 5.2   Shetland shellfish stock assessment programme

The shellfish fisheries around Shetland have been managed by the Shetland Shellfish Management Organisation (SSMO) using a Regulating Order since 2000. As a result of this legislation all vessels fishing within the six-mile limit must obtain a licence from the SSMO and fishermen are required to submit log sheets summarising their catch and effort data. This information, combined with data from surveys and applied research carried out by the North Atlantic Fisheries College Marine Centre, has resulted in one of the most detailed fisheries data sets in Europe.

The fisheries data are collected at a fine spatial scale using 5-mile statistical squares (Figure 5.8) producing detailed spatial information on catch and effort for each of six main commercial species: lobsters, edible crabs (Figure 5.9), velvet crabs, scallops, queen scallops and whelks. These and other data are used to carry out annual stock assessments to support the management process.

The stock assessments are carried out using standard approved techniques and provide vital information on the status of the shellfish stocks. Standard length cohort analysis (LCA) for crabs and lobsters and virtual population analysis (VPA) for scallops are used to assess stocks. Trends in landings per unit effort data (LPUE) from SSMO logbooks are also investigated, and further analysed within a generalized additive modelling (GAM) framework. The results of the stock assessments, LPUE trends and analysis and applied research are used to provide management recommendations based on the status of the shellfish stocks.

This data set represents a unique and very detailed resource, and is an extremely useful tool in the management of the shellfish fisheries around Shetland.

### Summary Assessment

| Parameter | Geographical region | Key factors & pressures | What the evidence shows | Trend | Status now | Confidence in assessment | Reason for overall status |
|---|---|---|---|---|---|---|---|
| Shellfish stock assessment | Six mile limit around Shetland | Fishing | Shetland shellfish stocks are in a healthy state | ↔ | ■ | ||| | High quality fisheries data at a fine spatial scale |

### Figure 5.9   Brown crabs

**Figure 5.8    Area covered by the Shetland Regulating Order**

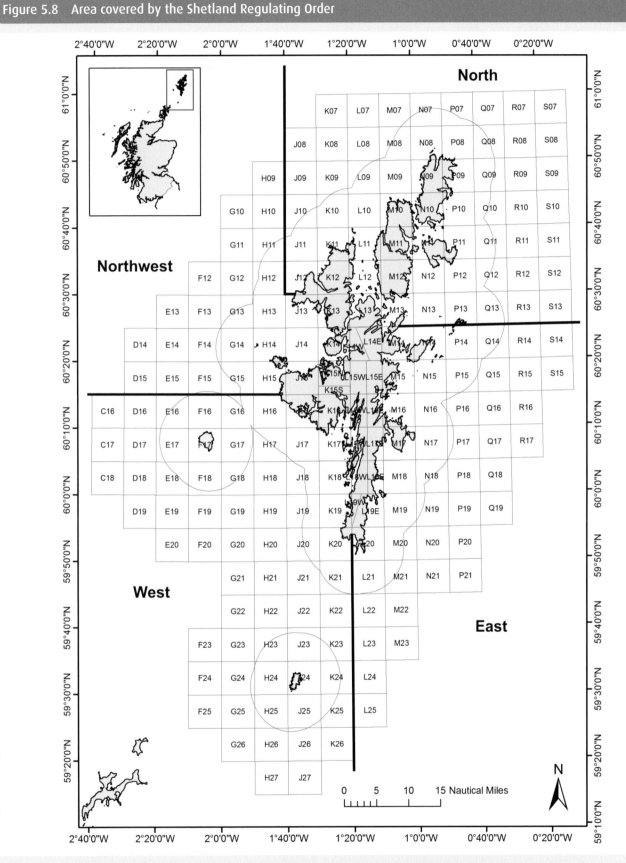

Figure shows the statistical squares used for data collection divided up into four geographical areas.

Potential interactions between aquaculture and the marine environment arise from the release of particulate organic matter, dissolved nutrients, veterinary medicines and anti-foulants, which may affect seabed and water quality, while escaped fish may interbreed with wild stocks.

The discharge of particulate organic matter from fish cages, in the form of faeces and waste feed, affects the sea bed in the immediate vicinity of the cages. High rates of carbon deposition significantly affect sediment chemistry and infaunal diversity. These effects are regulated under The Water Environment (Controlled Activities) (Scotland) Regulations (2005) (CAR) by SEPA through the issuing of discharge consents.

Monitoring of the sea bed conducted for licensing purposes, in addition to broader-scale monitoring of sediments in Scottish sea lochs, indicates that significant effects on sediment quality from fish farms are confined to areas very close (<100 m) to cages and that the majority of these effects are compliant with sediment Environmental Quality Standards (EQS).

The addition of nitrogen from anthropogenic sources (such as the feed fed to farmed fish) has the potential to cause deleterious effects resulting from accelerated planktonic growth. The quantities of nutrients discharged to Scottish waters as a result of fish farming activities have increased in line with production trends in the industry and improvements in the efficiency of farming practices (Figure 5.10).

An extensive monitoring programme conducted by FRS and SEPA between 2002 and 2006 assessed the eutrophication status of Scottish marine waters which were identified by modelling as most likely to be at risk of effects from nutrient enhancement from fish farms[12]. Nutrient concentrations, ratios and input trends were assessed along with the likely effects of nutrients on plankton, seaweeds, water and sediment chemistry, fish kills and algal toxins. No evidence of nutrient enhancement or accelerated growth of plankton or seaweeds was found. There was some evidence of harmful planktonic species, and their effects, however, these events are not thought to be caused by nutrients from fish farms.

Chemical discharges from fish farms include antibiotics, sea lice treatments and antifoulants. Since the development of a wide range of effective vaccines, the use of antibiotics has declined to low levels, however, in-feed and bath treatments for sea lice and copper-based antifoulants are widely used across the industry and regulated under CAR. SEPA sediment monitoring surveys have shown that there is no significant occurrence of medicines in sediments at concentrations above EQS at sites outside the immediate vicinity of fish farm cages. Unfortunately parasites, especially the sea louse, become immune to frequently used pesticides and there is a demand from the industry to use new active ingredients and new formulations to counter this problem.

There is potential for salmon farms to have deleterious effects on local populations of wild salmonids through genetic introgression or competition from fish farm escapes and as a result of potential increased disease prevalence in wild stocks through contact with diseased farm fish, for example through increased infective pressure from lice on farmed fish.

The majority of escapes involve Atlantic salmon and are caused by weather, equipment failure and damage caused by the action of predators. Reported numbers of escaped fish were approximately 1% of stock held during 2002–2007 (Figure. 5.11).

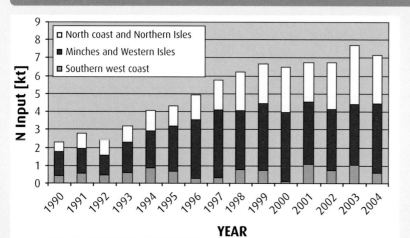

Southern west coast (Loch Ryan to Mull), Minches and Western Isles (Mull to Cape Wrath) and North coast / Northern Isles (Cape Wrath to Moray Firth).

## Figure 5.11   Escapes of farmed fish 2002–2007

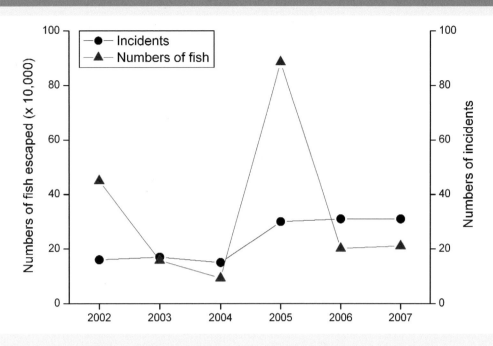

Overall, despite the dramatic rise in the production tonnage in the last two decades, the control measures in place by regulatory authorities address the main processes by which aquaculture may adversely affect the surrounding environment.

## Summary Assessment

| Parameter | Geographical region | Key factors & pressures | What the evidence shows | Trend | Status now | Confidence in assessment | Reason for overall status |
|---|---|---|---|---|---|---|---|
| Impacts on the seabed | Clyde, Minches & Malin Sea, Hebrides, North Scotland Coast, East Shetland, West Shetland | Particulate and chemical discharges from fish farms | Very localised significant impacts on sediment quality and infaunal diversity | ⟷ | ■ | III | Plethora of benthic monitoring data |
| Impacts on water column | Clyde, Minches & Malin Sea, Hebrides, North Scotland Coast, East Shetland, West Shetland | Nutrient discharges from fish farms | Increasing nutrient inputs in some areas but no significant enhancement or deleterious effects | X | ■ | III | Extensive eutrophication assessments of sea lochs |
| Effects on wild fisheries | Clyde, Minches & Malin Sea, Hebrides, North Scotland Coast, East Shetland, West Shetland | Escapes of farmed fish. Transmission of disease. | Large losses of farmed fish | ⟷ | ● | I | Room for reduction in escapes. Low confidence in effects on wild populations. |

## Oil and gas industry

Oil and gas exploitation has been a major activity in the waters around Scotland since the 1970s and has contributed significantly to the Scottish economy:

> approximately 145,000 jobs in Scotland are provided by the industry, representing 43% of the total UK oil and gas employment[13] according to Scottish Enterprise;

> there are over 2,000 Scottish companies involved in the industry;

> there is an onshore manufacturing industry for equipment, pumps and pipelines, etc; and

> in 2006, the UK continental shelf (no specific Scottish figures available) produced 70 million tonnes of oil[14] and 84 million cubic metres of gas[15].

The nearest production platform to shore is the Beatrice field in the outer Moray Firth which is on the territorial sea limit. The rest of the activity is well outside territorial waters and there are main clusters west of Shetland and east of Shetland which extends southwards to the southern North Sea. The nearest of these further platforms, Buzzard, is about 55 km NE of Rattray Head. However, oil and gas come ashore through a number of main export pipelines to facilities on Shetland (Sullom Voe) (3 import, 1 export) and Orkney (Scapa Flow) (1) for onward export in tankers or by pipeline to enhance oil recovery at other fields (1), and at St Fergus (6) and Cruden Bay (1) for onward transport by overland pipeline. There are tanker handling facilities at Sullom Voe, Flotta (Scapa Flow), Braefoot Bay, Hound Point (Firth of Forth) and Finnart.

For the industry to develop, major infrastructure emerged around the Scottish coast in the 1970s. Key supply bases remain at Aberdeen, Peterhead and Lerwick. There are large onshore oil, gas and chemical refineries at Grangemouth, Kinneil, St Fergus and Mossmorran. The initial platform construction yards at Hunterston, Ardyne Point, Kishorn and Ardersier are no longer in use with that at Nigg currently mothballed. The once busy pipeline fabrication centres at Tain and near Wick are now rarely used, although there is an active pipeline fabrication unit at Evanton in the Cromarty Firth.

The impacts that oil and gas activity can have on the marine environment, and therefore on the status of the seas, are:

> The initial construction of the onshore facilities. These impacts would be considered as part of an environmental assessment associated with the consenting regime at the time of construction. The majority of coastal facilities were constructed before the current environmental assessment regime was implemented. The effects of the actual build would probably be short-term in nature although any land reclamation would obviously make long-term physical changes to the coastline.

> The initial construction of the offshore facilities. A strategic environmental assessment (SEA) regime today accompanies each round of new exploration and production licences. Individual assessments are undertaken on the impacts of underwater acoustic releases associated with seismic survey and for all drilling and pipeline operations to be conducted offshore. Drill cuttings derived from operations using water-based muds may be placed on the seabed next to platforms but it should be noted that cuttings from oil-based mud use are no longer released to sea, all being either re-injected into the formation from which they came or returned to shore for processing and disposal.

> During the operational phase the discharge of substances either during normal operations or due to accidental or emergency events may impact upon the marine environment, see case study 3.6. Discharges of operational chemicals are controlled under BERR legislation based on a chemicals risk management system. FRS acts as an adviser to BERR on both the chemical and environmental risk posed by such discharges.

There may be some positive benefits of platform presence because of the creation of safety zones for 500 m around each installation, which restrict access, and because this may stimulate the creation of substrate for corals.

There are no Government targets associated with the oil and gas industry. It is a market-driven economic activity.

The Advisory Committee on Protection of the Sea (ACOPS) prepares an annual report on behalf of the Maritime and Coastguard Agency (MCA), the *Annual survey of reported discharges attributed to vessels and offshore oil and gas installations operating in the UK Pollution control zone 2005*.[16] The survey generates statistics concerning incidents involving discharges of oil, noxious liquid substances and garbage from all types of vessels and offshore oil and gas installations. Figure 5.12 shows the reporting areas used and Tables 5.7 and 5.8 show statistics from 2005.

**Table 5.7   Total pollution incidents associated with marine installations and shipping reported by category and area in 2005**

| Area | Mineral oils | Garbage | Vegetable & animal oils | Chemicals | Other substances | Totals |
|---|---|---|---|---|---|---|
| Western Scotland | 12 | 0 | 0 | 0 | 0 | 12 |
| Orkney & Shetland Islands | 10 | 0 | 0 | 0 | 0 | 10 |
| Eastern Scotland | 26 | 0 | 1 | 0 | 0 | 27 |
| UKCS oil & gas installations | 282 | 0 | 0 | 97 | 4 | 383 |
| UKCS vessels | 24 | 0 | 0 | 2 | 0 | 26 |
| Total | 354 | 0 | 1 | 99 | 4 | 458 |

**Table 5.8   Total incidents and amount of pollution reported by marine environmental area in 2005**

| Area | Open sea | Tidal river/ estuary | Bay/ near shore | Beach/ shore | Port/ harbour | Totals | 1-455 litres | 456-999 litres | 1-50 tonnes | > 50 tonnes | Not known |
|---|---|---|---|---|---|---|---|---|---|---|---|
| Western Scotland | 0 | 0 | 4 | 0 | 8 | 12 | 10 | 1 | 1 | 0 | 0 |
| Orkney & Shetland Islands | 3 | 0 | 1 | 0 | 6 | 10 | 7 | 0 | 1 | 1 | 1 |
| Eastern Scotland | 5 | 0 | 2 | 1 | 19 | 27 | 21 | 0 | 6 | 0 | 0 |
| UKCS oil & gas installations | 383 | 0 | 0 | 0 | 0 | 383 | 301 | 23 | 37 | 0 | 22 |
| UKCS vessels | 26 | 0 | 0 | 0 | 0 | 26 | 11 | 2 | 5 | 0 | 8 |
| Total | 417 | 0 | 7 | 1 | 33 | 458 | 350 | 26 | 50 | 1 | 31 |

## Figure 5.12 Areas used by ACOPS to report discharges from vessels or oil and gas installations

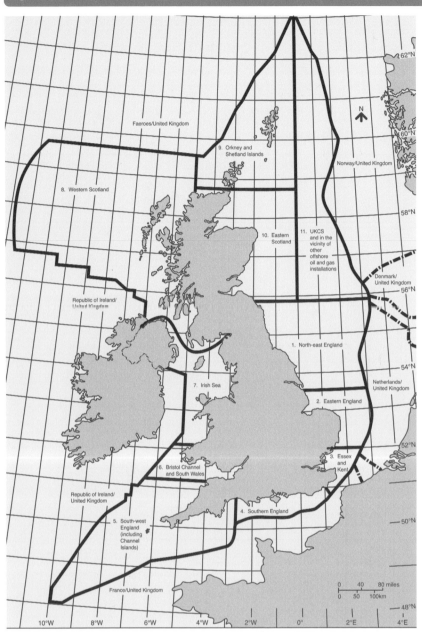

### Summary Assessment

| Parameter | Geographical region | Key factors & pressures | What the evidence shows | Trend | Status now | Confidence in assessment | Reason for overall status |
|---|---|---|---|---|---|---|---|
| Economic value of oil and gas industry | Continental shelf mainly beyond 12 nautical miles offshore | Global demand for oil and gas | A productive industry but some uncertainty about its value to Scotland even though most of the UK industry occurs on Continental Shelf adjacent to Scotland | √ | ■ | III | High level of historical investment; high national strategic importance; buoyant world market |
| Frequency and size of pollution incidents | Continental shelf mainly beyond 12 nautical miles offshore | High level of activity; aging infrastructure | Frequent though local and relatively small incidents | ↔ | ■ | III | Closely monitored and highly regulated |

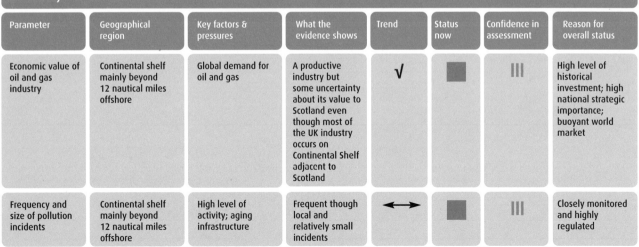

## Ports

There are over 100 ports in Scotland ranging from very small to those with major facilities. They include:

> large oil and gas terminals, e.g. Hound Point (Firth of Forth), Sullom Voe (Shetland), Flotta (Scapa Flow, Orkney);

> large quarry product port - Glensanda;

> large fishing ports, e.g. Peterhead, Fraserburgh;

> smaller fishing ports, e.g. Buckie, Mallaig;

> oil supply ports, e.g. Aberdeen (Figure 5.13), Cromarty Firth;

> multi-purpose ports, e.g. Leith, Clyde;

> large container ports - Grangemouth;

> major ferry ports serving Ireland and Europe – Cairnryan, Stranraer and Rosyth - as well as lifeline ferry services within Scotland;

> "marine Works" serving as pier heads for ferry services to Scotland's islands and for working boats associated with fish farm installations; and

> marina facilities, e.g. Fairlie, Craobh Haven, Port Edgar.

Eleven Scottish ports are classified by the Department for Transport under the EC Maritime Statistics Directive as major ports (generally because they handled at least 1 million tonnes (Mt), of cargo in 2001). These are: Forth (31.5 Mt in 2006), Sullom Voe (Shetland) (19.4 Mt), Clyde (14.9 Mt), Orkney (11.2 Mt), Glensanda (6 Mt), Aberdeen (4.6 Mt), Cromarty Firth (3.2 Mt), Cairnryan (3.1 Mt), Dundee (1.2 Mt), Stranraer (1.2 Mt) and Peterhead (0.9 Mt). Total cargo handled for all Scottish ports in 2006 was 101.5 Mt.

Some of the traffic flows between ports and the imports and export figures are shown in Table 5.9.

### Figure 5.13   Aberdeen oil base

### Table 5.9   Total traffic in Scottish ports in 2006

| Type of traffic | Volume (Mt) | | Type of traffic |
| --- | --- | --- | --- |
| | Exports | Imports | |
| "Coastwise" traffic to other ports in the UK (including Scotland) | 20.6 | 7.8 | "Coastwise" freight discharged in Scotland (including freight from elsewhere in Scotland) |
| "One port" traffic to offshore installations | 1.5 | 8.3 | "One port" traffic (nearly all from oil platforms) was discharged in Scotland |
| Exports from major Scottish ports | 44.0 | 17.9 | Imports at major Scottish ports |
| Freight lifted by water transport in Scotland - main categories | 66.1 | 34.0 | Freight landed by water transport in Scotland - main categories |

Source: *Scottish Transport Statistics No.26 2007 edition*, Scottish Government

The main types of cargo handled by the Scottish major ports in 2006 were crude oil (53.3 Mt), oil products (9.2 Mt), coal (10.9 Mt), "other dry bulk" (7.7 Mt) and liquefied gas (3.2 Mt).

Passenger traffic is also important. In 2006, 2 million passengers were carried between Scotland and Northern Ireland, the busiest port being Stranraer (1.2 million passengers). 112,000 passengers travelled between Rosyth and Belgium (Zeebrugge). In addition, around 8.1 million passengers were carried on internal Scottish ferry services (Cal Mac 5.4 million, Northlink 0.3 million, Orkney Ferries 0.3 million, Shetland Council 0.8 million, Western Ferries 1.3 million).

A new system for collecting detailed port traffic statistics was launched in 2000 to comply with the requirements of the EC Maritime Statistics Directive. Details can be found in the Department for Transport's publication, "Maritime Statistics" which can be found on the DfT Web site[17]. In terms of the economic activity of ports, no targets are set by Government or collectively by the industry. Market forces and commercial considerations will determine such activity, within the context of the legislative framework within which ports operate, which includes environmental responsibilities.

The main impacts that ports and shipping can have on the marine environment and therefore on the status of the seas are:

> The construction of the port facilities. These impacts are considered as part of an environmental assessment associated with the consenting regime at the time of construction. It is usually expected that any environmental effects of the actual construction would be short-term in nature. In future, hydromorphological effects will also be considered as part of WFD requirements.

> The discharge of substances from shipping either accidentally during normal operations or due to emergency events (see Tables 5.7 and 5.8).

> The disposal of dredged material removed from navigation channels, berths and turning channels to keep ports operational. All such disposal requires a licence under Part II of the Food and Environment Protection Act (FEPA) 1985 which is managed by FRS. The figures for amounts of dredged material disposed in 2006 are in Table 5.10. Most disposal takes place on the east coast. Historically, sediment concentrations of trace metals and polychlorinated biphenyls (PCBs) show values that do not preclude the sea disposal of dredged material. The list of contaminants used to assess the suitability of sediment for sea disposal has now been increased to include polycyclic aromatic hydrocarbons (PAHs) and tributyl tin (TBT). As part of its ongoing environmental monitoring programme, FRS samples disposal sites on a regular basis for the presence of heavy metals, PAHs, TBT and PCBs. To date, results have shown that average contaminant concentrations fall below thresholds recommended by Government[18,19] Therefore future disposal operations at these sites are possible, provided the quantity, quality and type of dredged material is consistent with previous disposal operations.

| Table 5.10   Dredge spoil disposal in 2006 (wet tonnes) | | | |
|---|---|---|---|
| Area of Dredging | Licensed Tonnage | Tonnes Disposed | Reporting Area |
| Girvan, Ayr, Troon, Glasgow, Greenock & Hunterston | 1,569,573 | 244,846 | Clyde |
| Bruichladdich, Port Ellen & Ullapool | 29,330 | 24,116 | Minches & Malin Sea |
| Foula | 1,750 | 1,750 | West Shetland |
| Burghead, Buckie, Findochty, Portknockie & Macduff | 169,649 | 43,535 | Moray Firth |
| Aberdeen, Montrose, Arbroath, Dundee & Berwick | 688,755 | 302,463 | East Scotland Coast |
| Upper Forth Crossing, Kincardine, Grangemouth, RNAD Crombie, Rosyth, Royal Forth Yacht Club & Leith | 4,739,699 | 1,087,908 | Forth |
| TOTAL | 7,198,756 | 1,704,618 | |

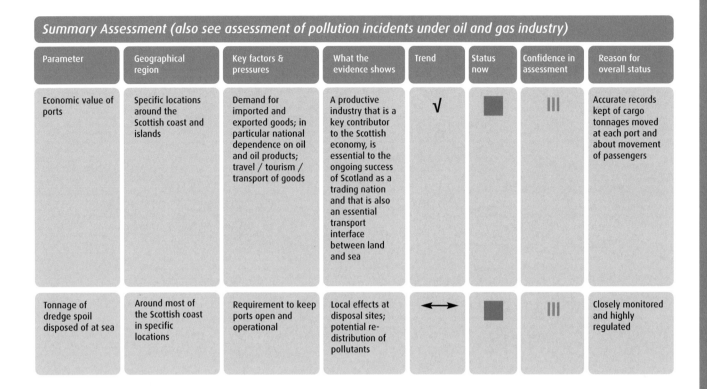

## Summary Assessment (also see assessment of pollution incidents under oil and gas industry)

| Parameter | Geographical region | Key factors & pressures | What the evidence shows | Trend | Status now | Confidence in assessment | Reason for overall status |
|---|---|---|---|---|---|---|---|
| Economic value of ports | Specific locations around the Scottish coast and islands | Demand for imported and exported goods; in particular national dependence on oil and oil products; travel / tourism / transport of goods | A productive industry that is a key contributor to the Scottish economy, is essential to the ongoing success of Scotland as a trading nation and that is also an essential transport interface between land and sea | √ | ■ | III | Accurate records kept of cargo tonnages moved at each port and about movement of passengers |
| Tonnage of dredge spoil disposed of at sea | Around most of the Scottish coast in specific locations | Requirement to keep ports open and operational | Local effects at disposal sites; potential re-distribution of pollutants | ↔ | ■ | III | Closely monitored and highly regulated |

### Aggregate extraction

Aggregate extraction is the process of taking sand and gravel from the seabed for the making of concrete or for providing sand for land reclamation. Traditionally the industry has been very small in Scotland due to an adequate land supply and lack of suitable and easily accessible resources on the seabed. Two licensed production areas exist; one of which lies in the Firth of Forth for the extraction of up to 6,000,000 m³ over 10 years. In 2005, 129,387 tonnes (86,260 m³) was removed to supply infill material for the Leith Western Dock Reclamation Project. This is the only extraction to date. A second area exists in the Firth of Tay (East Scotland Coast) and although this region has not been used for several years it could supply 66,000 m³ *per* year. The

Crown Estate publishes an annual report of aggregate extraction around the UK[20].

Aggregate dredging activity is subject to the approval of the Scottish Government who will require compliance conditions and that an Electronic Monitoring System is used to monitor the location of dredging. Further monitoring of the physical (sediment plume and bathymetry of the seabed), chemical (seabed sediment chemistry) and biological (benthic habitats and species; commercial fisheries; seabirds) effects of dredging also take place.

There are no Government targets for marine aggregate extraction.

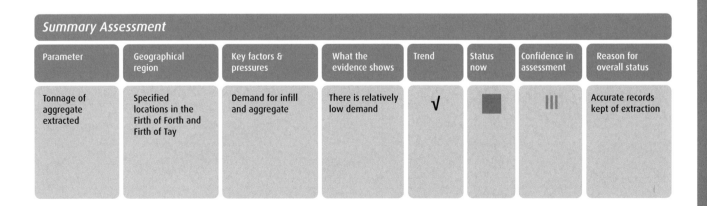

## Summary Assessment

| Parameter | Geographical region | Key factors & pressures | What the evidence shows | Trend | Status now | Confidence in assessment | Reason for overall status |
|---|---|---|---|---|---|---|---|
| Tonnage of aggregate extracted | Specified locations in the Firth of Forth and Firth of Tay | Demand for infill and aggregate | There is relatively low demand | √ | ■ | III | Accurate records kept of extraction |

### Leisure, recreation and the historic heritage

Leisure, recreation and Scotland's historic heritage are important parts of our economy. Scotland has a magnificent coastline and it is used widely for leisure and recreational pursuits including coastal footpaths (Figure 5.14). To estimate the value of all this activity to the economy and assess a measure of productivity is not easily achieved. Economic and employment statistics for coastal tourism, for instance, are not separated out in the wider tourism statistics. In the same way, figures are not centrally available for the overall value of marinas or moorings to the economy. Cruise ship visits to the Scottish coast have been increasing in recent years but the value of these visits is not identifiable.

However, specific studies at a local scale provide an indication of the economic value of particular sectors. For example, the coastal and underwater natural heritage attracts visitors and recreational divers to areas such as Orkney. Recreational diving has been calculated to contribute more than £1.5 million to the local economy of Orkney (see Table 5.12). See Case Study 5.4.

The Firth of Clyde and the west coast lochs are popular sailing destinations with a number of established marinas. New marinas have emerged in recent years on the east coast as small fishing harbours look to diversity and satisfy a growing demand.

The British Marine Federation (BMF) publishes key performance indicators for the UK leisure and small commercial marine industry. In its 2006/2007 report[21] (published January 2008 and updating earlier work) it estimates the total UK industry revenue to be £2,952 million, with a Value Added of £1,053 million (35.7% of turnover) with Scotland's share being £98.9 million (3.4% of the UK) and VA £35.3 million, quite significant figures. The report also estimates full-time equivalent employment to be 1,816 for Scotland. Scotland

may be able to generate more revenues in this sector and it may be currently underexploited.

In 2006, a report[22] for Scottish Enterprise and Highlands & Islands Enterprise which investigated the potential for future development in the Clyde Estuary said that **"Scotland is hailed as one of the top six sailing destinations in the world ... The main reasons given for sailing in the Clyde are scenery, safe waters, islands, uncrowded areas and the quality of the sailing"**. The report also concluded that "it would not be unreasonable to use a figure of £250 million as a conservative estimate of the current total economic value of the marine leisure industry to Scotland".

Recreational use of Scotland's seas is not without environmental impacts. Surveys of Loch Creran have identified damage on the seabed reefs. However, a management initiative to bring stakeholders together and develop good practice is set to address the problems (see Case Study 5.5).

### Figure 5.14    Coastal footpath signpost

## Summary Assessment

| Parameter | Geographical region | Key factors & pressures | What the evidence shows | Trend | Status now | Confidence in assessment | Reason for overall status |
|---|---|---|---|---|---|---|---|
| Economic value of marine leisure activities | Scottish continental shelf but mainly within firths, and sea lochs | Highly regarded for scenery and safe waters | A healthy and expanding industry | √ | ■ | ‖ | Data for Scotland as a whole are poor but local and general assessments are very positive |

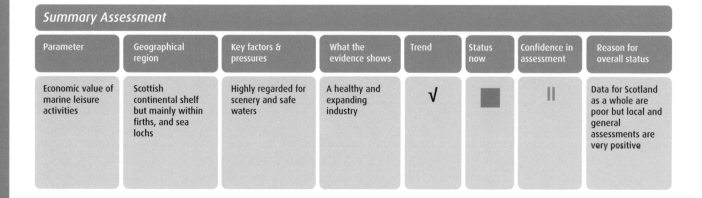

## CASE STUDY 5.4    Coastal and marine historic heritage

Scotland's coasts and seas have provided a source of food and energy, a means of defence from invasion, and a springboard for trade and communication between neighbouring communities and across oceans. The material remains of this historical association with the sea can be found at the coast edge and far out to sea.

Since the last Ice Age, the coast edge and sea bed have undergone constant change which continues to this day. For example, once-terrestrial sites may now be submerged; once-marine sites may now be on land. Fish-traps and crannogs in the intertidal zone experience cyclical inundation and exposure by tides, while lighthouses and harbours extend from dry land into the sea.

The wrecks of ships and aircraft, sometimes far offshore, are part of a wider maritime cultural landscape that may extend inland. For shipwrecks, this might encompass the yards where they were built, the ports they served, the lighthouses they passed, and the routes they crossed.

About 30% of the coast and foreshore has been surveyed as part of Historic Scotland's Coastal Zone Assessment programme[23] (Table 5.11). Extrapolation suggests about 38,000 historic buildings and monuments spanning 9,000 years of human activity lie close to our coasts. Underwater, 15 of the most important historic wreck sites so far discovered have statutory protection by law (Figure 5.15).

**Table 5.11    Royal Commission on the Ancient and Historic Monuments of Scotland (RCAHMS) maritime records (correct to April 2006), and Historic Scotland statistics on sub-tidal scheduled/designated marine historic assets**

| Headline indicator | Number |
|---|---|
| Total number of RCAHMS maritime records[D] | 12,049 |
| Identified sites where demonstrable remains have been identified | 1,425 |
| Historical references of a casualty at sea, some with only a vague location identifier | 10,223 |
| Recorded seabed obstructions (e.g. fishermens' net fastenings or other obstructions) | 297 |
| Aircraft | 61 |
| Numbers of subtidal marine historic assets with statutory protection[E] | 15 |
| Scheduled under the Ancient Monuments and Archaeological Areas Act 1979 | 2 monuments comprising 7 wrecks |
| Designated under the Protection of Wrecks Act 1973 | 8 |

Source: www.pastmap.org

## Figure 5.16    Multi-beam sonar image of SMS *Koln*, Scapa Flow, Orkney Islands

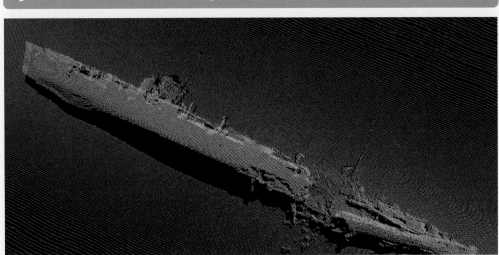

Scotland's marine historic environment has a positive contribution to make to the economic, social and cultural fabric of today's Scotland whether by direct visitor enjoyment of the remaining wrecks of the German High Seas Fleet scuttled in Scapa Flow in 1919 (Figure 5.16), or simply by understanding that remains dating the earliest recorded human occupation may be found at the coast edge (Figure 5.17) or further offshore.

Historic Scotland's recent review of existing information provides possible headline indicators for the historic environment as a whole[24]. Its 14 staffed coastal and maritime properties in care attracted over 310,000 visitors and generated on-site income of £1.4 million in 2006/7, with indirect local employment and income benefits. Skara Brae, the most complete Neolithic village in NW Europe and part of a World Heritage Site, attracts over 60,000 visitors per year. There are few published figures of the 'economic value' of the subtidal heritage. However, shipwrecks are a significant attraction for many of the 6,000 or more recreational divers based in Scotland, and thousands more who visit from further afield[25]. Table 5.12 indicates their contribution to the economy of the Orkney Islands.

Historic assets on the seabed introduce both positive and negative effects on the marine environment. Wrecks can act as artificial reefs supporting diverse communities of marine wildlife. Conversely, in some cases there is a risk of oil leakage such as that from HMS *Royal Oak* in the Orkney Islands, which is subject to routine monitoring.

Sea level rise and increased storminess threaten the integrity of numerous coastal sites such as Skara Brae[F]. Our marine historic assets are similarly susceptible to the effects of wave and tidal energy, and factors such as seabed sediment type, slope of seabed, water salinity and acidity/alkalinity, and levels of oxygenation. Marine historic assets can be at risk too from human activities such as construction projects, cable laying, salvage, dredging and fishing.

Techniques to investigate underwater sites remain in their infancy and less is known about marine historic assets than those on land. This is particularly true for submerged landscapes for which there is considerable potential, notably around the Western and Northern Isles. The majority of 'maritime records' relate to losses of ships but with no known seabed location. Enhancement of this knowledge base would greatly facilitate efforts to safeguard Scotland's most important marine historic assets.

### Table 5.12   Economic figures for Orkney Islands

| Subject | Headline Indicator | Value |
|---|---|---|
| Visitor access | • Numbers of visitors to the scheduled German Fleet wrecks in Scapa Flow each year<br>• Numbers of dives on the scheduled wrecks in 2006 | 2,500-3,500<br><br>14,415 |
| Contribution to economy | • Numbers of jobs directly connected with historic wreck tourism in Orkney<br>• Contribution by divers to the Orkney economy | >20<br>8% of tourist revenue to Orkney |

Source: Forbes, 2003 ScapaMap 2000-2002; Forbes, 2008, ScapaMap 2001-2006. Copies archived with RCAHMS, 16 Bernard Terrace, Edinburgh EH8 9NX.

### Summary Assessment

| Parameter | Geographical region | Key factors & pressures | What the evidence shows | Trend | Status now | Confidence in assessment | Reason for overall status |
|---|---|---|---|---|---|---|---|
| Condition of historic environment | Coast edge and foreshore | Coastal erosion and development pressure | Numerous sites/areas at risk | X | ▲ | III | 30% sample biased towards known high-risk areas |
| Knowledge of marine historic environment | Sub-tidal zones | Shortage of quality data and/or access to it | Potential for submerged terrestrial sites in places, numerous wrecks of ships, aircraft and associated sites | ? | ● | I | The existing record is an indicator of seabed archaeology; only a very few sites have been recorded in detail |

**Figure 5.15    Scheduled wrecks and designated sites in Scottish waters**

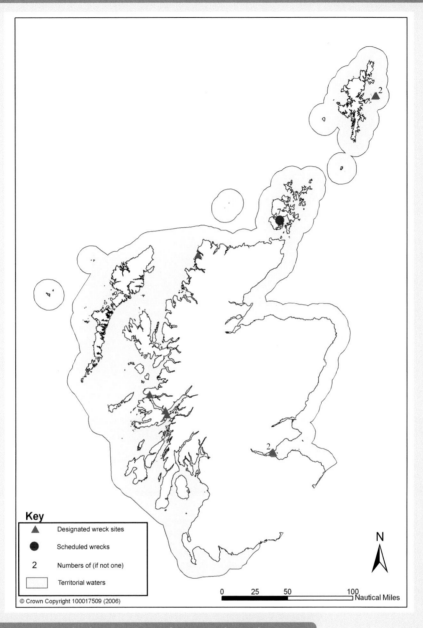

Key

▲    Designated wreck sites

●    Scheduled wrecks

2    Numbers of (if not one)

☐    Territorial waters

© Crown Copyright 100017509 (2006)

N

0    25    50    100
Nautical Miles

**Figure 5.17    Late Bronze Age logboat recovered in 2006 from the Tay Estuary**

Loch Creran is a relatively small but important loch in Argyll which has many economic activities occurring within it (e.g. fish and shellfish farming, fishing, recreation/marinas, ferry terminal for coastal quarry, local marine industry). Scientists from various institutes, including Heriot-Watt University and SAMS, have carried out numerous studies in the loch. The data produced has helped to justify the designation of the area as a marine SAC and to guide its management.

The presence of spectacular but fragile serpulid reefs (Figure 5.18) was one of the principal reasons for Loch Creran being designated as a marine SAC under the EC Habitats Directive (92/43/EEC) in 2005. Serpulid reefs have also been identified as a priority habitat by the UK Government's Biodiversity Action Plan (UK action under the UN Convention on Biological Diversity) and are on the Scottish Biodiversity List. In UK waters only *Serpula vermicularis* L. is known to form extensive subtidal reefs. Such reefs were reported to occur in Loch Sween, Scotland in 1975 although a number of subsequent unpublished surveys have revealed that only dead reef fragments now remain.

The only published records confirming the presence of living *S. vermicularis* reefs in the UK are for Loch Creran, Scotland[26-32], although in 2006 an area supporting a large number of smaller patches was discovered in Loch Teacuis, mid-west Scotland. Other known locations of these rare biogenic *S. vermicularis* reefs include Ardbear Lough and Killary Harbour in Ireland and Mar Piccolo di Taranto, Italy[33] although the reefs in Loch Creran are by far the most extensive.

Careful management is required to support all of Loch Creran's competing economic activities, and to maintain its biological health and conservation status. The Argyll Marine SACs Management Forum, coordinated by Argyll and Bute Council, was established in 2003 and includes representatives of all stakeholders, with independent scientific advice provided by Heriot Watt University and SAMS. Notable successes of the management process include the production of a Private and Commercial Moorings Pack and an anchoring leaflet to ensure that moorings and anchors are placed where they will not damage serpulid reef (Figure 5.19). In addition, zoning of fishing activities to protect the serpulid reefs and horse mussel beds has been achieved through the Inshore Fishing (Prohibited Methods of Fishing) (Loch Creran) Order 2007: SSI No. 185.

### Figure 5.18 A typical ovoid-shaped patch reef of *Serpula vermicularis*

### Figure 5.19 Dense reef rubble resulting from mooring damage

### Summary Assessment

| Parameter | Geographical region | Key factors & pressures | What the evidence shows | Trend | Status now | Confidence in assessment | Reason for overall status |
|---|---|---|---|---|---|---|---|
| Conservation Status of Biogenic Reefs | Loch Creran, Argyll & Bute | Fish dredging and vessel mooring | Limited damage to fragile reefs but now protected | √ | ▪ | III | Sufficient available, quality assured data |

## Marine renewable energy industry

Scotland has one of the best environments anywhere in the world for generating offshore renewable energy. The northern and western coastlines, and island areas, offer huge opportunities for the generation of wave and tidal energy. The eastern coast and further offshore provide strong offshore wind potential. It is not surprising that attempts are being made to harness this abundant renewable resource. At present there is a small number of offshore renewable energy installations in this emerging area but technology and projects are evolving quickly. Existing projects in Scotland include:

> Beatrice offshore wind demonstrator – Part of the DOWNViND project, this demonstrator has located wind turbines 25km from the Scottish shoreline and is the world's deepest offshore wind project. The 2 wind turbines with a capacity of 10 MW, power the Beatrice oil platform in Moray Firth (Figure 5.20).

> European Marine Energy Centre (Orkney) – EMEC provides custom test facilities for the wave and tidal energy sector. The Centre has four wave energy berths and five tidal energy berths. Several devices have already been tested at EMEC with more expected through 2008.

> LIMPET is a shoreline wave energy generator located on Islay. It produces electricity which is supplied to the National Grid and was the world's first commercial-scale wave energy device that generates wave energy for the grid.

Construction has started on the Robin Rigg Offshore wind farm in the Solway Firth. This will have a capacity of 216 MW. A small number of projects are at the planning stage including the Siadar Wave Energy Scheme, a 4 MW active breakwater device proposed for Siadar in Lewis and the Aberdeen offshore wind farm, a 165 MW proposal.

The environmental impact of renewable energy installations is considered as part of the initial consenting regime. In addition, there is a requirement for ongoing pre- and post-construction environmental monitoring, an example of this is the Robin Rigg Monitoring Group. Data on the level of production, economic activity and number of people employed are not currently collected. Figures are included as part of the overall energy sector.

In November 2007 the Scottish Government announced an increase in renewable electricity targets. Ministers want 31% of Scotland's electricity to come from renewable sources by 2011, and they have set a target of 50%, up from 40%, of all electricity from renewables by 2020[34]. Ministers are also committed to seeing 10 MW of wave and tidal energy deployed by 2010[35]. In addition, an SEA[36,37] for wave and tidal energy has identified what some of the likely environmental impacts of marine energy will be. Further work on environmental impact and locational guidance will be taken forward in response to the SEA.

### Figure 5.20 Beatrice offshore wind demonstrator

### Summary Assessment

| Parameter | Geographical region | Key factors & pressures | What the evidence shows | Trend | Status now | Confidence in assessment | Reason for overall status |
|---|---|---|---|---|---|---|---|
| Megawatts of power; number of experimental power generation systems tested | Wind and wave: Offshore around most of the Scottish coast<br><br>Tidal: specific sites | Government targets to achieve targets for renewable energy | High level of activity in the development and installation of new capacity | √ | | III | Technological challenges remain. Uncertain environmental effects. |

### Other activities

There are a number of other activities that take place in the coastal and marine environment and contribute to the marine economy of Scotland. To develop a comprehensive assessment of the productivity of Scotland's seas requires them all to be considered. The next section briefly describes what could be included. All of these will be considered further to determine how much can be included in the 2010 report.

**Ship and boat building and repairs** – the once large industry for which Scotland was famous and the term Clyde Built meant quality, is now a shadow of its former self. However, a number of shipyards remain that provide important economic activity. The Input-Output approach includes some details of this sector.

**Shipping operations, navigation and safety** – this could include Scottish seafarers, value of Scottish shipping company operations and the work of various safety organisations in Scotland, although many of these are not Scottish-based.

**Construction industry** – construction projects such as port extensions, new jetties, coastal defence and coastal flood protection work and building of offshore renewable energy projects are economic activities that are marine-based. However, economic details of such, usually one-off, projects are not collected. Their ongoing value to the Scottish economy would be included in the statistics for the main activity, for example, ports.

**Telecommunications industry** – the Scottish seabed is covered by a large network of both inter-island (domestic) and transcontinental (international) telecommunication cables. Marine economic activity is created during the laying operations of the cable laying ships. It is uncertain as to how much of the economic value of the traffic that passes through such cables could be attributed to the value of the marine economy.

**Defence** – the Ministry of Defence has a number of large Scottish coastal bases. These will have a local economic value that could be attributed to the marine economy, since without the sea the bases would not exist.

**Business services** – these usually include activities such as ship finance, ship broking and chartering. The extent of these in Scotland has not been investigated for this report.

**Licence and rental** – a payment is usually made for development activity on the foreshore and the seabed to its owner, whether this is the Crown Estate (the largest such owner) or one of the many other owners. This creates economic value but has not been included in this report.

**Marine research and development and education** – Scotland has some world class centres which create economic value which has not been investigated for this report.

**Marine environment** – this could include the operation of coastal waste water treatments plants, in future the decommissioning of oil and gas platforms and the work of Scotland's environmental organisations such as FRS, SEPA and SNH.

### WHAT GAPS ARE THERE IN OUR KNOWLEDGE?

Assessing whether the seas are productive requires a comparison between current levels of production and agreed target levels. It is apparent that except for fishery quotas, which are a form of target, targets are not set for human activities. It is normal that activity responds to market forces. As such, this initial assessment has many gaps, in particular assessing "are the seas being productive enough?". Equally, the various sectors have responsibility for their own statistics of levels of activity that have been collected in a similar way for many years. Comparing sector by sector is therefore not possible and also raises the question "would it be appropriate to do so anyway?".

Currently statistics are collected based on a variety of geographical areas, compare the fisheries catch statistics with the ACOPS oil spill figures for example. If an integrated assessment of the seas is to report on the basis of the areas in chapter 1, then a method is needed to reconcile the various reporting mechanisms.

Another gap is the difficulty in identifying the economic value of the seas to Scotland. This assessment has included in the Input-Output Table approach, figures derived from government economic statistics. Individual industries may not always agree that this gives a full assessment of their particular industry.

Detailed knowledge of the impact of some sectors on the marine environment remains a gap as is the lack of contribution to this report from the many sectors identified. To give a comprehensive overview of both the economic benefits and the environmental impacts of the various activities, a wide engagement will be required with industry for the *State of Scotland's Seas* in 2010.

### CONCLUSION

There is little doubt that Scotland's seas are productive. In 2006 379,200 tonnes of live fish worth £368.5 million was landed, about 150,000 tonnes of salmon and shellfish farmed worth about £280 million; a significant share of the UK's 70 million tonnes of oil and 84 million cubic metres of gas produced in waters off Scotland; a total cargo of 101.5 million tonnes handled at all Scottish ports and about 10 million passengers carried on ferries. Analysis of the Scottish Government Input-Output tables show that in 2004, the total value to the Scottish economy of the identified marine related industries was estimated to be £2.2 billion and employing around 50,000 full time equivalent employees. This represents 2.6% of the total Scottish GVA (£83 billion) and 2.4% of total Scottish full time equivalent employment (around 2 million). Overall, all these figures demonstrate productivity but not a measure of 'how productive Scotland's seas could be' nor indeed 'whether this level of productivity is sustainable'. In addition, there was much activity at the coast with many visitors to historical sites and a new renewable energy industry emerging. There are also many activities, such as ship and boat building that this report has not investigated. Data about the impacts of some activities have been identified, for example aquaculture, and the number of spills from shipping and oil activity is carefully monitored (458 in 2005) but from the case study in Chapter 3 the impact of oil production is shown to be limited. Scotland has many active ports but only 1.7 million tonnes of dredge spoil deposited in 2006. Moorings can have damaging effects as the photograph in case study 5.2 shows but management arrangements can be put in place to mitigate this for the future.

# Chapter 6
# Assessment of Climate Change Impacts on Scottish Seas

## INTRODUCTION

Research and advice on climate change in the marine environment can be divided into two areas. The first is **observation of past change** and research to understand how it has affected the marine environment. The second is **prediction of future change** which can then be used for management planning and mitigation.

In 2007, the Intergovernmental Panel on Climate Change (IPCC) published their fourth assessment report[1], presenting strong evidence that anthropogenic inputs of greenhouse gases to the atmosphere are the most likely cause of the observed average increase in global temperatures over the last 100 years. Global atmosphere and oceans have warmed at a rate of 0.07°C per decade[1] over the past 100 years and the warming has also been observed to have accelerated over the last decade, a trend which is particularly apparent in sea-surface temperatures.

Although the long-term global average trend is one of warming, there is considerable regional and temporal variability and there are also changes in other parameters. For this reason the term Global Climate Change is used rather than Global Warming to describe these effects.

The recent, since approximately the early 1990s, accelerated rise in global average temperature is more rapid than predicted by climate models[2]. At the same time there has also been a more rapid than predicted rise in global mean sea-level. The reasons for the recent more rapid warming are as yet difficult to determine. It is possible that they can be attributed to natural variability in the climate system added on top of the effects of Global Climate Change. Another possibility is that the climate models underestimated the future rate of warming.

As will be explained in this chapter, the waters around Scotland are strongly influenced by Global Climate Change and also show natural variability. The term Atlantic Multi-decadal Oscillation (AMO) is often used to describe the long-term pattern of change evident in both the atmosphere and the North Atlantic Ocean. It is also clear that there is a complex relationship between Global Climate Change and the Meridional Overturning Circulation (MOC; see Chapter 2) which is not yet fully understood.

## OBSERVED CHANGES IN OCEAN CLIMATE IN SCOTTISH WATERS

### Changes in temperature

Regional effects mean that changes observed at a local level, which includes scales equivalent to Scottish waters, are likely to be different to the global average. In fact, the observed warming in Scottish waters since the early 1990s has been more rapid than the global and northern hemisphere averages (see below).

Data on climate trends in the waters around Scotland are gathered by a number of institutes and summarised in the *Scottish Ocean Climate Status Report* published by FRS[3]. For the purpose of this report, data from the longest datasets (those extending further than 10 years) are summarised here.

FRS maintains a network of coastal temperature monitoring stations around the coast of Scotland (Figure 6.1) and at three of these sites (Millport, Fair Isle and Peterhead) data have been collected for more than 25 years. Researchers at SAMS maintain a mooring in the Tiree Passage recording temperature, salinity and flow variability data in waters on the west coast of Scotland (see Case Study 2.1).

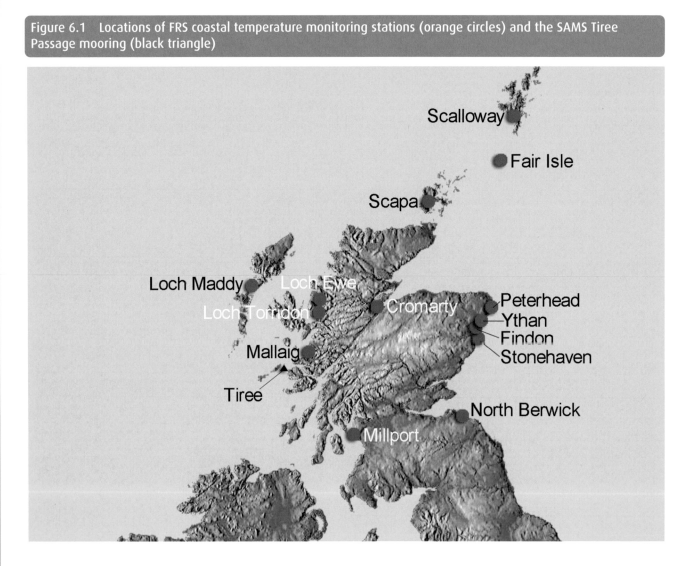

FRS also surveys three offshore sections, two across the Faroe-Shetland Channel (Figure 6.2; also see Figure 2.1) and a third in the North Sea, extending eastward from Orkney (the JONSIS Line). The measurements of temperature and salinity in the Faroe-Shetland Channel date back to 1893 and are one of the longest oceanographic time-series in the world.

Since 1975, researchers at SAMS and the National Oceanography Centre Southampton (NOCS) have measured temperature and salinity on a short section (the Ellett Line) across the Rockall Trough, a deep ocean basin to the west of Scotland (Figure 6.2, also see Figure 2.1). Since 1996 SAMS and NOCS have been occupying an extended version of the Ellett Line that runs all the way to Iceland. The Extended Ellett Line is important oceanographically because it completes the measurements of the warm salty water flowing into the Nordic Seas from the eastern North Atlantic. It also measures around half of the returning deep and cold current, the overflow water, the rest returning to

the Atlantic via the Denmark Strait which is west of Iceland.

Since the end of the 1980s, the temperature of oceanic water flowing past Scotland has increased at a rate of between 0.22-0.40°C per decade, with a longer-term (1990-2006) trend of around 0.04°C (Figure 6.3a). These changes observed in Scottish waters are similar, both in their patterns of variability and long term trends, to those observed in the wider North Sea and north-eastern Atlantic[4]. For all the offshore sites, temperatures observed in 2003-2004 were the warmest on record, with 2006 being the second highest on record (Figure 6.3). The temperature data from all monitoring sites show an overall warming trend since the late 1980s. The variability in coastal waters is higher than that observed in oceanic waters and more closely coupled to atmospheric effects, and the warming trend is generally higher than observed further offshore (Figure 6.3d).

## Figure 6.2   Offshore long-term hydrographic sections in Scottish waters

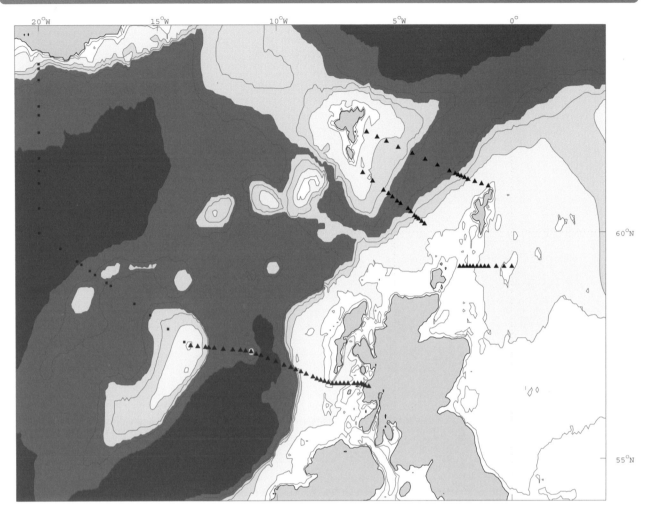

Red triangles (▲) in the Faroe-Shetland Channel (also see Figure 2.1) and East of Orkney (JONSIS Line) are occupied 3 times per year by FRS. Blue triangles (▲) indicate the Ellett Line occupied at least once per year by SAMS/NOCS. Blue squares (■) indicate the Extended Ellett Line started in 1996. Contours are at 50, 100, 250, 500, 1,000, 2,000 and 3,000 m.

Although the changes observed since 1980 have been marked, they must be considered in context with longer-term variability. There is evidence that across the North Atlantic a warmer period between 1930 and 1960 was followed by a cooler period between 1960 and 1980[5]. These warmer and cooler periods can be observed in the oceanic water flowing past Scotland (Figure 6.3a) and are likely to be related to the long-term pattern of variability in the North Atlantic, known as the AMO.

## Figure 6.3 Variability of temperature and salinity in Scottish waters

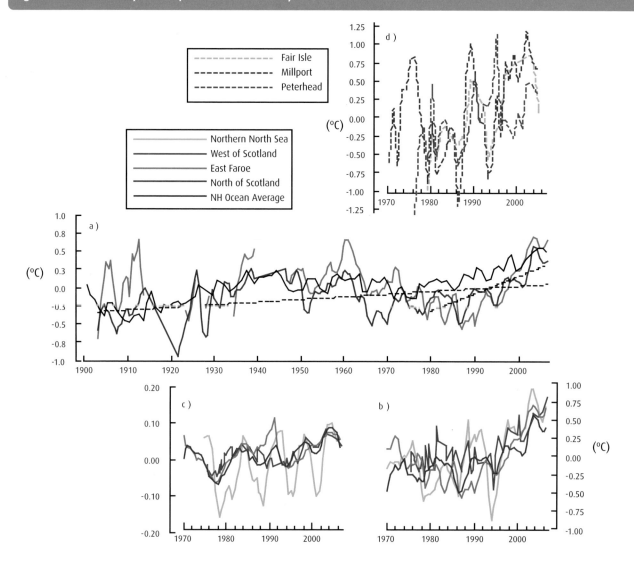

a) long-term (1900-2006) variability in oceanic temperatures to the north of Scotland and east of Faroe[3]. To compare the long-term variability in Scottish oceanic waters with wider-scale trends, the Northern Hemisphere (NH) Ocean Average temperature time series, as collated by the National Ocean and Atmospheric Administration, is included. Dashed lines show the linear trend from 1980-2006 (0.24°C per decade) and from 1900-2006 (0.04°C per decade).

b) variability in oceanic temperatures (1970-2006) to the north of Scotland, east of Faroe, west of Scotland and the northern North Sea[3].

c) variability in salinity (1970-2006) to the north of Scotland, east of Faroe, west of Scotland and the northern North Sea[3].

d) variability in surface temperature of coastal waters around Scotland.

To focus on long-term variability, the mean conditions, and where necessary the seasonal cycle, have been removed. The data are therefore presented as anomalies, which are the difference from the long-term mean after the seasonal trends have been removed.

### Changes in salinity

The salinity data also show clear evidence of decadal and longer-term variability. Alternating salty and fresh periods are closely associated with changes in the wider circulation patterns in the North Atlantic. The freshwater content of the whole North Atlantic has decreased over the last 50 years (1955-2006) leading to an increase in salinity in the upper layers[6]. This trend to higher salinity is clearly seen in the offshore salinity data (Figure 6.3c). In the North Sea, the variability in salinity is much larger than in offshore regions. This is because at a local level salinity is affected both by influx of water from the North Atlantic and also from freshwater inputs (rivers and rainfall). Over the wider North Sea, it is more difficult to determine a clear trend in salinity[3] (Figure 6.3c).

All of the offshore temperature and salinity data also show strong evidence of concurrent variability over the shorter periods (decadal scale). This variability is likely to be related both to changes in oceanic circulation and atmospheric conditions over the North Atlantic. As Scotland's weather is strongly influenced by Atlantic pressure patterns, the North Atlantic Oscillation index (NAO), which provides a simple measure of changes in Atlantic pressure differences, has in the past been used to explain this variability. However, the NAO has, since the end of the 1990s, been weak and variable as the dominant pattern of atmospheric pressure across the North Atlantic has not been that of a typical NAO pattern.

*Changes in sea-level*
Sea-level rise, as a result of Global Climate Change, is thought to be due to both the thermal expansion of water and the melting of land glaciers. Global sea levels have risen by between 10 and 20 cm during the 20th century, and like sea temperature, appear to have accelerated since the late 1990s[2]. Long-term measurements at Aberdeen show a trend over the last 100 years of around 0.7 mm/year[7]. All other Scottish mainland tide gauges have also recorded a sea-level rise over the same period. In contrast, a tide gauge in Lerwick (Shetland Islands) has recorded a fall in sea-level since 1957. Increases in sea-level are offset, in some areas, by the rise in the Scottish land mass which has continued since the melting of the overlaying ice sheets at the end of the last ice age. Estimates of current sea-level change for Scotland, adjusted to take account of uplift movements, are shown in Figure 6.4. It is worth noting that coastal erosion is occurring along 12% of the Scottish coastline.

*Other evidence for the impact of climate change in the marine environment*
Whether the recent rapid warming can be attributed to Global Climate Change alone, or a combination of Global Climate Change and natural climate variability, there is no doubt that the effects have been marked, for example see Marine Climate Change Impacts Partnership (MCCIP) Annual Report Card[7], with observed consequences throughout the marine environment. Many organisations have collected data so that observations of past changes can be made and have also attempted to understand how climate change has affected the marine environment. Areas studied are diverse and include aquaculture, coastal flooding and harmful algal blooms (Table 6.1).

**Figure 6.4    Present rates of relative sea-level change in Scotland[8]**

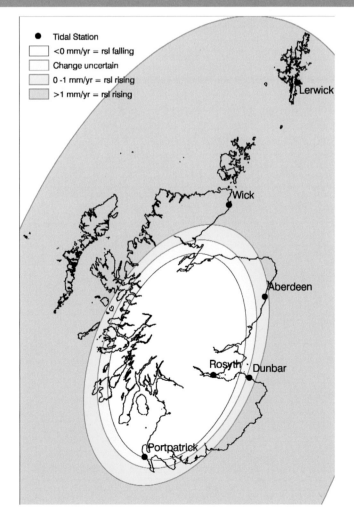

| Table 6.1 | Summary of data collected on the impact of climate change in the marine environment |
|---|---|
| **Indicators of the impact of climate change** | **Organisations collecting data** |
| Aquaculture | FRS |
| Built structures | Cefas, Oil & Gas industry |
| Coastal flooding | Met Office Hadley Centre, POL |
| Coastal habitats | SNH |
| Fisheries | FRS |
| Harmful Algal Blooms (HABs) | Cefas, FRS, SAHFOS |
| Nutrient enrichment | FRS, SEPA, SAHFOS, Satellite Observing Systems Ltd |
| Species abundance and distribution (including seabed, intertidal and non-native species, fish, birds and marine mammals) | Cefas, Centre for Ecology and Hydrology (CEH), FRS, JNCC, MBA, Sea Watch Foundation, SMRU, SAHFOS, SAMS, University of Aberdeen, University of Cambridge |
| Tourism | Natural England, University of Maastricht |

MCCIP brings together experts throughout the UK to summarise what is currently known about the impact of climate change on the marine environment[7]. The impacts of physical changes are observed at all levels within the marine ecosystem, from plankton through to fisheries, although the complex nature of the marine ecosystem means that it is difficult to isolate climate effects from other pressures. Much of the information reported by MCCIP, detailing what is already happening, relates to the UK as a whole with only a limited amount of regional information available. However, it is hoped that regional reporting will evolve such that a Scottish regional report will be integral to a future Report Card.

The changes in the climate of the marine environment around Scotland have already been described and what is happening in terms of temperature, salinity and sea-level are reported with a high level of confidence in the Report Card. It is not the purpose of this report to reproduce the Report Card, however, it is appropriate to note that it summarises:

> the climate of the marine environment;

> the impacts of climate change on the vision for a healthy and biologically diverse marine ecosystem;

> the impacts of climate change on the vision for clean and safe seas; and

> the impacts of climate change on the vision for commercially productive seas.

As outlined in the Report Card, climate change impacts on the vision for a healthy and biologically diverse marine ecosystem include:

> a decrease in biomass by 70% since the 1960s of the cold-water zooplankton species *Calanus finmarchicus*;

> earlier phytoplankton blooms;

> an indication of metabolic stress in cod and eelpout during warmer years;

> the spread of non-native species as a result of climate change as well as migration and human introduction; and

> some warm-water invertebrates and algae have extended their ranges around northern Scotland.

It should be noted that investigations into the effects of climate change on marine biodiversity, specifically key intertidal species whose abundance has been shown to fluctuate with changes in climatic conditions, were undertaken in the UK through the Marine Biodiversity and Climate Change (MarClim) programme[9].

There is generally less confidence in determining how climate change is impacting on the vision for clean and safe seas. There are, however, indications that harmful algal blooms are being driven largely by ocean climate forcing, with nutrient enrichment only relevant in some cases.

Finally, in terms of the vision for commercially productive seas, there is again low confidence in reporting what is already happening. This includes the possible impacts of climate change on aquaculture; the current view is that in the short-term, climate change is unlikely to have a significant effect on farmed marine fish, over 99% of which are cultivated in Scotland. What is reported for north-west Europe is that there will be an increasing frequency of months when conditions are more comfortable for tourists. What exactly this will mean for Scotland is unclear.

## PREDICTIONS FOR THE FUTURE

Future climate change can be predicted using global and/or regional climate models using estimates of the atmospheric concentration of greenhouse gases. As this is uncertain and depends upon society's response to the concerns about climate change, predictions based on a number of different future scenarios are often presented.

In 2002 the UK Climate Impacts Programme (UKCIP) published a detailed set of future scenarios for the UK[10] based on low, medium–low, medium-high and high estimates of future greenhouse gas concentrations. The resolution of the scenarios was very coarse with a 50 km resolution throughout the UK. At this resolution many of the small Scottish islands were not well represented. To address this problem the British-Irish Council commissioned a further report that used the results of a regional model at 25 km resolution and provided improved scenarios for Scottish Islands such as Orkney, Shetland and the Western Isles[11]. Later in 2008 UKCIP will publish new and updated scenarios that will include information about changes in the marine environment[12] and provide a better basis for future assessments.

Future sea-level rise, and an increased risk of storm surges, are likely to lead to more coastal flooding with knock-on impacts on coastal erosion, coastal habitats and built structures. Wave conditions in Scottish waters are most likely to be affected through changes in weather patterns and increased storminess. In order to better understand these changing conditions four WaveNet buoys[13] are to be installed in Scottish waters in 2008; two on both the east and west coasts.

It seems that in terms of future climate change, alterations in pH will have a widespread effect, although most probably through a cumulative effect with changes in other environmental conditions. Ocean acidification will be influential not only for marine primary producers through effects on nutrient speciation and biogeochemical processes, but also for shell-forming organisms where lower pH will hinder the formation of shells and skeletons. The latter will have greatest impact on the shellfish fisheries which will also be affected indirectly by changes in food web structure attributable to acidification.

Existing predictions from regional models indicate that annual mean air temperatures in Europe are likely to increase faster than the global mean, winter temperatures are likely to rise faster and annual precipitation is likely to increase. Many climate models predict that the MOC will weaken in the future, but at the moment the effects of this weakening are thought likely to be less than the overall warming[1].

## CONCLUSION

There is strong evidence that anthropogenic inputs of greenhouse gases to the atmosphere are the most likely cause of the observed average increase in global temperatures over the last 100 years. The rate of change in temperature appears to have increased in recent years such that the linear trend from 1980-2006 in Scottish waters equates to 0.24°C per decade. However, for some of the indicators discussed in this chapter there is low confidence in the interpretation and predictions drawn from them; indeed the current and future impacts of climate change remain poorly understood. As such, there is a clear need to ensure that the required research and monitoring is in place to gather the appropriate data. This requires both national and international collaboration since many of the measurements are costly and cover significant geographical regions (e.g. the global Argo Buoy network[14]). Scotland contributes actively to the assessment of climate change in the North Atlantic as summarised in the *ICES Report on Ocean Climate*[4]. Due to the considerable maritime influences on Scotland, it is inevitable that changes in the seas caused by climate change will have environmental and socio-economic impacts on Scotland. There is a need to improve our confidence in both understanding what is happening and in predicting the likely consequences that climate change will have on the seas around Scotland.

# Chapter 7
# Preparing a State of Scotland's Seas 2010

## INTRODUCTION

The Scottish Government has a vision for seas that are "clean, healthy, safe, productive and biologically diverse...managed to meet the long term needs of nature and people". To ensure that this vision is achieved, the status of the marine environment must be assessed and the impacts and effects arising from the various pressures must be monitored. Such assessments can be undertaken on different scales. Although this report focuses on Scottish waters, it takes account of the dynamic nature of the marine environment and the influence of larger-scale processes such as inflow from the Atlantic Ocean, and smaller-scale processes such as the general northward flow along the west coast of the UK. There is also a need to consider how the present assessment fits into the wider picture at the UK (UKMMAS), regional (OSPAR), European and global scales.  Assessment programmes report at regular intervals at these scales; in 2010 both the UKMMAS, through *Charting Progress 2*, and OSPAR, through *Quality Status Report* (QSR) 2010, will report and it is therefore important that Scotland should

also report in 2010. Not only will a Scottish report provide a higher degree of granularity than is possible in reports such as QSR 2010, it will also provide information that can be used in these broader reports. In 2009 the first River Basin Plans required by the European Water Framework Directive must be complete. These plans, together covering the whole of the UK, must identify objectives for improvement and programmes of measures to achieve these objectives. The initial assessment under the European Marine Strategy Framework Directive must be completed by 2012, with specific attention given to the 11 qualitative descriptors for determining Good Environmental Status (see Table 1.2) and the detailed characteristics, and pressures and impacts (see Table 1.3). This report has begun considering these descriptors from a Scottish perspective including how current monitoring programmes provide relevant information. In addition, this report identifies gaps and lays the foundation for a comprehensive assessment about the *State of Scotland's Seas* in 2010.

### Figure 7.1   Scotland's seas

From the shores to the deep waters to the west of Scotland, there is a need to assess the pressures and impacts such that relevant action can be taken so as to maintain the quality of Scotland's marine environment and the diversity of plants and animals that are integral to it.

## MAJOR GAPS

### Co-ordinated science and industry involvement

Scotland has over 11,000 km of coastline, approximately 60% of the UK coastline, and one of the largest inshore areas (88,414 km²; for comparison the land mass of Scotland is 78,811 km²) in Europe. Assessing the status of the Scottish marine environment will need co-ordinated scientific research both with respect to data gathering and data assessment. In recent years there have been some significant developments within the UK to which Scotland has contributed greatly. These include:

> the UK Marine Monitoring and Assessment Strategy (UKMMAS), the overall aim of which is to shape the UK's capability, within National and International waters, to provide, and respond, within a changing climate, to the evidence required for sustainable development within a clean, healthy, safe, productive and biologically diverse marine ecosystem;

> the UK Directory of Marine Observing Systems (UKDMOS), a project designed to overcome the current lack of information on where, when and what is being monitored by the UK in the marine environment; and

> the Marine Data and Information Partnership (MDIP), which will soon merge with the Marine Environmental Data Action Group (MEDAG)[A], and which will provide an overarching framework for data management in the UK *via* a system of Data Archive Centres (DACs), interoperability and standards.

In addition, as part of this report, details of the various marine monitoring programmes and data collection surveys undertaken by FRS, SEPA, SNH and the wider community are provided (Annex 2). However, not all monitoring and research activities undertaken in Scottish waters are listed; only limited information is provided on the data gathered by the many other industries using the marine environment. Marine research being undertaken within the academic community also needs to be integrated within future plans for overall data collection, interpretation and management. These issues will be addressed during the preparation of the 2010 report.

### Stakeholder involvement

The importance of stakeholder involvement is now a feature of how Scotland manages the marine environment (for example, as detailed in *A Strategic Framework for Scottish Aquaculture*[1] and *A Strategic Framework for Inshore Fisheries in Scotland*[2]). Consultation with stakeholders is also one of the keystones in the rolling out of the Water Framework Directive with national and area advisory groups committed to consulting widely at every stage. Furthermore, Marine Science Scotland is a new

initiative that will coordinate the activities of marine scientists across Scotland as a way of ensuring that research activities are focused upon policy needs. It is important that the purpose of these initiatives and frameworks, and their contribution to ensuring a sustainable marine environment, is well understood to ensure that they are complementary in nature and there is minimal overlap. With appropriate coordination, these processes will provide a coherent approach to understanding and managing the Scottish marine environment. These initiatives and their objectives will be considered in more detail in the 2010 report.

### Status indicators and reporting areas

In order to describe the state of Scotland's seas there is a need for a greater range of indicators to be developed that can then be used to provide appropriate assessments. Summary assessments have been provided within various case studies (see Chapters 2–5) and for some human activities (see Chapter 5). The assessments provide information on trends, status and confidence in the assessment for a given indicator within a geographical region. All three categories of status (acceptable, room for improvement and unacceptable) have been used in the assessments made within this report. At the same time, confidence in the assessment ranges from low to high. The reasons for low confidence in the assessment include the need for improved models, the requirement for improved spatial resolution, the availability of only partial data and insufficient length of data timeseries. The last of these can only be resolved through the maintenance of on-going monitoring programmes, because detecting the causes and the true magnitude of variation in the marine environment often requires data to be collected over at least 10 years. Such issues have prompted a review of sampling methodologies which would allow assessments of designated areas. This has resulted in stratified random sampling becoming an integral part of the Clean Safe seas Environmental Monitoring Programme (CSEMP, see Figure 3.12 and Chapter 3) and led to the adoption of specific reporting areas in UK waters (Figure 1.7). Future monitoring programmes will need to be aligned to these reporting areas, and future reports, and hopefully as early as the 2010 report, should present the types of assessment illustrated in Figure 7.2.

In line with one of the recommendations made by the Advisory Group on Marine and Coastal Strategy (AGMACS), there remains a need to focus on the development of indicators which help inform managers and provide information to the public. Scotland must continue to contribute to the development of appropriate indicators within the broader UK and international framework.

**Figure 7.2 Revised representation of the Summary Assessment from Case Study 3.6 describing the impact of the offshore oil and gas industry on the sediment hydrocarbon concentration and composition**

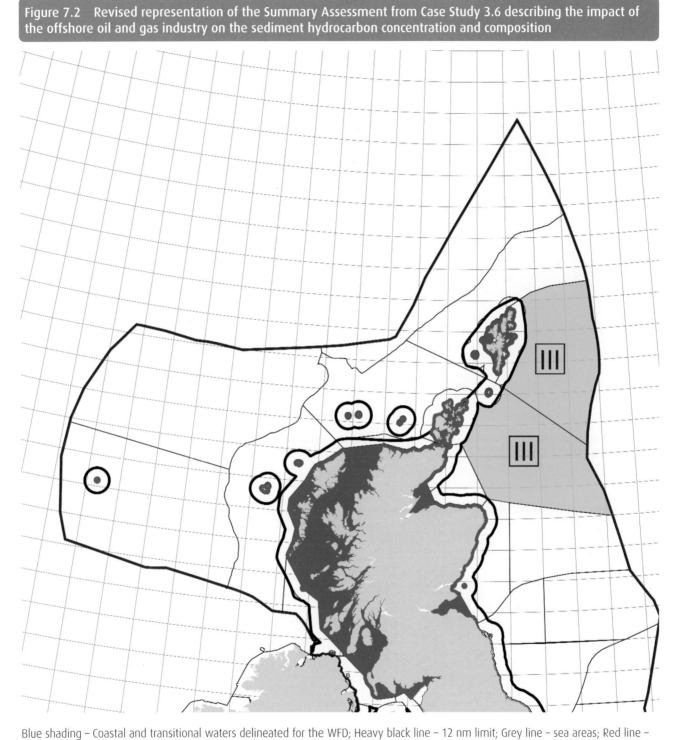

Blue shading – Coastal and transitional waters delineated for the WFD; Heavy black line – 12 nm limit; Grey line – sea areas; Red line – fisheries limits. The green shading illustrates that the status within sea areas East Shetland and Fladen is acceptable with respect to sediment hydrocarbon concentration and composition. The Roman Number within the green shaded area is the 'confidence of assessment' which in this case is 'III' corresponding to 'High' (see Table 1.9).

### Integrating assessment of human impacts

Historically, the effects of different human impacts have been treated separately. However, any area of the sea is likely to be exposed to several impacts. There is a need to develop tools which can discriminate and assess these multiple impacts. For example, a recent report has, for the first time, presented a global assessment of human impacts on marine ecosystems[3]. This type of integrated assessment requires detailed information and consideration of weighting factors for the different anthropogenic activities and it illustrates an approach to ecosystem-based assessment. For the 2010 report, it is intended to start producing integrated ecosystem-based assessments of multiple human impacts where possible.

### Knowledge of offshore waters

As highlighted in Chapter 3, new legislation requires monitoring to take place in areas assumed to be clean. It also requires an improved knowledge of deeper, offshore waters. The initial assessment required under the European Marine Strategy Framework Directive in 2012 will require information on sea areas to the west of Scotland, including Bailey and Rockall (Figure 1.7). Both SEPA and FRS have extended data collection into these regions but it will also be necessary to use other sources of data, such as those collected regularly by the academic community, to enable assessment of the deeper waters to be made. These data need to be sourced as part of the process of producing a report on the **State of Scotland's Seas** in 2010.

### Areas outside designated sites

There is a need to gather information from outside designated sites, which presently cover less than 0.5% of Scotland's territorial waters and have been the primary focus of most ecological monitoring to date. Filling such a gap before the 2010 report will not be possible, but the 2010 report will consider how this might be achieved.

### Impacts of global climate change

There is a need to improve confidence in both understanding what is happening and in predicting the likely consequences that global climate change will have on the seas around Scotland.

## WHAT NEEDS TO BE DONE?

The current report provides a starting point for the 2010 report but gathering the views of stakeholders is an important process that will lead to modification and improvement. Consequently, the authors welcome this feedback and encourage the completion of the short questionnaire at the back of the report. Alternatively comments can be sent to StateofScotlandsSeas2010@scotland.gsi.gov.uk

Scotland is fully engaged in the UKMMAS and associated production of **Charting Progress 2**. It is important that the work undertaken to produce the Scottish report dovetails with that required of Scotland in respect of **Charting Progress 2**. Consequently, the structure of this report is consistent with the developing structure of **Charting Progress 2**.

There is a need to build on the cooperation received from many organisations in the preparation of this report. Such input to date has ensured a more holistic report than would have been possible if the information used had been limited to that available from FRS, SEPA and SNH.

In preparing **Scotland's Seas: Towards Understanding their State,** it is apparent that there is a considerable body of knowledge available about Scotland's diverse seas (Figure 7.3) and that this is continuing to expand, but there are also gaps and uncertainties. Confidence in some of the assessments is also low and it would be helpful if there was a focused effort to reduce this uncertainty.

As a maritime nation, Scotland makes extensive use of its seas. To be confident that Scotland continues to use its seas in a sustainable manner into the future requires a continuing cycle of monitoring, research and assessment as well as the implementation of new management approaches should problems be identified.

## Figure 7.3    Scotland's diverse seas

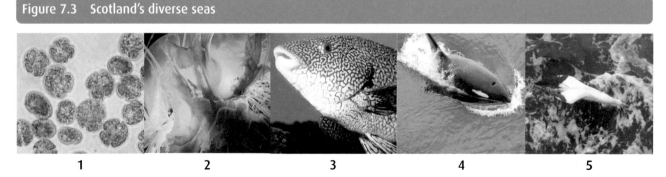

|   1   |   2   |   3   |   4   |   5   |

1. phytoplankton (*Karenia mikimotoi*), 2. lion's mane jelly fish, 3. ballen wrasse, 4. orca and 5. gannet.

# Notes

### Chapter 1
[A] ICES working definition of Ecosystem Approach: integrated management of human activities based on our knowledge of ecosystem dynamics to achieve sustainable use of ecosystem goods and services, and maintenance of ecosystem integrity. Bergen Declaration, 2002. 5th International Conference on the Protection of the North Sea.

### Chapter 2
[A] The term 'bank' is used to described a region that is shallower (in terms of water depth) than its surroundings.

### Chapter 3
[A] OSPAR Convention, Definition of [Marine] Pollution - The introduction by man, directly or indirectly, of substances or energy into the maritime area which results, or is likely to result, in hazards to human health, harm to living resources and marine ecosystems, damage to amenities or interference with other legitimate uses of the sea.

### Chapter 4
[A] Compiled results for the first six year cycle of monitoring in the UK are available on the JNCC website at: http://www.jncc.gov.uk/page-3520. Specific results for each feature in Scotland are accessible via the SNH website, via the SiteLink tool: http://www.snh.org.uk/snhi/

[B] The Scottish Biodiversity list is available from: http://www.biodiversityscotland.gov.uk/pageType2.php?id=35 &type=2&navID=92 and satisfies the requirements of Section 2(4) of the Nature Conservation (Scotland) Act 2004.

[C] Results are reported to JNCC and Scottish Government and are available upon the SNH website, via SiteLink: http://www.snh.org.uk/snhi/

[D] The preliminary analysis of CPR A Route data was funded by the UHI Millennium Institute. Thanks are due to the Sir Alister Hardy Foundation for Ocean Science for making these data available, and to the owners and crews of the ships that collected it.

[E] SNH's SCM and broadscale mapping reports are available at http://www.snh.org.uk/pubs/cr.asp

[F] The Scottish Biodiversity Strategy satisfies the requirements of Section 2(1) of the Nature Conservation (Scotland) Act 2004.

[G] ICES – details of the organisation, its working groups and advice can be found at http://www.ices.dk/

### Chapter 5
[A] Partial Input-Output category core employment figures are based upon estimated output share applied to employment figures for the whole Input-Output category. Indirect and supported upstream figures are estimated using the Input-Output model. Each of the identified marine industries indirect and supported upstream effects will include activity between other marine industries. To prevent double counting, this activity is not included for the marine sector as a whole. As a result, the all marine sector totals will always be lower than the sum of the identified industries, except for the core industry columns.

[B] Crofters who own a boat and engage in occasional fishing activity to supplement their crofting are included in the statistics.

[C] When the Register of Buyers and Sellers (RBS) was introduced in September 2005, Sales Notes were not initially required for sales of shellfish and information on the value of such landings is consequently missing. The value has therefore been estimated for a number of landings, mostly shellfish, relating to voyages starting on or after 1 September 2005.

[D] Figures are courtesy of the Royal Commission on the Ancient and Historical Monuments of Scotland (RCAHMS): see http://www.rcahms.gov.uk. RCAHMS report that the total number of records is expected to rise to 20-25,000 on completion of data entry.

[E] In addition, the Protection of Military Remains Act 1986 provides for the protection by the Ministry of Defence of all aircraft and designated wrecks lost in military service after 4 August 1914.

[F] Along the 30% of Scotland's coast recorded by the HS coastal zone assessments, 3525 monuments were recommended for further action. Of these, urgent action is likely to be necessary at c.200.

### Chapter 7
[A] The Marine Data and Information Partnership (MDIP) will merge in 2008 with the Marine Environmental Data Action Group (MEDAG) to form the Marine Environmental Data and Information Network (MEDIN).

# Glossary

| | |
|---|---|
| ACOPS | Advisory Committee on Protection of the Sea |
| AGMACS | Advisory Group on Marine and Coastal Strategy |
| AMO | Atlantic Multi-decadal Oscillation |
| ASP | Amnesic shellfish poisoning |
| $B_{lim}$ | ICES SSB 'limit' reference point - low biomass, serious risk to reproductive capacity |
| $B_{pa}$ | ICES precautionary biomass reference point - biomass below which management action required to increase biomass |
| BAC | Background Assessment Concentration |
| BC | Background Concentration |
| BERR | Department of Business, Enterprise and Regulatory Reform (previously DTI) |
| BGS | British Geological Survey |
| BMF | British Marine Federation |
| BODC | British Oceanographic Data Centre |
| BTO | British Trust for Ornithology |
| CAMP | Comprehensive Atmospheric Monitoring Programme |
| CAR | Controlled Activities (Scotland) Regulations 2005 |
| CBD | Convention on Biological Diversity |
| CD | Compact Disc |
| CDOM | Colour Dissolved Organic Matter |
| Cefas | Centre for Environment, Fisheries and Aquaculture Science |
| CEH | Centre for Ecology and Hydrology |
| CEMP | Co-ordinated Environmental Monitoring Programme |
| CMO | Contributory Marine Objective |
| CPR | Continuous Plankton Recorder |
| CSSEG | Clean Safe Seas Evidence Group |
| CSEMP | Clean Safe seas Environmental Monitoring Programme |
| DAC | Data Archive Centre |
| DBA | Dibenz[$a,h$]anthracene |
| DDT | Dichloro-diphenyl-trichloroethane or 4,4'-(2,2,2-trichloroethane-1,1-diyl)bis(chlorobenzene) |
| DEHP | Diethylhexylphthalate |
| DfT | Department for Transport |
| DJFM | December, January, February, March (winter) |
| DNA | Deoxyribonucleic acid |
| DPAG | Dounreay Particles Advisory Group |
| DSP | Diarrhetic shellfish poisoning |
| DTI | Department of Trade and Industry (now BERR) |
| EAC | Ecotoxicological Assessment Criteria |
| EC | European Council |
| EEC | European Economic Community |
| EMEC | European Marine Energy Centre |
| EMEP | Co-operative Programme for Monitoring and Evaluation of the Long-range Transmission of Air Pollutants in Europe |
| EcoQ | Ecological Quality |
| EcoQO | Ecological Quality Objective |
| EQS | Environmental Quality Standards |
| E&RDC | Environment and Rural Affairs Committee (Scottish Parliament) |
| ERSEM | European Regional Seas Ecosystem Model |
| ESAI | East Shetland Atlantic Inflow |
| EU | European Union |
| $F_{lim}$ | ICES fishing mortality 'limit' reference point - high fishing rate likely to drive biomass below $B_{lim}$ |

| | |
|---|---|
| $F_{pa}$ | ICES precautionary fishing mortality rate reference point - fishing rate above which management action required |
| FEPA | Food and Environment Protection Act 1985 |
| FIC | Fair Isle Current |
| FRS | Fisheries Research Services |
| FSAS | Food Standards Agency Scotland |
| GAM | Generalised Additive Modelling framework |
| GDP | Gross Domestic Product |
| GES | Good Environmental Status (under MSFD) |
| GEcS | Good Ecological Status (under WFD) |
| GSDP | Glasgow Strategic Drainage Plan |
| GVA | Gross Value Added |
| HBDC | Hexabromocyclododecane |
| HBDSEG | Healthy and Biologically Diverse Seas Evidence Group |
| HMNB | Her Majesty's Naval Base |
| HMS | (UK) Hamonised Monitoring Scheme |
| ICES | International Council for the Exploration of the Sea |
| IMO | International Maritime Organisation |
| IPCC | Intergovernmental Panel on Climate Change |
| JAMP | Joint Assessment and Monitoring Programme |
| JNCC | Joint Nature Conservation Committee |
| KIMO | Kommunenes Internasjonale Miljorganisasjon (local authorities international environmental organisation) |
| Li | Lithium |
| LCA | Length Cohort Analysis |
| LPUE | Landings per unit effort |
| MAPC | Marine Assessment Policy Committee |
| MARCLIM | Marine Biodiversity and Climate Change Project |
| MARG | Marine Assessment Reporting Group |
| MBA | Marine Biological Association |
| MCA | Maritime and Coastguard Agency |
| MCCIP | Marine Climate Change Impacts Partnership |
| MDIP | Marine Data and Information Partnership |
| MEDAG | Marine Environmental Data Action Group |
| MESH | Mapping European Seabed Habitats |
| MoD | Ministry of Defence |
| MNCR | Marine Nature Conservation Review |
| MOC | Meridional Overturning Circulation |
| MPA | Marine Protected Area |
| MSL | Mean Sea Level |
| MSFD | Marine Strategy Framework Directive |
| Mt | Million Tonnes |
| MT | Motor tanker |
| MW | Megawatts |
| NAFCMC | North Atlantic Fisheries College Marine Centre |
| NAO | North Atlantic Oscillation index |
| NCOF | National Centre for Ocean Forecasting |
| NOCS | National Oceanography Centre Southampton |
| OSPAR | Oslo & Paris OSPAR Commission for the Protection of the Marine Environment of the North-East Atlantic |
| PA | Problem Area (in respect of OSPAR Comprehensive Procedure) |
| PAH | Polycyclic aromatic hydrocarbon |
| PBDE | Polybrominated diphenyl ether |
| PCB | Polychlorinated biphenyl (sometimes abbreviated to CB) |
| PCI | Phytoplankton Colour Index |
| PNP | Potential new primary production |

| | | | | |
|---|---|---|---|---|
| POL | Proudman Oceanographic Laboratory | | SPA | Special Protection Area |
| POP | Persistent Organic Pollutant | | SPM | Suspended particulate material |
| PPA | Potential Problem Area (in respect of OSPAR Comprehensive Procedure) | | SPRI | Scottish Pollutant Release Inventory |
| | | | SSB | Spawning stock biomass |
| PSEG | Productive Seas Evidence Group | | SSMO | Shetland Shellfish Management Organisation |
| PSP | Paralytic shellfish poisoning | | SSSI | Site of Special Scientific Interest |
| PSR | Pressure State Response framework | | SST | Sea surface temperature |
| qPCR | Quantitative polymerase chain reaction | | SR | Stratified random (sampling) |
| QSR | Quality Status Report (OSPAR) | | TAC | Total Allowable Catch |
| RCAHMS | Royal Commission on the Ancient and Historic Monuments of Scotland | | TBT | Tributyltin |
| | | | TIG | Turtle Implementation Group |
| RID | Comprehensive Study on Riverine Inputs and Direct Discharges | | TRAC | Transitional and Coastal Waters (under WFD) |
| | | | UHI | University of the Highlands and Islands |
| RIFE | Radioactivity in Food and the Environment | | UK | United Kingdom |
| RNAD | Royal Navy Armourments Depot | | UKAEA | United Kingdom Atomic Energy Authority |
| RSA 93 | Radioactive Substances Act 1993 | | UKBAP | UK Biodiversity Action Plan |
| RSPB | Royal Society for the Protection of Birds | | UKCIP | United Kingdom Climate Impacts Programme |
| SAC | Special Area of Conservation | | UKCS | United Kingdom continental shelf |
| SAHFOS | Sir Alister Hardy Foundation for Ocean Science | | UKDMOS | United Kingdom Database of Marine Observing Systems |
| SAMS | Scottish Association for Marine Science | | UKMMAS | United Kingdom Marine Monitoring and Assessment Strategy |
| SARF | Scottish Aquaculture Research Forum | | | |
| SBS | Scottish Biodiversity Strategy | | UN | United Nations |
| SCM | Site Condition Monitoring | | UVF | Ultraviolet fluorescence |
| SEA | Strategic Environmental Assessment | | UWWTD | Urban Waste Water Treatment Directive |
| SEPA | Scottish Environment Protection Agency | | VA | Value Added |
| SG | Systematic grid (sampling) | | VPA | Virtual Population Analysis |
| SGMD | Scottish Government Marine Directorate | | WEWS | Water Environment Water Services Act 2003 |
| SMP | Seabird Monitoring Programme | | WFD | Water Framework Directive |
| SMRU | Sea Mammal Research Unit | | WSSD | World Summit on Sustainable Development |
| SNH | Scottish Natural Heritage | | | |
| SOTEAG | Shetland Oil Terminal Environmental Advisory Group | | | |

# Common and scientific names used in report

## Chapter 2

| Common name | Scientific name |
| --- | --- |
| herring | *Clupea harengus* |
| Norway pout | *Trisopterus esmarkii* |
| sandeel | *Ammodytes spp* |
| sprat | *Sprattus sprattus* |

## Chapter 3

| Common name | Scientific name |
| --- | --- |
| eider | *Somateria mollissima* |
| greylag geese | *Anser anser* |
| pink-footed geese | *Anser brachyrhynchus* |
| redshank | *Tringa totanus* |
| shelduck | *Tadorna tadorna* |
| widgeon | *Anas penelope* |

## Chapter 4

| Common name | Scientific name |
| --- | --- |
| Allis shad | *Alosa alosa* |
| arrow worm | *Sagitta spp.* |
| Atlantic salt meadows | *Glauco-Puccinellietalia maritimae* |
| black-legged kittiwake | *Rissa tridactyla* |
| bottlenose dolphin | *Tursiops truncatus* |
| cod | *Gadus morhua* |
| common guillemot | *Uria aalge* |
| common seal | *Phoca vitulina* |
| copepod | *Euchaeta hebes* |
| copepod | *Calanus finmarchicus* |
| copepod | *Candacia armata* |
| copepod | *Metridia lucens* |
| copepod | *Acartia clausii* |
| copepod | *Temora longicornis* |
| copepod | *Pseudocalanus elongatus* |
| copepod | *Calanus spp.* |
| Greenland shark | *Somniosus microcephalus* |
| grey seal | *Halichoerus grypus* |
| haddock | *Melanogrammus aeglefinus* |
| harbour porpoise | *Phocoena Phocoena* |
| herring | *Clupea harengus* |
| horse mussel | *Modiolus modiolus* |
| langoustine | *Nephrops norveigicus* |
| leatherback turtle | *Dermochelys coriacea* |
| lesser sandeel | *Ammodytes marinus* |
| mackerel | *Scomber scombrus* |
| Mediterranean and thermo-Atlantic halophilous scrubs | *Sarcocornetea fruticosi* |
| monkfish | *Lophius piscatorius* |
| northern gannet | *Morus bassanus* |
| otter | *Lutra lutra* |
| pteropod | *Limacina retroversa* |
| red mullet | *Mullus sumuletus* |
| saithe | *Pollachius virens* |
| sea lamprey | *Petromyzon marinus* |
| serpulid worm | *Serpula vermicularis* |
| skeleton shrimp | *Caprella mutica* |
| snake pipefish | *Entelurus aequoreus* |
| spartina swards | *Spartinion maritimae* |
| sprat | *Sprattus sprattus* |
| twaite shad | *Alosa fallax* |
| whiting | *Merlangius merlangus* |
| wireweed | *Sargassum muticum* |

## Chapter 5

| Common name | Scientific name |
| --- | --- |
| Atlantic salmon | *Salmo salar* |
| cod | *Gadus morhua* |
| common mussel | *Mytilus edulis* |
| edible crabs | *Cancer pagurus* |
| haddock | *Melanogrammus aeglefinus* |
| halibut | *Hippoglossus hippoglossus* |
| herring | *Clupea harengus* |
| lemon sole | *Microstomus kitt* |
| lobsters | *Homarus gammarus* |
| mackerel | *Scomber scombrus* |
| monkfish (anglerfish) | *Lophius piscatorius* |
| native oyster | *Ostrea edulis* |
| *Nephrops* | *Nephrops norvegicus* |
| Pacific oyster | *Crassostrea gigas* |
| pollack | *Pollachius pollachius* |
| queen scallops | *Aequipecten opercularis / Chlamys opercularis* |
| rainbow trout | *Oncorhynchus mykiss* |
| saithe | *Pollachius virens* |
| scallop | *Pecten maximus* |
| trout | *Salmo trutta* |
| turbot | *Scophthalmus maximus* |
| velvet crabs | *Necora puber* |
| whiting | *Merlangius merlangus* |
| whelks | *Buccinum undatum* |

## Chapter 6

| | |
| --- | --- |
| cod | *Gadus morhua* |
| eelpout | *Zoarces viviparous* |

# Contributors and acknowledgements

**CASE STUDIES – CHAPTER 2**

Case study 2.1 – Climatic variability in the seas to the west of Scotland
Mark Inall and Colin Griffiths, Scottish Association for Marine Science

Case study 2.2 – Seabed sediment
Alan Stevenson, Dave Long and Robert Gatliff, British Geological Survey

Case study 2.3 – Modelling bathymetric data
Alan Hills, SEPA

Case study 2.4 – New primary production in Scottish waters, 1960-2003
Mike Heath, FRS and Doug Beare, Institute for the Protection and Security of the Citizen

**CASE STUDIES – CHAPTER 3**

Case study 3.1 – Loadings on Riverine Inputs and Direct Discharges (RID)
Brian Miller, SEPA

Case study 3.2 – Coastal and estuarine water quality classification
Brian Cowan and Peter Holmes, SEPA

Case study 3.3 – Water Framework Directive classification of transitional and coastal waters
David Ross, SEPA

Case study 3.4 – Persistent organic pollutants in Scottish harbour (common) seals
Ailsa Hall, Sea Mammal Research Unit

Case study 3.5 – Geochemical analysis of sediment on the seabed
Alan Stevenson, Dave Long and Robert Gatliff, British Geological Survey

Case study 3.6 – The impact of the offshore oil and gas industry on the sediment of potentially accumulative areas of the North Sea
Lynda Webster, Pam Walsham, Marie Russell, Gill Packer, Abdulwaheed Ahmed and Colin Moffat, FRS

Case study 3.7 – Evaluating the effects of environmental stressors on marine wildlife. Emerging techniques and approaches: DNA microarrays and qPCR arrays
John Craft, Glasgow Caledonian University

Case study 3.8 – Scottish Pollutant Release Inventory
Brian Miller, SEPA

Case study 3.9 – Eutrophication in Scottish marine waters
Brian Miller and Judy Dobson, SEPA

Case study 3.10 – Radioactive substances
Mark Toner, SEPA

**CASE STUDIES – CHAPTER 4**

Case study 4.1 – Analysis of Continuous Plankton Recorder (CPR) Data
Ian Napier, NAFC Marine Centre

Case study 4.2 – Stonehaven ecosystem monitoring site – Phytoplankton
Eileen Bresnan, FRS

Case study 4.3 – Stonehaven ecosystem monitoring site – Zooplankton
Jens Rasmussen and Steve Hay, FRS

Case study 4.4 – Deep sea biodiversity around Scotland
Bhavani E Narayanaswamy, Scottish Association for Marine Science

Case study 4.5 – Commercially exploited fish stocks
Bill Turrell and Nick Bailey, FRS

Case study 4.6 – Implications of climate change for Scottish seabirds
Sarah Wanless, Centre for Ecology and Hydrology

**CASE STUDIES – CHAPTER 5**

Case study 5.1 – Safeguarding shellfish quality
Keith Davidson, Scottish Association for Marine Sciences; Jacqui McElhiney and Lorna Murray, Food Standards Agency Scotland and Myriam Algoet, Centre for Environment, Fisheries, and Aquaculture Science

Case study 5.2 – Shetland shellfish stock assessment programme
B. Leslie, C. Laurenson, R. Shelmerdine & D.Riley, NAFC Marine Centre

Case study 5.3 – Marine finfish aquaculture interactions with the environment
Matt Gubbins, FRS and Ewan Gillespie, SEPA

Case study 5.4 – Coastal and marine historic heritage
Philip Robertson, Historic Scotland

Case study 5.5 – Competing activities in the Loch Creran marine Special Area of Conservation
Hamish Mair, Heriot Watt University

# Contributors and acknowledgements (contd:)

| | |
|---|---|
| Kevin O'Carroll | BERR |
| Alan Stevenson | BGS |
| Mark Charlesworth | British Oceanographic Data Centre |
| Nick Bailey | FRS |
| Barbara Berx | FRS |
| Ian Davies | FRS |
| Steve Hay | FRS |
| Sarah Hughes | FRS |
| Colin Megginson | FRS |
| Colin Moffat | FRS |
| Tracy McCollin | FRS |
| Keith Mutch | FRS |
| Bill Turrell | FRS |
| David Connor | JNCC |
| Matt Frost | Marine Biological Association |
| Ian Boyd | Marine Science Scotland |
| Mike Bell | Meteorological Office |
| Alan Hughes | National Oceanographic Centre, Southampton |
| Steve Gontarek | SAMS |
| Mike Burrows | SAMS |
| Rhona Fairgrieve | Scottish Coastal Forum |
| Alan Hills | SEPA |
| Peter Holmes | SEPA |
| Tom Leatherland | SEPA |
| Monica Straughan | SEPA |

| | |
|---|---|
| Jenny Brough | Scottish Government |
| Martyn Cox | Scottish Government |
| Stevan Croasdale | Scottish Government |
| Louise Cunningham | Scottish Government |
| David Dunkley | Scottish Government |
| Zoe McGuire | Scottish Government |
| Ian Mitchell | Scottish Government |
| Heather Holmes | Scottish Government |
| Alan McPherson | Scottish Government |
| Dominic Munro | Scottish Government |
| Angela Robinson | Scottish Government |
| Jane Rougvie | Scottish Government |
| James Thomson | Scottish Government |
| Marlene Walker | Scottish Government |
| Ailsa Hall | SMRU |
| John Baxter | SNH |
| Rhys Bullman | SNH |
| Dominic Counsell | SNH |
| David Donnan | SNH |
| Martin Gaywood | SNH |
| Ben James | SNH |
| George Lees | SNH |
| Shona MacLellan | SNH |

Preparation of the report was overseen by a steering group of Peter Holmes (SEPA), John Baxter (SNH), Ian Boyd (Marine Science Scotland), Martyn Cox and Louise Cunningham (Scottish Government) and chaired by Colin Moffat (FRS).

# Photograph/image copyrights

**Frontispiece**
British Geological Survey

**Foreword/Executive Summary**
SNH

**Chapter 1**
Title page - FRS
1.1 Steve Gontarek, SAMS (Bathymetry and elevations based on GebcoCE and GTOPO30 datasets).
1.2 OSPAR secretariat
1.7 UKMMAS

**Chapter 2**
Title page - SNH
2.1 Steve Gontarek, SAMS (Bathymetry and elevations based on GebcoCE and GTOPO30 datasets) and Keith Mutch, FRS
2.2 United Kingdom Hydrographic Office
2.3 Mike Bell, Crown Copyright 2008, the Met Office
2.4 Sarah Hughes and Keith Mutch, FRS
2.5 and 2.11 K O'Carroll, BERR, Atlas of Marine Renewable Energy (Bathymetry, Waves, Wind, Tides)
http://www.berr.gov.uk/energy/sources/renewables/explained/wind/page27741.html
2.6 Connor, D.W., Gilliland, P.M., Golding, N, Robinson, P., Todd, D., & Verling, E. 2006. *UKSeaMap: the mapping of seabed and water column features of UK seas.* Joint Nature Conservation Committee, Peterborough
2.7, 2.8, 2.9 SAMS
2.10 SEPA and Keith Mutch, FRS
2.12 Barbara Berx, FRS
2.13 Colin Moffat, FRS
2.14 and 2.15 BGS
2.16 MCA, ABP Ports, Google Earth

**Chapter 3**
Title page - SNH
3.3 SEPA
3.5, 3.6 SMRU
3.7 BGS
3.8, 3.9, 3.10 FRS
3.11 Marie Russell, FRS
3.12 FRS and SEPA
3.13 Glasgow Caledonian University
3.14, 3.15, 3.16, 3.17 SEPA
3.18, 3.19, 3.20 SEPA

**Chapter 4**
Title Page - SNH
4.1, 4.2 SNH
4.3 FRS
4.4 SAHFOS
4.9 SEPA
4.12 Jens Rasmussen, FRS
4.16 MNCR/SNH
4.17, 4.19 SNH
4.20 D. Leaver
4.21 FRS
4.22 SNH

4.23 Sue Scott
4.24 Christine Howson
4.25 SAMS
4.27 Lorne Gill/SNH
4.28 Ashley Coutts
4.30 SNH
4.33, 4.34, 4.35 SMRU
4.36 Marine Environmental Monitoring
4.37 SNH
4.38 Mike Harris, CEH
4.42 Akinori Takahashi, CEH

**Chapter 5**
Title page - SNH
5.1, 5.2, 5.3, 5.4, 5.5 FRS
5.6, 5.7 FSAS and SAMS
5.8, 5.9 NAFC
5.10, 5.11 FRS
5.12 ACOPS
5.13 FRS
5.14 Colin Moffat, FRS
5.15 Historic Scotland
5.16 ScapaMap project
5.17 Perth and Kinross Heritage Trust
5.18, 5.19 Heriot Watt University
5.20 Marie Russell, FRS

**Chapter 6**
Title page - SNH
6.1, 6.2, 6.3 FRS
6.4 Natural Heritage Trends, The Seas Around Scotland 2004, SNH

**Chapter 7**
Title page - SNH
7.1 Colin Moffat, FRS
7.2 FRS
7.3 (1) Eileen Bresnan, (2 & 3) Simon Greenstreet, (4) Craig Davies, (5) John Dunn; FRS

# References

Chapter 1

(1) Directive of the European Parliament and of the Council establishing a Framework for (Community Action in the field of Marine Environmental Policy (Marine Strategy Framework Directive) http://www.europarl.europa.eu/sides/getDoc.do?type=TA&language=EN&reference=P6-TA-2007-0595

(2) http://www.cbd.int/

(3) Defra, 2005. Charting Progress - An Integrated Assessment of the State of UK Seas. Department for Environment, Food and Rural Affairs, London. pp. 120. http://www.defra.gov.uk/environment/water/marine/uk/stateofsea/index.htm

(4) OSPAR, 2000. Quality Status Report 2000 for the North-East Atlantic. Oslo and Paris Commissions, London. pp. 108. http://www.ospar.org/eng/html/welcome.html

(5) OSPAR, 2006. Overview of OSPAR Assessments 1998 – 2006. Oslo and Paris Commissions, London. pp. 89. http://www.ospar.org/eng/html/welcome.html

(6) http://eur-lex.europa.eu/LexUriServ/LexUriServ.do?uri=COM:2007:0575:FIN:EN:PDF

(7) http://ec.europa.eu/maritimeaffairs/pdf/ActionPaper/action_plan_en.pdf

(8) Defra, 2002. Safeguarding our Seas - Conservation and Sustainable Development of our Marine Environment. Department for Environment, Food and Rural Affairs, London. pp. 80. http://www.defra.gov.uk/environment/water/marine/uk/stewardship/index.htm

(9) ). Marine Environment Monitoring Group, 2004. UK National Marine Monitoring Programme – 2nd report (1999-2001) Cefas, Lowestoft. pp. 136. http://www.cefas.co.uk/publications/files/nmmp2.pdf

(10) Scottish Executive, 2005. Seas the Opportunity – a strategy for the long term sustainability of Scotland's coasts and seas. Scottish Executive, Edinburgh. pp. 40. http://www.scotland.gov.uk/Publications/2005/08/26102543/25444

(11) Recommendations of the Advisory Group on Marine and Coastal Strategy: A Follow up to Seas the Opportunity: A Strategy for the Long Term Sustainability of Scotland's Coasts and Seas, 2007. Scottish Executive, Edinburgh. pp. 79. http://www.scotland.gov.uk/Publications/2007/03/08103826/0

(12) Scottish Parliament, 2007. Report on Inquiry into the Marine Environment. Environment and Rural Development Committee, Edinburgh. pp. 36. SP Paper 774. http://www.scottish.parliament.uk/business/committees/environment/reports-07/rar07-04-00.htm

Chapter 2

(1) http://www.defra.gov.uk/environment/statistics/inlwater/iwrainfall.htm

(2) Fehling, J., Davidson, K., and Bates, S.S., 2005. Growth dynamics of non-toxic Pseudo-nitzchia delicatissima and toxic P. seriat (Bacillariophyceae) under simulated spring and summer photperiods. Harmful Algae 4, 763 – 769.

(3) Inall, M.E., Gillibrand, P.A., Griffiths, C.R., MacDougal, N. and Blackwell, K., 2008. Temperature, Salinity and Flow Variability on the North-West European Shelf. Journal of Marine Systems (in press).

(4) Hickey, K.R., 2001. The storm of 31 January to 1 February 1953 and its impact on Scotland, Scottish Journal of Geography 117, 283-295.

(5) McKee, D., Cunningham, A. and Jones K.J., 2002. Optical and hydrographic consequences of freshwater run-off during spring phytoplankton growth in a Scottish fjord. Journal of Plankton Research 24 (11), 1163-1171.

(6) Heath, M.R., Edwards, A.C., Pätsch, J. and Turrell, W.R., 2002. Scottish Executive Central Research Unit contract: Modelling the behaviour of nutrients in the coastal waters of Scotland, Final Report. Fisheries Research Services Report 10/02.

(7) ICES., 2007. Report of the Workshop on the Significance of Changes in Surface CO2 and Ocean pH in ICES Shelf Sea Ecosystems (WKCpH). ICES C.M. 2007/OCC:12

(8) Blackford, J. and Gilbert, F., 2007. pH variability and CO2 induced acidification in the North Sea. Journal of Marine Systems 64, 229-241.

(9) Andrews, I.J., Long, D., Richards, P.C., Thomson, A.R., Brown, S., Chesher, J.A. and McCormac, M., 1990. United Kingdom offshore regional report: The Geology of the Moray Firth. London: HMSO for the British Geological Survey.

(10) Fyfe, J.A., Long, D. and Evans, D., 1993. United Kingdom offshore regional report: the geology of the Malin-Hebrides sea area. London: HMSO for the British Geological Survey.

(11) Gatliff, R.W., Richards, P.C., Smith, K., Graham, C.C., McCormac, M., Smith, N.J.P., Jeffery, D., Long, D., Cameron, T.D.J., Evans, D., Stevenson, A.G., Bulat, J. and Ritchie, J.D., 1993. United Kingdom offshore regional report: the geology of the central North Sea. London: HMSO for the British Geological Survey.

(12) Jackson, D.I., Jackson, A.A., Evans, D., Wingfield, R.T.R., Barnes, R.P. and Arthur, M.J., 1995. United Kingdom offshore regional report: the geology of the Irish Sea. London: HMSO for the British Geological Survey.

(13) Johnson, H., Richards, P.C., Long, D. and Graham, C.C., 1993. United Kingdom offshore regional report: the geology of the northern North Sea. London: HMSO for the British Geological Survey.

(14) Stoker, M.S., Hitchen, K. and Graham, C.C., 1993. United Kingdom offshore regional report: the geology of the Hebrides and West Shetland shelves, and adjacent deep-water areas. London: HMSO for the British Geological Survey.

Chapter 3

(1) www.sepa.org.uk/publications/state_of/2006/main/e_nutrient.html

(2) www.sepa.org.uk/data/classification/index.htm Trends in Water quality from 1996

(3) www.sepa.org.uk/wfd/index.htm

(4) Ross, P.S., Vos, J.G., Birnbaum, L.S. and Osterhaus, A.D.M.E., 2000. PCBs are a health risk for humans and wildlife. Science 289, 1878-1879.

(5) Kannan, K., Blankenship, A.L., Jones, P.D. and Giesy, J.P., 2000. Toxicity reference values for the toxic effects of polychlorinated biphenyls to aquatic mammals. Human and Ecological Risk Assessment 6, 181-201.

(6) Hall, A. J., Law, R.J., Wells, D.E., Harwood, J., Ross, H.M., Kennedy, S., Allchin, C.R., Campbell, L.A. and Pomeroy, P.P., 1992. Organochlorine levels in common seals (Phoca vitulina) that were victims and survivors of the 1988 phocine distemper epizootic. Science of the Total Environment 115, 145-162.

(7) Hall, A.J. and Thomas, G.O., 2005. Population impacts of endocrine disrupters on UK seals - effects on juvenile survival and interactions with disease. Contract No. AE1142, Endocrine Disrupters in the Aquatic Environment, Department for the Environment, Food and Rural Affairs, London.

(8) Hall, A.J. and Thomas, G.O., 2007. Polychlorinated biphenyls, DDT, polybrominated diphenyl ethers and organic pesticides in United Kingdom harbor seals - mixed exposures and thyroid homeostasis. Environmental Toxicology and Chemistry 26, 851-861.

(9) Edgar, P.J., Hursthouse, A.S., Matthews, J.E. and Davies, I.M., 2003. An investigation of geochemical factors controlling the distribution of PCBs in intertidal sediments at a contamination hot spot, the Clyde Estuary, UK. Applied Geochemistry 18, 327-338.

(10) Law, R.J., Bersuder, P., Allchin, C.R. and Barry, J., 2006. Levels of the flame retardants hexabromocyclododecane and tetrabromobisphenol A in the blubber of harbor porpoises (*Phocoena phocoena*) stranded or bycaught in the UK, with evidence for an increase in HBCD concentrations in recent years. Environmental Science & Technology 40, 2177-2183.

(11) www.marlab.ac.uk/Delivery/standaloneM.aspx?contentid=2202leather

(12) www.sepa.org.uk/spri/index.htm

(13) www.**sepa**.org.uk/publications/**state**_of/index.htm

(14) www.ospar.org/documents/dbase/publications/p00189_Eutrophication%20Status%20Report%202003.pdf

(15) www.sepa.org.uk/dpag

(16) www.crwm.org.uk/content-0 Recommendations of the Committee of Radioactive Waste management (CoRWM)

(17) www.**sepa**.org.uk/publications/**rife**/index.htm

(18) www.cefasdirect.co.uk/publications/aquatic/aemr59.pdf Radioactivity in Coastal Waters

(19) www.fwr.org/**sniffer**.htm Identification and Assessment of Alternative Disposal Options for Radioactive Oilfield Wastes - Summary Guidance

(20) www.wdcs.org/dan/publishing.nsf/c525f7df6cbf01ef802569d600573108/48a0c8d9c559fa0680256d2b004027d4/$FILE/Oceansofnoise.pdf
Simmonds, M., Dolman, S. & Weilgart, L. (eds.), 2003. Oceans of Noise [on-line]. Chippenham: Whale and Dolphin Conservation Society [cited 31/10/03].

(21) www.marlab.ac.uk/FRS.Web/Uploads/Documents/Impacts%20of%20Marine%20Litter.pdf Impacts of Marine Litter

Chapter 4
(1) Scottish Government. 2007. *Scotland's Biodiversity Indicators*. The Scottish Government, Edinburgh. pp. 50.
http://www.scotland.gov.uk/Publications/2007/11/09155020/0

(2) http://www.searchnbn.net/

(3) http://www.searchmesh.net/

(4) http://www.snh.org.uk/pubs/cr.asp

(5) Batten, S.D., Clark, R., Flinkman, J., Hays, G., John, E., John, A.W.G., Jonas, T., Lindley, J.A., Stevens, D.P. and Walne, A., 2003. CPR sampling: the technical background, materials and methods, consistency and comparability. Progress in Oceanography 58, 193-215.
http://www.sahfos.ac.uk/PDF_files/symposium manuscripts/PIO 58 Batten 193-215.pdf

(6) Corten, A., 1999. Evidence from plankton for multi-annual variations of Atlantic inflow in the northwestern North Sea. Journal of Sea Research 42, 191-205.

(7) Edwards, M., John, A.W.G., Hunt, H.G. and Lindley, J.A., 1999. Exceptional influx of oceanic species into the North Sea. Journal of the Marine Biological Association of the UK 79, 737-739.

(8) Mavor, R.A., Parsons, M., Heubeck, M. and Schmitt, S., 2005. Seabird numbers and breeding success in Britain and Ireland, 2004. UK Nature Conservation, No. 29., Joint Nature Conservation Committee, Peterborough.

(9) Reid, P.C., Edwards, M., Beaugrand, G., Stevens, D. and Wootton, M., 2005. Marine Habitats and Species: Chapter 2: State of Plankton. In: Charting Progress: An Integrated Assessment of the State of the UK Seas. DEFRA, London, pp. 59-100.
http://www.defra.gov.uk/environment/water/marine/uk/stateofsea/chartprogress-3.pdf

(10) Edwards, M., Johns, D.G., Licandro, P., John, A.W.G. and Stevens, D.P., 2007. Ecological Status Report: results from the CPR survey 2005/2006. SAHFOS Technical Report 4, 1-8.
http://www.sahfos.ac.uk/annual_reports/ecological%20status%20report%20(ebook)%202006.pdf

(11) Defra, 2005. Charting Progress: An integrated assessment of the State of the UK Seas. Department for Environment, Food and Rural Affairs, London. pp 120.

(12) Saunders, G. 2004. Natural heritage trends: the seas around Scotland 2004. Scottish Natural Heritage, Perth. pp. 158.

(13) Scottish Biodiversity Forum, 2004. Scotland's biodiversity: it's in your hands. A strategy for the conservation and enhancement of biodiversity in Scotland. An overview of the implementation plans 2005 - 2008. Scottish Executive, Edinburgh. pp. 38.

(14) Williams, J.M., ed. 2006. Common Standards Monitoring for Designated Sites: First Six Year Report. Joint Nature Conservation Committee, Peterborough. pp 16.

(15) Scottish Natural Heritage, in-prep. Site Condition Monitoring. The results from the First Six Years. Scottish Natural Heritage, Perth.

(16) Turrell, W.R., Slesser, G., Adams, R.D., Payne, R. and Gillibrand, P.A., 1999. Decadal variability in the composition of Faroe Shetland Channel bottom water. Deep Sea Research 46, 1-25.

(17) Minchin, D. and Eno, C., 2002. Exotics of coastal and inland waters of Ireland and Britain. In: Invasive Aquatic Species in Europe. Edited by Leppäkoski, E., Gollasch, S. and Olenin, S., Kluwer, Dordrecht. 267-275.

(18) Willis, K.J., Cook, E.J., Lozano-Fernandez, M. and Takeuchi, I., 2004. First record of the alien caprellid amphipod, *Caprella mutica*, for the UK. Journal of the Marine Biological Association of the United Kingdom 84, 1027-1028.

(19) Eno, C., Clark, R.A., and Sanderson, W.G. (Editors), 1997. Non-native marine species in British waters: a review and directory. Joint Nature Conservation Committee, Peterborough. pp. 152.

(20) ICES, 2005. ICES Code of Practice on the Introductions and Transfers of Marine Organisms 2005. International Council for the Exploration og the Sea, Copenhagen. pp. 30.

(21) Davison, D.M., 1996. An estimation of the total number of marine species that occur in Scottish coastal waters. Scottish Natural Heritage Review No 63. Scottish National Heritage, Edinburgh. pp. 31

(22) Poxton, M.G., 1992. Towards a strategy for the conservation of marine fish in Scotland. Proceedings of the Royal Society of Edinburgh 100B, 141-167.

(23) Hammond, P.S. and Grellier, K., 2005. Grey seal diet composition and fish consumption in the North Sea. Department for Environment, Food and Rural Affairs under project MF0319, 1-54.

(24) Hammond, P.S. and Harris, R.N., 2006. Grey seal diet composition and prey consumption off western Scotland and Shetland. Final report to Scottish Executive Environment and Rural Affairs Department and Scottish Natural Heritage. pp. 41

(25) Wanless, S., Wright, P.J., Harris, M.P. and Elston, D.A., 2004. Evidence for decrease in size of lesser sandeels *Ammodytes marinus* in a North Sea aggregation over a 30-yr period. Marine Ecology Progress Series 279, 237-246.

(26) Jennings, S. and Reynolds, J.D. 2000. Impacts of fishing on diversity: from pattern to process. In: Effects of fishing on non-target species and habitats: biological, conservation and socio-economic issues. Edited by. Kaiser, M.J. and de Groot, S.J. Blackwell Science, Oxford, pp. 235-250.

(27) Edwards, M., Johns, D.G., Licandro, P., John, A.W.G. and Stevens, D.P., 2007. Ecological Status Report: results from the CPR survey 2005/2006. SAHFOS Technical Report 4, 1-8. http://biology.st-and.ac.uk/scans2/

(29) Thompson, P.M., Corkrey, R., Lusseau, D., Lusseau, S.M., Quick, N., Durban, J.W., Parsons, K.M. and Hammond, P.S., 2006. An assessment of the current condition of the Moray Firth bottlenose dolphin population. Scottish Natural Heritage Commissioned Report No. 175, pp. 27

(30) http://smub.st-and.ac.uk/CurrentResearch.htm/scos.htm

(31) Lonergan, M., Duck, C.D., Thompson, D., Mackey, B.L., Cunningham, L. and Boyd, I.L., 2007. Using sparse survey data to investigate the declining abundance of British harbour seals. Journal of Zoology 271(3), 261-269.

(32) http://www.strandings.com/Wales.html

(33) Penrose, R.S. and Gander, L.R., 2008. UK & Republic of Ireland Marine Turtle Strandings & Sightings Annual Report 2007. Marine Environmental Monitoring, pp. 28.

(34) Mitchell, P.I., Newton, S.F., Ratcliffe, N. and Dunn, T.E., 2004. Seabird Populations of Britain and Ireland. T. & A.D. Poyser , London. pp. 511.

(35) Parsons, M., Mitchell, P. I., Butler, A., Mavor, R., Ratcliffe, N. and Foster, S., 2006. Natural Heritage Trends: Abundance of Breeding Seabirds. Scottish Natural Heritage Commissioned Report No. 222 F05NB01, pp. 74.

(36) Mavor, R.A., Parsons, M., Heubeck, M. and Schmitt, S.. 2005. Seabird numbers and breeding success in Britain and Ireland, 2004. UK Nature Conservation, No. 29, Joint Nature Conservation Committee, Peterborough, pp. 104

(37) Parsons, M., Mitchell, P.I., Butler, A., Ratcliffe, N., Frederiksen, M., Foster, S. and Reid, J.B., 2008. NATURAL HERITAGE TRENDS: Productivity of Breeding Seabirds in Scotland 1986 – 2006. Scottish Natural Heritage Commissioned Report. pp. 28.

(38) Arnott, S.A. and Ruxton, G. D., 2002. Sandeel recruitment in the North Sea: demographic, climatic and trophic effects. Marine Ecology Progress Series 238, 199-210.

(39) Frederiksen, M., Wanless, S., Harris, M.P., Rothery, P. and Wilson, L. J., 2004b. The role of industrial fishery and oceanographic changes in the decline of the North Sea black-legged kittiwakes. Journal of Applied Ecology 41, 1129-1139.

(40) Frederiksen, M., Mavor, R. A. and Wanless, S., in press. Seabirds as environmental indicators: the advantages of combining data sets. Marine Ecology Progress Series.

(41) Furness, R.W. and Tasker, M.L., 2000. Seabird-fishery interactions: quantifying the sensitivity of seabirds to reductions in sandeel abundance and identification of key areas for sensitive seabirds in the North Sea. Marine Ecology Progress Series 202, 253-264.

(42) Wanless, S., Wright, P.J., Harris, M.P. and Elston, D. A., 2004. Evidence for decrease in size of lesser sandeels *Ammodytes marinus* in a North Sea aggregation over a 30-yr period. Marine Ecology Progress Series 279, 237-246.

(43) Wanless, S., Harris, M.P., Redman, P. and Speakman, J. R., 2005. Low energy values of fish as a probable cause of a major seabird breeding failure in the North Sea. Marine Ecology Progress Series 294, 1-8.

(44) Beaugrand, G., Brander, K.M., Lindley, A., Souissi, S. and Reid, P.C., 2003. Plankton effect on cod recruitment in the North Sea. Nature 426, 661-664.

(45) Harris, M.P., Anker-Nilssen, T., McCleery, R.H., Erikstad, K.E., Shaw, D.N. and Grosbois, V., 2005. Effect of wintering area and climate on the survival of adult Atlantic puffins *Fratercula arctica* in the eastern Atlantic. Marine Ecology Progress Series 297, 283-296.

(46) Grosbois, V. and Thompson, P.M., 2005. North Atlantic climate variation influences survival in adult fulmars. Oikos 109, 273-290.

(47) Votier, S.C., Hatchwell, B.J., Beckerman, A., McCleery, R.H., Hunter, F.M., Pellatt, J., Trinder, M. and Birkhead, T.R., 2005. Oil pollution and climate have wide-scale impacts on seabird demographics. Ecology Letters 8, 1157-1164.

(48) Kirby, R.R., Johns, D.G. and Lindley, J.A., 2006. Fathers in hot water: rising sea temperatures and a Northeastern Atlantic pipefish baby boom. Biology Letters 2, 597-600.

(49) Harris, M.P., Beare, D., Toresen, R., Nøttestad, L., Kloppmann, M., Dörner, H., Peach, K., Rushton, D.R.A., Foster-Smith, J. and Wanless, S., 2007. A major increase in snake pipefish (*Entelurus aequoreus*) in northern European seas since 2003: potential implications for seabird breeding success. Marine Biology 151, 973-983.

(50) Harris, M.P., Newell, M., Daunt, F., Speakman, J.R. and Wanless, S., in press. Snake pipefish (*Entelurus aequoreus*) are poor food for seabirds. Ibis.

Chapter 5
(1)
http://www.scotland.gov.uk/Topics/Statistics/Browse/Economy/Input-Output

(2) Pugh, D.T., 2008. Socio-economic indicators of marine-related activities in the UK economy. Marine Estate Research Report, The Crown Estate, March 2008. pp. 81.

(3) Pugh, D.T. and Skinner, L., 2002. A new analysis of marine-related activities in the UK economy with supporting science and technology. IACMST, August 2002. pp. 48.

(4)
http://www.statistics.gov.uk/methods_quality/sic/downloads/UK_SIC_Vol1(2003).pdf

(5) Topping, G., Davies, J.M., Mackie, P.R. and Moffat, C.F., 1997 The impact of the Braer spill on commercial fish and shellfish. In: The Impact of an oil spill in Turbulent Waters: the Braer. Edited by Davies, J.M. and Topping, G, The Stationery Office, Edinburgh, UK, 121 – 143.

(6) Table 1, Statistical Bulletin No Fis/2007/1. September 2007. FRS. http://www.frs-scotland.gov.uk/FRS.Web/Uploads/Documents/SCSB06%20web.pdf

(7) Figure 8. Statistical Bulletin No Fis/2007/1. September 2007. FRS. http://www.frs-scotland.gov.uk/FRS.Web/Uploads/Documents/SCSB06%20web.pdf

(8)
http://www.scotland.gov.uk/Publications/2003/03/16842/20502

(9) Fisheries Research Services, 2007. Scottish Fish Farms Annual Production Survey 2006. Fisheries Research Services, Aberdeen, pp. 53 http://www.frs-scotland.gov.uk/Delivery/Information_Resources/information_resources_view_document.aspx?contentid=2220

(10)
http://www.sarf.org.uk/Project%20Final%20Reports/SARF024%20-%20Final%20Reports%20and%20Templates/EIA%20Guidelines%20FINAL+%20Templates.pdf

(11) http://www.scottishsalmon.co.uk/dlDocs/CoGp.pdf

(12) Gubbins, M.J., McCollin, T., Lichtman, D., Miller, B.S., Dobson, J. and Davies, I.M., 2006. Eutrophication assessment of Scottish coastal waters supporting aquaculture 2004 – 2005. OSPAR EUC 06/02/Info.1. pp. 303.

(13) Scottish Enterprise http://www.scottish-enterprise.com/sedotcom_home/sig/sig-energy/energy_sector/energykeyfacts.htm?siblingtoggle=1

(14) http://www.og.dti.gov.uk/information/bb_updates/appendices/Appendix9.htm

(15) http://www.og.dti.gov.uk/information/bb_updates/appendices/Appendix10.htm

(16) http://www.mcga.gov.uk/c4mca/mcga-environmental/mcga-dops_cp_environmental-counter-pollution.htm

(17) http://www.dft.gov.uk/pgr/statistics/datatablespublications/maritime/compendium

(18) Hayes, P., Russell, M. and Packer, G., 2005. Surveys of dredged material and wastewater sludge sea disposal sites for the east coast of Scotland. Fisheries Research Services Report No. 08/05, 1 – 55.

(19) Hayes, P., Russell, M. and Packer, G., 2005. Assessment of the quality of sediment polycyclic aromatic hydrocarbons and tributyl tin samples collected from Aberdeen harbour and Aberdeen sea disposal site. Fisheries Research Services Report No. 07/05, 1 – 36.

(20) http://www.thecrownestate.co.uk/43_landing_port_statistics_2006.pdf

(21) UK leisure and small commercial marine industry. Key Performance Indicators. British Marine Federation January 2008. www.britishmarine.co.uk/docimages/2038.pdf

(22) Sailing in the Clyde Estuary, The Potential For Future Development, A Market Assessment, Economic Impact Study and Action Plan, 2006. Scottish Enterprise. pp. 81. http://www.scottish-enterprise.com/publications/sailing_in_the_clyde_estuary_june_2006.pdf

(23) www.scapetrust.org

(24) Historic Scotland, 2007. A review of existing information for Scotland's Historic Environment Audit (SHEA). http://www.heritageaudit.org.uk/

(25) Figures obtained from the Scottish Sub-Aqua Club http://www.scotsac.com

(26) Smith, W.A., 1887. Loch Creran Notes from the West Highlands. Gardner, A. Paisley.

(27) Connor, D., 1990. Survey of Lochs Linnhe, Eil, Creran and Aline. Nature Conservancy Council, CSD Report No. 1073. Nature Conservancy Council, Peterborough. pp. 170.

(28) Moore, C.G., Saunders, G.R., Harries, D.B., 1998. The status and distributional ecology of reefs of Serpula vermicularis L. (Polychaeta: Serpulidae) in Scotland. Aquatic Conservation: Marine and Freshwater Ecosystems, 8, 645-656.

(29) Moore, C.G., Harries, D.B., Lyndon, A.R., Saunders, G.R. and Conway, T.R., 2003. Quantification of serpulid biogenic reef coverage of the sea bed (Polychaeta: Serpulidae) using a video transect technique. Aquatic Conservation: Marine and Freshwater Ecosystems, 13, 137-146.

(30) Chapman, N.D., Moore, C.G., Harries, D.B. andLyndon, A,R., 2007. Patterns of recruitment in Serpula vermicularis L. (Polychaeta: Serpulidae). Estuarine Coastal and Shelf Science 73, 598-606.

(31) Moore, C.G., Bates, C.R., Mair, J.M., Saunders, G.R., Harries, D.B. and Lyndon, A.R., in press. Mapping serpulid worm reefs (Polychaeta: Serpulidae) for conservation management. Aquatic Conservation: Marine and Freshwater Ecosystems.

(32) Poloczanska, E.S., Hughes, D.J. and Burrows, M.T., 2004. Underwater television observations of Serpula vermicularis (L.) reefs and associated mobile fauna in Loch Creran, Scotland. Estuarine, Coastal and Shelf Science 61, 425-435.

(33) Ten Hove, H.A. and Van den Hurk, P., 1993. A review of recent and fossil serpulid 'reefs'; actuopalaeontology and the 'Upper Malm' serpulid limestones in NW Germany. Geologie en Mijnbouw 72, 23-67.

(34) http://www.scotland.gov.uk/News/Releases/2007/11/27095600

(35) http://www.scotland.gov.uk/Publications/2007/11/13092240/0 page 13

(36) http://www.scotland.gov.uk/Topics/Business-Industry/Energy/19185/WaveTidalSEA

(37) http://www.seaenergyscotland.co.uk/WhatisSEA.htm

Chapter 6

(1) Intergovernmental Panel on Climate Change, 2007. Climate Change 2007: Impacts, Adaptation and Vulnerability. Contribution of Working Group II to the Fourth Assessment Report of the Intergovernmental Panel on Climate Change (IPCC). Edited by Parry, M.L., Canziani, O.F., Palutikof, J.P., van der Linden P.L. and Hanson, C.E. Cambridge University Press, Cambridge, UK. pp. 976.

(2) Rahmstorf, S., Cazenave, A., Church, J.A., Hansen, J.E., Keeling, R.F., Parker, D.E. and Somerville, R.C.J., 2007. Recent Climate Observations Compared to Projections. Science 316 (5825), pp. 709.

(3) Fisheries Research Services, 2007. Scottish Ocean Climate Status Report 2004 and 2005. Edited by Hughes S.L. Fisheries Research Services, Aberdeen. pp. 40.

(4) Hughes, S.L. and Holliday, N.P. (Editors). 2007. ICES Report on Ocean Climate 2006. ICES Cooperative Research Report No. 289, International Council for the Exploration of the Sea. pp. 55.

(5) Holliday, N.P., Hughes, S., Bacon, S., Beszczynska-Möller, A., Hansen, B., Lavín, A., Loeng, A.H., Mork, K.A., Østerhus, S., Sherwin, T. and Walczowski, W., in press. Reversal of the 1960s - 1990s Freshening Trend in the North Atlantic and Nordic Seas, Geophysical Research Letters.

(6) Boyer, T., Levitus, S., Antonov, J., Locarnini, R., Mishonov, A., Garcia, H. and Josey, S.A., 2007. Changes in freshwater content in the North Atlantic Ocean 1955-2006. Geophysical Research Letters 34.

(7) Marine Climate Change Impacts Partnership, 2008. Marine Climate Change Impacts Annual Report Card 2007–2008. Edited by Baxter, J.M., Buckley, P.J. and Wallace, C.J. Summary Report, MCCIP, Lowestoft, pp. 8.

(8) Dawson, A., Smith, D.E. and Dawson, S., 2001. The Potential Impacts of Climate Change on Sea Levels around Scotland. Scottish Natural Heritage Research Survey and Monitoring Report, No. 178. Scottish Natural Heritage, Edinburgh. pp. 77.

(9) http://www.mba.ac.uk/marclim/

(10) Hulme, M., Jenkins, G.J., Lu, X., Turnpenny, J.R., Mitchell, T.D., Jones, R.G., Lowe, J., Murphy, J.M., Hassell, D., Boorman, P., McDonald, R. and Hill, S., 2002. Climate Change Scenarios for the United Kingdom: The UKCIP02 Scientific Report. Tyndall Centre for Climate Change Research, School of Environmental Sciences, University of East Anglia, Norwich, UK. pp. 120.

(11) British-Irish Council, 2003. Scenarios of climate change for islands within the BIC region. Edited by Jenkins, G., Cooper, C., Hassell D. and Jones, R. UK Met Office, Bracknell. pp. 48.

(12) UK Climate Impacts Programme (UKCIP) Scenarios gateway – UKCIP08: http://www.ukcip.org.uk/scenarios/ukcip08/what_is_ukcip08.asp

(13) www.cefas.co.uk/data/wavenet

(14) http://www.argo.ucsd.edu/index.html

Chapter 7

(1) http://www.scotland.gov.uk/Publications/2003/03/16842/20502

(2) http://www.scotland.gov.uk/Publications/2005/03/sfifs/0

(3). Halpern, B., Walbridge, S., Selkoe, K.A., Kappel, C.V., Micheli, F. et al., 2008. A Global map of human impact on marine ecosystems. Science 319, 948 – 952.

# List of Figures

# List of Tables